Multivariate Approximation for solving ODE and PDE

Multivariate Approximation for solving ODE and PDE

Editor

Clemente Cesarano

MDPI • Basel • Beijing • Wuhan • Barcelona • Belgrade • Manchester • Tokyo • Cluj • Tianjin

Editor
Clemente Cesarano
Uninettuno University
Italy

Editorial Office
MDPI
St. Alban-Anlage 66
4052 Basel, Switzerland

This is a reprint of articles from the Special Issue published online in the open access journal *Mathematics* (ISSN 2227-7390) (available at: https://www.mdpi.com/journal/mathematics/special_issues/Multivariate_Approximation_Solving_ODE_PDE).

For citation purposes, cite each article independently as indicated on the article page online and as indicated below:

LastName, A.A.; LastName, B.B.; LastName, C.C. Article Title. *Journal Name* **Year**, *Article Number*, Page Range.

ISBN 978-3-03943-603-3 (Hbk)
ISBN 978-3-03943-604-0 (PDF)

Contents

About the Editor

Clemente Cesarano is an associate professor of Numerical Analysis and the director of the Section of Mathematics—Uninettuno University, Rome, Italy; he is the coordinator of the doctoral college in Technological Innovation Engineering, coordinator of the Section of Mathematics, vice-dean of the Faculty of Engineering, president of the Degree Course in Management Engineering, director of the Master in Project Management Techniques, and a coordinator of the Master in Applied and Industrial Mathematics. He is also a member of the Research Project "Modeling and Simulation of the Fractionary and Medical Center", Complutense University of Madrid (Spain), and the head of the national group from 2015, member of the Research Project (Serbian Ministry of Education and Science) "Approximation of Integral and Differential Operators and Applications", University of Belgrade (Serbia) and coordinator of the national group since 2011), a member of the Doctoral College in Mathematics at the Department of Mathematics of the University of Mazandaran (Iran), expert (Reprise) at the Ministry of Education, University and Research, for the ERC sectors: Analysis, Operator Algebras and Functional Analysis, and Numerical Analysis. Clemente Cesarano is an honorary fellow of the Australian Institute of High Energetic Materials, affiliated with the National Institute of High Mathematics (INdAM), as well as with the International Research Center for the "Mathematics & Mechanics of Complex Systems" (MEMOCS)—University of L'Aquila, associate of the CNR at the Institute of Complex Systems (ISC), affiliated with the "Research Italian Network on Approximation (RITA)" as the head of the Uninettuno office. Finally, he is a member of the UMI and the SIMAI

Preface to "Multivariate Approximation for solving ODE and PDE"

Multivariate approximation is an extension of approximation theory and approximation algorithms. In general, approximations can be provided via interpolation, as approximation/ polynomials' interpolation and approximation/interpolation with radial basis functions or more in general, with kernel functions. In this book, we have covered the field through spectral problems, exponential integrators for ODE systems, and some applications for the numerical solution of evolutionary PDE, also discretized, by using the concepts and the related formalism of special functions and orthogonal polynomials, which represent a powerful tool to simplify computation. Since the theory of multivariate approximation meets different branches of mathematics and is applied in various areas such as physics, engineering, and computational mechanics, this book contains a large variety of contributions.

Clemente Cesarano

Editor

Article

Unbiased Least-Squares Modelling

Marta Gatto and Fabio Marcuzzi *

Department of Mathematics, "Tullio Levi Civita", University of Padova, Via Trieste 63, 35131 Padova, Italy; mgatto@math.unipd.it

* Correspondence: marcuzzi@math.unipd.it

Received: 25 May 2020; Accepted: 11 June 2020; Published: 16 June 2020

Abstract: In this paper we analyze the bias in a general linear least-squares parameter estimation problem, when it is caused by deterministic variables that have not been included in the model. We propose a method to substantially reduce this bias, under the hypothesis that some a-priori information on the magnitude of the modelled and unmodelled components of the model is known. We call this method Unbiased Least-Squares (ULS) parameter estimation and present here its essential properties and some numerical results on an applied example.

Keywords: parameter estimation; physical modelling; oblique decomposition; least-squares

---

1. Introduction

The well known least-squares problem [1], very often used to estimate the parameters of a mathematical model, assumes an equivalence between a matrix-vector product Ax on the left, and a vector b on the right hand side: the matrix A is produced by the true model equations, evaluated at some operating conditions, the vector x contains the unknown parameters and the vector b are measurements, corrupted by white, Gaussian noise. This equivalence cannot be satisfied exactly, but the least-squares solution yields a minimum variance, maximum likelihood estimate of the parameters x, with a nice geometric interpretation: the resulting predictions Ax are at the minimum Euclidean distance from the true measurements b and the vector of residuals is orthogonal w.r.t. the subspace of all possible predictions.

Unfortunately, each violation of these assumptions produces in general a bias in the estimates. Various modifications have been introduced in the literature to cope with some of them: mainly, colored noise on b and/or A due to model error and/or colored measurement noise. The model error is often assumed as an additive stochastic term in the model, e.g., error-in-variables [2,3], with consequent solution methods like Total Least-Squares [4] and Extended Least-Squares [5], to cite a few. All these techniques let the model to be modified to describe, in some sense, the model error.

Here, instead, we assume that the model error depends from deterministic variables in a way that has not been included in the model, i.e., we suppose to use a reduced model of the real system, as it is often the case in applications. In this paper we propose a method to cope with the bias in the parameter estimates of the approximate model by exploiting the geometric properties of least-squares and using small additional a-priori information about the norm of the modelled and un-modelled components of the system response, available with some approximation in most applications. To eliminate the bias on the parameter estimates we perturb the right-hand-side without modifying the reduced model, since we assume it describes accurately one part of the true model.

2. Model Problem

In applied mathematics, physical models are often available, usually rather precise at describing quantitatively the main phenomena, but not satisfactory at the level of detail required by the application at hand. Here we refer to models described by differential equations, with ordinary and/or partial derivatives, commonly used in engineering and applied sciences. We assume, therefore, that there are two models at hand: a true, unknown model $\mathcal{M}$ and an approximate, known model $\mathcal{M}_a$. These models are usually parametric and they must be tuned to describe a specific physical system, using a-priori knowledge about the application and experimental measurements. Model tuning, and in particular parameter estimation, is usually done with a prediction error minimization criterion that makes the model response to be a good approximation of the dynamics shown by the measured variables used in the estimation process. Assuming that the true model $\mathcal{M}$ is linear in the parameters that must be estimated, the application of this criterion brings to a linear least-squares problem:

$$\bar{x} = \underset{x' \in \mathbb{R}^n}{\operatorname{argmin}} \|Ax' - \bar{f}\|^2, \tag{1}$$

where, from here on, $\|\cdot\|$ is the Euclidean norm, $A \in \mathbb{R}^{m \times n}$ is supposed full rank $\operatorname{rank}(A) = n$, $m \geq n$, $\bar{x} \in \mathbb{R}^{n \times 1}$, Ax' are the model response values and $\bar{f}$ is the vector of experimental measurements. Usually the measured data contain noise, i.e., we measure $f = \bar{f} + \epsilon$, with ϵ a certain kind of additive noise (e.g., white Gaussian). Since we are interested here in algebraic and geometric aspects of the problem, we suppose $\epsilon = 0$ and set $f = \bar{f}$. Moreover, we assume ideally that $\bar{f} = A\bar{x}$ holds exactly. Let us consider also the estimation problem for the approximate model $\mathcal{M}_a$:

$$x^{\|} = \underset{x' \in \mathbb{R}^{n_a}}{\operatorname{argmin}} \|A_a x' - \bar{f}\|^2, \tag{2}$$

where $A_a \in \mathbb{R}^{m \times n_a}$, $x^{\|} \in \mathbb{R}^{n_a \times 1}$, with $n_a < n$. The choice of the notation for $x^{\|}$ is to remind that the least-squares solution satisfies $A_a x^{\|} = P_{A_a}(f) =: f^{\|}$, where $f^{\|}$ is the orthogonal projection of $\bar{f}$ on the subspace generated by A_a, and the residual $A_a x^{\|} - \bar{f}$ is orthogonal to this subspace. Let us suppose that A_a corresponds to the first n_a columns of A, which means that the approximate model $\mathcal{M}_a$ is exactly one part of the true model $\mathcal{M}$, i.e., $A = [A_a, A_u]$ and so the solution $\bar{x}$ of (1) can be decomposed in two parts such that

$$A\bar{x} = [A_a, A_u] \begin{bmatrix} \bar{x}_a \\ \bar{x}_u \end{bmatrix} = A_a \bar{x}_a + A_u \bar{x}_u = \bar{f}. \tag{3}$$

This means that the model error corresponds to an additive term $A_u \bar{x}_u$ in the estimation problem.

Note that the columns of A_a are linearly independent since A is supposed to be of full rank. We do not consider the case in which A_a is rank-deficient, because it would mean that the model is not well parametrized. Moreover, some noise in the data is sufficient to determine a full rank matrix.

For brevity, we will call $\mathcal{A}$ the subspace generated by the columns of A and $\mathcal{A}_a$, $\mathcal{A}_u$ the subspaces generated by the columns of A_a, A_u respectively. Note that if $\mathcal{A}_a$ and $\mathcal{A}_u$ were orthogonal, decomposition (3) would be orthogonal. However, in the following we will consider the case in which the two subspaces are not orthogonal, as it commonly happens in practice. Oblique projections, even if not as common as orthogonal ones, have a large literature, e.g., [6,7].

Now, it is well known and easy to demonstrate that, when we solve problem (2) and A_u is not orthogonal to A_a, we get a biased solution, i.e., $x^{\|} \neq \bar{x}_a$:

Lemma 1. *Given $A \in \mathbb{R}^{m \times n}$ with $n \geq 2$ and $A = [A_a, A_u]$, and given $b \in \mathbb{R}^{m \times 1} \notin \mathcal{I}_m(A_a)$, call x the least-squares solution of (2) and $\bar{x} = [\bar{x}_a, \bar{x}_u]$ the solution of (1) decomposed as in (3). Then*

(i) if $A_u \perp A_a$ then $x^{\|} = \bar{x}_a$,
(ii) if $A_u \not\perp A_a$ then $x^{\|} \neq \bar{x}_a$.

Proof. The least-squares problem $Ax = f$ boils down to finding x such that $Ax = P_{\mathcal{A}_a}(f)$. Let us consider the unique decomposition of f on $\mathcal{A}_a$ and $\mathcal{A}_a^{\perp}$ as $f = f^{\|} + f^{\perp}$ with $f^{\|} = P_{\mathcal{A}_a}(f)$ and $f^{\perp} = P_{\mathcal{A}_a^{\perp}}(f)$. Call $f = f_a + f_u$ the decomposition on $\mathcal{A}_a$ and $\mathcal{A}_u$, hence there exist two vectors $x_a \in \mathbb{R}^{n_a}$, $x_u \in \mathbb{R}^{n-n_a}$ such that $f_a = A_a x_a$ and $f_u = A_u x_u$. If $\mathcal{A}_u \perp \mathcal{A}_a$ then the two decompositions are the same, hence $f^{\|} = f_a$ and so $x^{\|} = \bar{x}_a$. Otherwise, for the definition of orthogonal projection ([6], third point of Def at page 429), it must hold $x^{\|} \neq \bar{x}_a$. □

3. Analysis of the Parameter Estimation Error

The aim of this paper is to propose a method to decrease substantially the bias of the solution of the approximated problem (2), with the smallest additional information about the norms of the model error and of the modelled part responses.

In this section we will introduce sufficient conditions to remove the bias and retrieve the true solution in a unique way, as summarized in Lemma 4. Let us start with a definition.

Definition 1 (Intensity Ratio). *The intensity ratio I_f between modelled and un-modelled dynamics is defined as*

$$I_f = \frac{\|A_a x_a\|}{\|A_u x_u\|}.$$

In the following we assume that a good approximation of this intensity ratio is available and that its magnitude is sufficiently big, i.e., we have an approximate model that is quite accurate. This information about the model error will be used to reduce the bias, as shown in the following sections. Moreover we will consider also the norm $N_f = \|A_a x_a\|$ (or, equivalently, the norm $\|A_u x_u\|$).

3.1. The Case of Exact Knowledge about I_f and N_f

Here we assume, initially, to know the exact values of I_f and N_f, i.e.,

$$\begin{cases} N_f = \bar{N}_f = \|A_a \bar{x}_a\|, \\ I_f = \bar{I}_f = \frac{\|A_a \bar{x}_a\|}{\|A_u \bar{x}_u\|}. \end{cases} \tag{4}$$

This ideal setting is important to figure out the problem also with more practical assumptions. First of all, let us show a nice geometric property that relates x_a and f_a under a condition like (4).

Lemma 2. *The problem of finding the set of $x_a \in \mathbb{R}^n$ that give a constant, prescribed value for I_f and N_f is equivalent to that of finding the set of $f_a = A_a x_a \in \mathcal{A}_a$ of the decomposition $f = f_a + f_u$ (see the proof of Lemma 1) lying on the intersection of $\mathcal{A}_a$ and the boundaries of two n-dimensional balls in $\mathbb{R}^n$. In fact, it holds:*

$$\begin{cases} N_f = \|A_a x_a\| \\ I_f = \frac{\|A_a x_a\|}{\|A_u x_u\|} \end{cases} \iff \begin{cases} f_a \in \partial B_n(0, N_f) \\ f_a \in \partial B_n(f^{\|}, T_f) \end{cases} \quad \text{with} \quad T_f := \sqrt{\left(\frac{N_f}{I_f}\right)^2 - \|f^{\perp}\|^2}. \tag{5}$$

Proof. For every $x_a \in \mathbb{R}^{n_a}$ holds,

$$\begin{cases} N_f = \|f_a\| = \|A_a x_a\| \\ I_f = \frac{\|f_a\|}{\|f_u\|} = \frac{N_f}{\|f_u^{\perp} + f_u^{\|}\|} = \frac{N_f}{\sqrt{\|f^{\perp}\|^2 + \|f^{\|} - A_a x_a\|^2}} = \frac{N_f}{\sqrt{\|f^{\perp}\|^2 + \|f^{\|} - f_a\|^2}} \end{cases} \iff \tag{6}$$

$$\iff \begin{cases} \|f_a\| = N_f \\ \|f^{\|} - f_a\| = \sqrt{\left(\frac{N_f}{I_f}\right)^2 - \|f^{\perp}\|^2} =: T_f, \end{cases} \tag{7}$$

where we used the fact that $f_u = f_u^{\|} + f_u^{\perp}$ with $f_u^{\perp} := P_{A_a^{\perp}}(f_u) = f^{\perp}$, $f_u^{\|} := P_{A_a}(f_u) = A_a \delta x_a = f^{\|} - A_a x_a$, and $\delta x_a = (x^{\|} - x_a)$. Hence the equivalence (5) is proved. □

Given I_f and N_f, we call the feasible set of accurate model responses all the f_a that satisfy the relations (5). Now we will see that Lemma 2 allows us to reformulate problem (2) in the problem of finding a feasible f_a that, replaced to $\tilde{f}$ in (2), gives as solution an unbiased estimate of $\bar{x}_a$. Indeed, it is easy to note that $A_a\bar{x}_a$ belongs to this feasible set. Moreover, since $f_a \in \mathcal{A}_a$, we can reduce the dimensionality of the problem and work on the subspace $\mathcal{A}_a$ which has dimension n_a, instead of the global space $\mathcal{A}$ of dimension n. To this aim, let us consider U_a the matrix of the SVD decomposition of A_a, $A_a = U_a S_a V_a^T$, and complete its columns to an orthonormal basis of $\mathbb{R}^n$ to obtain a matrix U. Since the vectors $f_a, f^{\|} \in \mathbb{R}^n$ belong to the subspace $\mathcal{A}_a$, the vectors $\tilde{f}_a, \tilde{f}^{\|} \in \mathbb{R}^n$ defined such that $f_a = U\tilde{f}_a$ and $f^{\|} = U\tilde{f}^{\|}$ must have zeros on the last $n - n_a$ components. Since U has orthonormal columns, it preserves the norms and so $\|f^{\|}\| = \|\tilde{f}^{\|}\|$ and $\|f_a\| = \|\tilde{f}_a\|$. If we call $\hat{f}_a, \hat{f}^{\|} \in \mathbb{R}^{n_a}$ the first n_a components of the vectors $\tilde{f}_a, \tilde{f}^{\|}$ (which have again the same norms of the full vectors in $\mathbb{R}^n$) respectively, we have

$$\begin{cases} \hat{f}_a \in \partial B_{n_a}(0, N_f), \\ \hat{f}_a \in \partial B_{n_a}(f^{\|}, T_f). \end{cases} \tag{8}$$

In this way the problem depends only on the dimension of the known subspace, i.e., the value of n_a, and does not depend on the dimensions $m \gg n_a$ and $n > n_a$. From (8) we can deduce the equation of the $(n_a - 2)$-dimensional boundary of an $(n_a - 1)$-ball to which the vector $f_a = A_a x_a$ must belong. In the following we discuss the various cases.

3.1.1. Case $n_a = 1$

In this case, we have one unique solution when both conditions on I_f and N_f are imposed. When only one of these two is imposed, two solutions are found, shown in Figure 1a,c. Figure 1b shows the intensity ratio I_f.

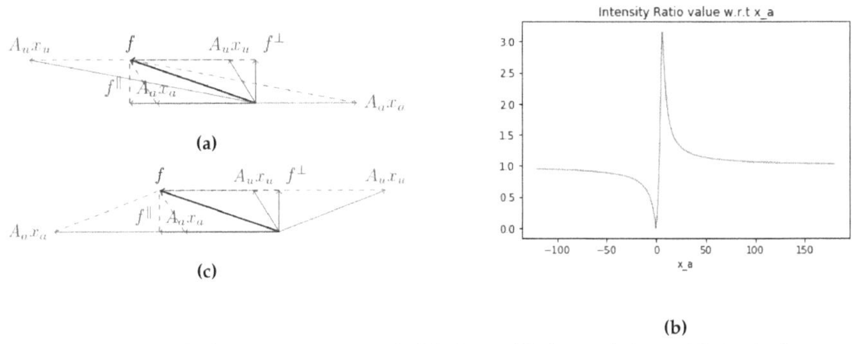

(b)

Figure 1. Case $n_a = 1$. (**a**): Case $n_a = 1, m = n = 2$. Solutions with the condition on N_f. In the figure: the true decomposition obtained imposing both the conditions (blue), the orthogonal decomposition (red), another possible decomposition (green) that satisfy the same norm condition N_f, but different I_f; (**b**): Case $n_a = 1$. Intensity Ratio value w.r.t the norm of the vector $A_a x_a$: given a fixed value of Intensity Ratio there can be two solution, i.e. two possible decomposition of f as sum of two vectors with the same Intensity Ratio; (**c**): Case $n_a = 1, m = n = 2$. Solutions with the condition on I_f. In the figure: the true decomposition obtained imposing both the conditions (blue), the orthogonal decomposition (red), another possible decomposition (green) with the same intensity ratio I_f, but different N_f.

3.1.2. Case $n_a = 2$

Consider the vectors $\hat{f}_a, \hat{f}^{\|} \in \mathbb{R}^{n_a=2}$ as defined previously, in particular we are looking for $\hat{f}_a = [\xi_1, \xi_2] \in \mathbb{R}^2$. Hence, conditions (8) can be written as

$$\begin{cases} \xi_1^2 + \xi_2^2 = N_f^2 \\ (\xi_1 - \hat{f}^{\|}_{\xi_1})^2 + (\xi_2 - \hat{f}^{\|}_{\xi_2})^2 = T_f^2 \end{cases} \longrightarrow \quad \mathcal{F}: \quad (\hat{f}^{\|}_{\xi_1})^2 - 2\hat{f}^{\|}_{\xi_1}\xi_1 + (\hat{f}^{\|}_{\xi_2})^2 - 2\hat{f}^{\|}_{\xi_2}\xi_2 = N_f^2 - T_f^2, \tag{9}$$

where the right equation is the $(n_a - 1) = 1$-dimensional subspace (line) $\mathcal{F}$ obtained subtracting the first equation to the second. This subspace has to be intersected with one of the beginning circumferences to obtain the feasible vectors $\hat{f}_a$, as can be seen in Figure 2a and its projection on $\mathcal{A}_a$ in Figure 2b. The intersection of the two circumferences (5) can have different solutions depending on the value of $(N_f - \|f^{\|}\|) - T_f$. When this value is strictly positive there are zero solutions, this means that the estimates of I_f and N_f are not correct: we are not interested in this case because we suppose the two values to be sufficiently well estimated. When the value is strictly negative there are two solutions, that coincide when the value is zero.

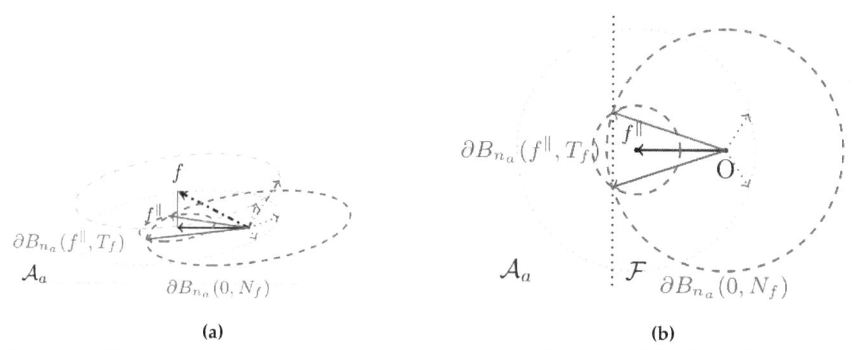

Figure 2. Case $n_a = 2$. (**a**): Case $n_a = 2$, $m = n = 3$, with $A_a x_a = [A_a(1)A_a(2)][x_a(1)x_a(2)]^T$. In the figure: the true decomposition (blue), the orthogonal decomposition (red), another possible decomposition of the infinite ones (green); (**b**): Case $n_a = 2$, $m = n = 3$. Projection of the two circumferences on the subspace $\mathcal{A}_a$, and projections of the possible decompositions of f (red, blue and green).

When there are two solutions, we have no sufficient information to determine which one of the two solutions is the true one, i.e., the one that gives $f_a = A_a\bar{x}_a$: we cannot choose the one that has minimum residual, neither the vector f_a that has the minimum angle with f, because both solutions have the same values of these two quantities. However, since we are supposing the linear system to be originated by an input/output system, where the matrix A_a is a function also of the input and f are the measurements of the output, we can take two tests with different inputs. Since all the solution sets contain the true parameter vector, we can determine the true solution from their intersection, unless the solutions of the two tests are coincident. The condition for coincidence is expressed in Lemma 3.

Let us call $A_{a,i} \in \mathbb{R}^{n \times n_a}$ the matrix of the test $i = 1, 2$, to which correspond a vector f_i. The line on which lie the two feasible vectors f_a of the same test i is $\mathcal{F}_i$ and $\mathcal{S}_i = A^{\dagger}_{a,i}\mathcal{F}_i$ is the line through the two solution points. To have two tests with non-coincident solutions, we need that these two lines $\mathcal{S}_1, \mathcal{S}_2$ do not have more than one common point, that in the case $n_a = 2$ is equivalent to $\mathcal{S}_1 \neq \mathcal{S}_2$, i.e., $A^{\dagger}_{a,1}\mathcal{F}_1 \neq A^{\dagger}_{a,2}\mathcal{F}_2$, i.e., $\mathcal{F}_1 \neq A_{a,1}A^{\dagger}_{a,2}\mathcal{F}_2 =: \mathcal{F}_{12}$. We represent the lines $\mathcal{F}_i$ by means of their orthogonal vector from the origin $f^{ort,i} = l_{ort,i}\frac{f_i^{\|}}{\|f_i^{\|}\|}$. We introduce the matrices C_a, C_f, C_{fp} such that $A_{a,2} = C_a A_{a,1}$, $f_2 = C_f f_1$, $f_2^{\|} = C_{fp} f_1^{\|}$ and k_f such that $\|f_2^{\|}\| = k_f \|f_1^{\|}\|$.

Lemma 3. *Consider two tests $i = 1, 2$ from the same system with $n_a = 2$ with the above notation. Then it holds $\mathcal{F}_1 = \mathcal{F}_{12}$ if and only if $C_a = C_{fp}$.*

Proof. From the relation $f_i^{\|} = \mathcal{P}_{A_{a,i}}(f_i) = A_{a,i}(A_{a,i}^T A_{a,i})^{-1} A_{a,i}^T f_i$, we have

$$f_2^{\|} = A_{a,2}(A_{a,2}^T A_{a,2})^{-1} A_{a,2}^T f_2 = C_a A_{a,1}(A_{a,1}^T C_a^T C_a A_{a,1})^{-1} A_{a,1}^T C_a^T C_f f_1. \tag{10}$$

It holds $\mathcal{F}_1 = \mathcal{F}_{12} \iff f^{ort,1} = f^{ort,12} := A_{a,1} A_{a,2}^{\dagger} f^{ort,2}$, hence we will show this second equivalence. We note that $l_{ort,2} = k_f l_{ort,1}$ and calculate

$$f^{ort,12} = A_{a,1} A_{a,2}^{\dagger} f^{ort,2} = A_{a,1} A_{a,1}^{\dagger} C_a^{\dagger} \left(l_{ort,2} \frac{f_2^{\|}}{\|f_2^{\|}\|} \right) = A_{a,1} A_{a,1}^{\dagger} C_a^{\dagger} \left(k_f l_{ort,1} \frac{C_{fp} f_1^{\|}}{k_f \|f_1^{\|}\|} \right) = A_{a,1} A_{a,1}^{\dagger} C_a^{\dagger} C_{fp} f^{ort,1}. \tag{11}$$

Now let us call $s^{ort,1}$ the vector such that $f^{ort,1} = A_{a,1} s^{ort,1}$, then, using the fact that $C_a = C_{fp}$ we obtain

$$f^{ort,12} = A_{a,1} A_{a,1}^{\dagger} C_a^{\dagger} C_{fp} A_{a,1} s^{ort,1} = A_{a,1}(A_{a,1}^{\dagger} A_{a,1}) s^{ort,1} = (\text{since} A_{a,1}^{\dagger} A_{a,1} = I_{n_a}) = A_{a,1} s^{ort,1} \tag{12}$$

Hence we have $\mathcal{F}_{12} = \mathcal{F}_1 \iff A_{a,1} A_{a,1}^{\dagger} C_a^{\dagger} C_{fp} f^{ort,1} = f^{ort,1} \iff C_a^{\dagger} C_{fp} = I.$ □

3.1.3. Case $n_a \geq 3$

More generally, for the case $n_a \geq 3$, consider the vectors $\hat{f}_a, \hat{f}^{\|} \in \mathbb{R}^{n_a}$ as defined previously, in particular we are looking for $\hat{f}_a = [\xi_1, \ldots, \xi_{n_a}] \in \mathbb{R}^{n_a}$. Conditions (8) can be written as

$$\begin{cases} \sum_{i=1}^{n_a} \xi_i^2 = N_f^2 \\ \sum_{i=1}^{n_a} (\xi_i - \hat{f}_{\xi_i}^{\|})^2 = T_f^2 \end{cases} \longrightarrow \mathcal{F}: \sum_{i=1}^{n_a} ((\hat{f}_{\xi_i}^{\|})^2 - 2\hat{f}_{\xi_i}^{\|} \xi_i) = N_f^2 - T_f^2, \tag{13}$$

where the two equations on the left are two $(n_a - 1)$-spheres, i.e., the boundaries of two n_a-dimensional balls. Analogously to the case $n_a = 2$, the intersection of these equations can be empty, one point or the boundary of a $(n_a - 1)$-dimensional ball (with the same conditions on $(N_f - \|f^{\|}\|) - T_f$). The equation on the right of (13) is the $(n_a - 1)$-dimensional subspace $\mathcal{F}$ on which lies the boundary of the $(n_a - 1)$-dimensional ball of the feasible vectors f_a, and is obtained subtracting the first equation to the second one. In Figure 3a the graphical representation of the decomposition $f^{\|} = f_a + f_u^{\|}$ for the case $n_a = 3$ is shown, and in Figure 3b the solution ellipsoids of 3 tests whose intersection is one point. Figure 4a shows the solution hyperellipsoids of 4 tests whose intersection is one point, in the case $n_a = 4$.

We note that, to obtain one unique solution x_a we must intersect the solutions of at least two tests. Let us give a more precise idea of what happens in general. Given $i = 1, \ldots, n_a$ tests we call, as in the previous case, $f^{ort,i}$ the vector orthogonal to the $(n_a - 1)$-dimensional subspace $\mathcal{F}_i$ that contains the feasible f_a, and $\mathcal{S}_i = A_{a,i}^{\dagger} \mathcal{F}_i$. We project this subspace on $\mathcal{A}_{a,1}$ and obtain $\mathcal{F}_{1i} = A_{a,1} A_{a,i}^{\dagger} \mathcal{F}_i$ that we describe through its orthogonal vector $f^{ort,1i} = A_{a,1} A_{a,i}^{\dagger} f^{ort,i}$. If the vectors $f^{ort,1}, f^{ort,12}, \ldots f^{ort,1n_a}$ are linearly independent, it means that the $(n_a - 1)$-dimensional subspaces $\mathcal{F}_1, \mathcal{F}_{12}, \ldots \mathcal{F}_{1n_a}$ intersect themselves in one point. In Figure 4b it is shown an example in which, in the case $n_a = 3$ the vectors $f^{ort,1}, f^{ort,12}, f^{ort,13}$ are not linearly independent. The three solution sets of this example will intersect in two points, hence, for $n_a = 3$, three tests are not always sufficient to determine a unique solution.

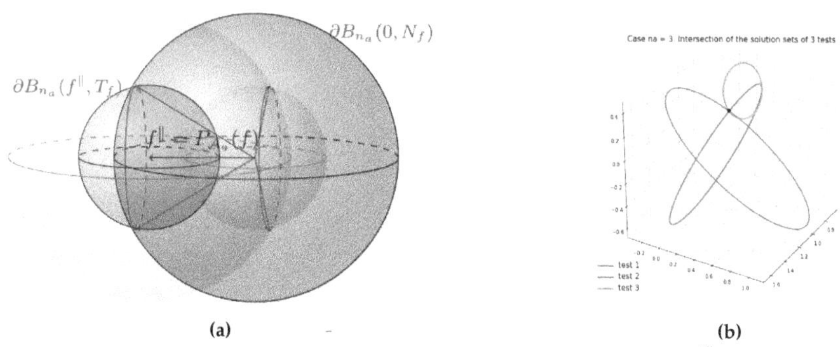

(a) (b)

Figure 3. Case $n_a = 3$. (**a**): Case $n_a = 3$, $m = n = 4$, $n - n_a = 1$: in the picture $\bar{f}^{\|}$, i.e., the projection of f on $\mathcal{A}_a$. The decompositions that satisfies the conditions on I_f and N_f are the ones with f_a that lies on the red circumference on the left. The spheres determined by the conditions are shown in yellow for the vector f_a and in blue for the vector $f^{\|} - a_a$. Two feasible decompositions are shown in blue and green; (**b**): Case $n_a = 3$. Intersection of three hyperellipsoids, set of the solutions x_a of three different tests, in the space $\mathbb{R}^{n_a=3}$.

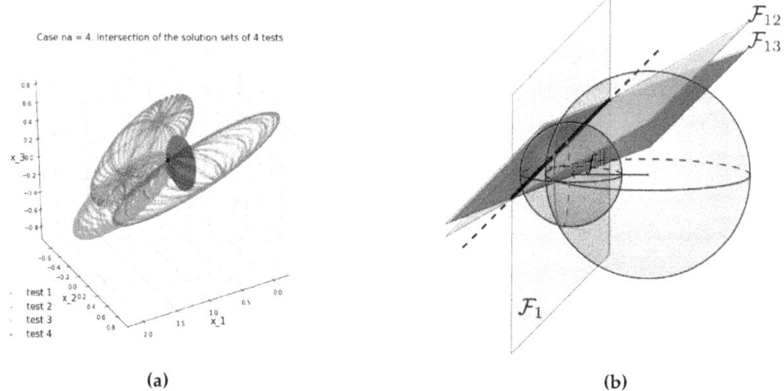

(a) (b)

Figure 4. Case $n_a \geq 3$. (**a**): Case $n_a = 4$. Intersection of four hyperellipsoids, set of the solutions x_a of four different tests, in the space $\mathbb{R}^{n_a=4}$; (**b**): Case $n_a = 3$. Example of three tests for which the solution has an intersection bigger than one single point. The three $(n_a - 1)$-dimensional subspaces $\mathcal{F}_1, \mathcal{F}_{12}, \mathcal{F}_{13}$ in the space generated by $A_{a,1}$ intersect in a line and their three orthogonal vectors are not linearly independent.

Lemma 4. *For all $n_a > 1$, the condition that, given $i = 1, \ldots, n_a$ tests, the n_a hyperplanes $\mathcal{S}_i = A^{\dagger}_{a,i}\mathcal{F}_i$ previously defined have linearly independent normal vectors is sufficient to determine one unique intersection, i.e., one unique solution vector $\bar{x}_a$, that satisfies the system of conditions (4) for each test.*

Proof. The intersection of n_a independent hyperplanes in $\mathbb{R}^{n_a}$ is a point. Given a test i and $\mathcal{S}_i = A^{\dagger}_{a,i}\mathcal{F}_i$ the affine subspace of that test

$$\mathcal{S}_i = v_i + W_i = \{v_i + w \in \mathbb{R}^{n_a} \, : \, w \cdot \mathbf{n}_i = 0\} = \{x \in \mathbb{R}^{n_a} \, : \, \mathbf{n}_i^T(x - v_i) = 0\},$$

where $\mathbf{n}_i$ is the normal vector of the linear subspace and v_i the translation with respect to the origin.

The conditions on $\mathcal{S}_i$ relative to n_a tests correspond to a linear system $Ax = b$, where $\mathbf{n}_i$ is the i-th row of A and each component of the vector b given by $b_i = \mathbf{n}_i^T v_i$. The matrix A has full rank because of the linear independence condition of the vectors $\mathbf{n}_i$, hence the solution of the linear system is unique.

The unique intersection is due to the hypothesis of full column rank of the matrices $A_{a,i}$: this condition implies that the matrices $A_{a,i}$ map the surfaces $\mathcal{F}_i$ to hyperplanes $\mathcal{S}_i = A_{a,i}\mathcal{F}_i$. □

For example, with $n_a = 2$ (Lemma 3) this condition is equal to considering two tests with non-coincident lines $\mathcal{S}_1, \mathcal{S}_2$, i.e., two non-coincident $\mathcal{F}_1, \mathcal{F}_{12}$.

3.2. *The Case of Approximate Knowledge of I_f and N_f Values*

Let us consider N tests and call $I_{f,i}$, $N_{f,i}$ and $T_{f,i}$ the values as defined in Lemma 2, relative to test i. Since the system of conditions

$$\begin{cases} N_{f,i} = \|A_{a,i}x_a\| \\ I_{f,i} = \frac{\|A_{a,i}x_a\|}{\|z_i - A_{a,i}x_a\|} \end{cases} \quad \text{and} \quad \begin{cases} N_{f,i} = \|A_{a,i}x_a\| \\ T_{f,i} = \|f_i^{\|} - A_{a,i}x_a\| \end{cases} \tag{14}$$

is equivalent, as shown in Lemma 2, we will take into account the system on the right for its simplicity: the equation on $T_{f,i}$ represents an hyperellipsoid, translated with respect to the origin.

In a real application, we can assume to know only an interval in which the true values of I_f is contained and, analogously, an interval for N_f values. Supposing we know the bounds on I_f and N_f, then the bounds on T_f can be easily computed. Let us call these extreme values $N_f^{max}, N_f^{min}, T_f^{max}, T_f^{min}$, we will assume it always holds

$$\begin{cases} N_f^{max} \geq max_i(N_{f,i}), \\ N_f^{min} \leq min_i(N_{f,i}), \end{cases} \quad \text{and} \quad \begin{cases} T_f^{max} \geq max_i(T_{f,i}), \\ T_f^{min} \leq min_i(T_{f,i}), \end{cases} \tag{15}$$

for each i-th test of the considered set $i = 0, \ldots, N$.

Condition (4) is now relaxed as follows: the true solution $\bar{x}_a$ satisfies

$$\begin{cases} \|A_{a,i}\bar{x}_a\| \leq N_f^{max}, \\ \|A_{a,i}\bar{x}_a\| \geq N_f^{min}, \end{cases} \quad \text{and} \quad \begin{cases} \|A_{a,i}\bar{x}_a - f_i^{\|}\| \leq T_f^{max}, \\ \|A_{a,i}\bar{x}_a - f_i^{\|}\| \geq T_f^{min}, \end{cases} \tag{16}$$

for each i-th test of the considered set $i = 0, \ldots, N$.

Assuming the extremes to be non-coincident ($N_f^{min} \neq N_f^{max}$ and $T_f^{min} \neq T_f^{max}$), these conditions do not define a single point, i.e., the unique solution $\bar{x}_a$ (as in (4) of Section 3.1), but an entire closed region of the space that may be even not connected, and contains infinite possible solutions x different from $\bar{x}_a$.

In Figure 5 two examples, with $n_a = 2$, of the conditions for a single test are shown: on the left in the case of exact knowledge of the $N_{f,i}$ and $T_{f,i}$ values, and on the right with the knowledge of two intervals containing the right values.

Given a single test, the conditions (16) on a point x can be easily characterized. Given the condition

$$\|f_a\| = \|A_a x_a\| = N_f,$$

we write $x_a = \sum \chi_i v_i$ with v_i the vectors of the orthogonal basis, given by the columns V of the SVD decomposition $A_a = USV^T$. Then

$$f_a = A_a x_a = USV^T(\sum_i \chi_i v_i) = US(\sum_i \chi_i e_i) = U(\sum_i s_i \chi_i e_i) = \sum_i s_i \chi_i \mathbf{u}_i.$$

Since the norm condition $\|f_a\|^2 = \sum_i (s_i \chi_i)^2 = N_f^2$ holds, then we obtain the equation of the hyperellipsoid for x_a as:

$$\sum_i (s_i \chi_i)^2 = \sum_i \frac{\chi_i^2}{(\frac{1}{s_i})^2} = N_f^2. \tag{17}$$

The bounded conditions hence gives the region inside the two hyperellipsoids centered in the origin:

$$N_f^{min} \leq \sum_i \frac{\chi_i^2}{(\frac{1}{s_i})^2} \leq N_f^{max}. \tag{18}$$

Analogously for the I_f condition, the region inside the two translated hyperellipsoids:

$$T_f^{min} \leq \sum_i \frac{\chi_i^2}{(\frac{1}{s_i})^2} - f^{\|} \leq T_f^{max}. \tag{19}$$

Given a test i, each of the conditions (18) and (19), constrain $\bar{x}_a$ to lie inside a thick hyperellipsoid, i.e., the region between the two concentric hyperellipsoids. The intersection of these two conditions for test i is a zero-residual region that we call Z_{r_i}

$$Z_{r_i} = \{x \in \mathbb{R}^{n_a} \mid (18) \text{ and } (19) \text{ hold } \}. \tag{20}$$

It is easy to verify that if $N_{f,i}$ is equal to the assumed N_f^{min} or N_f^{max}, or $T_{f,i}$ is equal to the assumed T_f^{min} or T_f^{max}, the true solution will be on a border of the region Z_{r_i}, and if it holds for both $N_{f,i}$ and $T_{f,i}$ it will lie on a vertex.

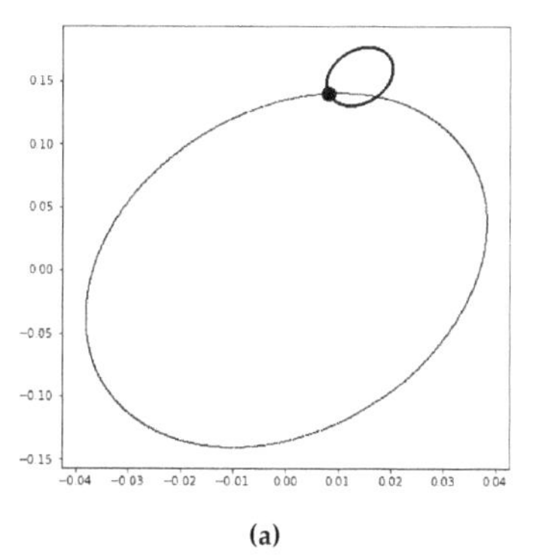

(a)

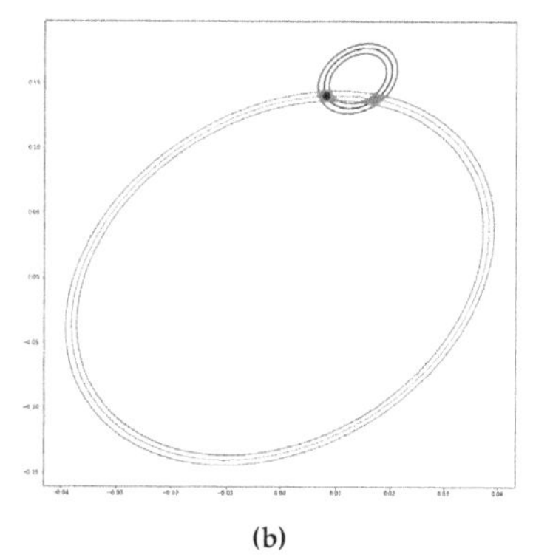

(b)

Figure 5. Examples of the exact and approximated conditions on a test with $n_a = 2$. In the left equation the two black ellipsoids are the two constraints of the right system of (14), while in the right figure the two couples of concentric ellipsoids are the borders of the thick ellipsoids defined by (16) and the blue region Z_{r_i} is the intersection of (18) and (19). The black dot in both the figures is the true solution. (**a**): Exact conditions on N_f and T_f; (**b**): Approximated conditions on N_f and T_f.

When more tests $i = 1, \ldots, N$ are put together, we have to consider the points that belong to the intersection of all these regions Z_{r_i}, i.e.,

$$I_{zr} = \bigcap_{i=0,\ldots,N} Z_{r_i}. \tag{21}$$

These points minimize, with zero residual, the following optimization problem:

$$\begin{aligned} \min_x \sum_{i=1}^{N} min(0, \|A_{a,i}x\| - N_f^{min})^2 + \sum_{i=1}^{N} max(0, \|A_{a,i}x\| - N_f^{max})^2 + \\ + \sum_{i=1}^{N} min(0, \|A_{a,i}x - f_i^{\|}\| - T_f^{min})^2 + \sum_{i=1}^{N} max(0, \|A_{a,i}x - f_i^{\|}\| - T_f^{max})^2. \end{aligned} \tag{22}$$

It is also easy to verify that, if the true solution lies on an edge/vertex of one of the regions Z_{r_i}, it will lie on an edge/vertex of their intersection.

The intersected region I_{zr} tends to monotonically shrink in a way that depends from the properties of the added tests. We are interested to study the conditions that make it reduce to a point, or at least to a small region. A sufficient condition to obtain a point is given in Theorem 1.

Let us first consider the function that, given a point in the space $\mathbb{R}^{n_a}$, returns the squared norm of its image through the matrix A_a:

$$N_f^2(x) = \|A_a x\|_2^2 = \|U\Sigma V^T x\|_2^2 = \|\Sigma V^T x\|_2^2 = (\Sigma V^T x)^T(\Sigma V^T x) = x^T(V\Sigma^T\Sigma V^T)x = \\ = \| \begin{bmatrix} \sigma_1 v_1^T x \\ \sigma_2 v_2^T x \\ \vdots \end{bmatrix} \|_2^2 = \sigma_1^2(v_1^T x)^2 + \sigma_2^2(v_2^T x)^2 + \ldots, \tag{23}$$

where v_i are the columns of V and $x = [x(1)\, x(2) \ldots, x(n_a)]$.

The direction of maximum increase of this function is given by its gradient

$$\nabla N_f^2(x) = 2(V\Sigma^2 V^T)x = \begin{bmatrix} 2\sigma_1^2 v_1^T x v_1(1) + 2\sigma_2^2 v_2^T x v_2(1) + \cdots + 2\sigma_{n_a}^2 v_{n_a}^T x v_{n_a}(1) \\ 2\sigma_1^2 v_1^T x v_1(2) + 2\sigma_2^2 v_2^T x v_2(2) + \cdots + 2\sigma_{n_a}^2 v_{n_a}^T x v_{n_a}(2) \\ \vdots \end{bmatrix}. \tag{24}$$

Analogously, define the function $T_f^2(x)$ as

$$T_f^2(x) = \|A_a x - f^{\|}\|_2^2 = \|U\Sigma V^T x - f^{\|}\|_2^2 = \|\Sigma V^T x - f^{\|}\|_2^2 = \\ = (\Sigma V^T x - f^{\|})^T(\Sigma V^T x - f^{\|}) = (\Sigma V^T x)^T(\Sigma V^T x) - 2(\Sigma V^T x)^T f^{\|} + (f^{\|})^T(f^{\|}) \\ = x(V\Sigma^2 V^T)x - 2(x)^T V\Sigma f^{\|} + (f^{\|})^T(f^{\|}) = \\ = \left\| \begin{bmatrix} \sigma_1 v_1^T x \\ \sigma_2 v_2^T x \\ \vdots \end{bmatrix} - f^{\|} \right\|_2^2 \tag{25}$$

with gradient

$$\nabla T_f^2(x) = 2(V\Sigma^2 V^T)x - 2V\Sigma f^{\|} = \\ = \begin{bmatrix} 2\sigma_1^2 v_1^T x v_1(1) + 2\sigma_2^2 v_2^T x v_2(1) + \cdots + 2\sigma_{n_a}^2 v_{n_a}^T x v_{n_a}(1) \\ \vdots \\ 2\sigma_1^2 v_1^T x v_1(j) + 2\sigma_2^2 v_2^T x v_2(j) + \cdots + 2\sigma_{n_a}^2 v_{n_a}^T x v_{n_a}(j) \\ \vdots \end{bmatrix} - \begin{bmatrix} -2\sigma_i^2 \sum_i f^{\|}(i) v_i(1) \\ \vdots \\ -2\sigma_i^2 \sum_i f^{\|}(i) v_i(j) \\ \vdots \end{bmatrix}. \tag{26}$$

Definition 2. *(Upward/Downward Outgoing Gradients) Take a test i, and the functions $N_f^2(x)$ and $T_f^2(x)$ as in (23) and (25), with the formulas of the gradient vectors of these two functions $\nabla N_{f,i}(x)$, $\nabla T_{f,i}(x)$ as in (24) and (26). Given the two extreme values $N_f^{min/max}$ and $T_f^{min/max}$ for each test, let us define*

- *the downward outgoing gradients as the set of gradients calculated on the points on the minimum hyperellipsoid*

$$\{-\nabla N_{f,i}(x) \mid N_{f,i}(x) = N_f^{min}\} \quad \text{and} \quad \{-\nabla T_{f,i}(x) \mid T_{f,i}(x) = T_f^{min}\} \tag{27}$$

  they point inward to the region of the thick hyperellipsoid.
- *the Upward Outgoing Gradients as the set of negative gradients of points on the maximum hyperellipsoid*

$$\{\nabla N_{f,i}(x) \mid N_{f,i}(x) = N_f^{max}\} \quad \text{and} \quad \{\nabla T_{f,i}(x) \mid T_{f,i}(x) = T_f^{max}\} \tag{28}$$

they point outward the region.

Note that the upward/downward outgoing gradient of function $N_f^2(x)$ (or $T_f^2(x)$) on point x is the normal vector to the tangent plane on the hyperellipsoid on which the point lies. Moreover, these vectors point outward the region defined by Equation (18) (and (19) respectively). In Figure 6, an example of some upward/downward outgoing gradients of function $N_f^2(x)$ is shown.

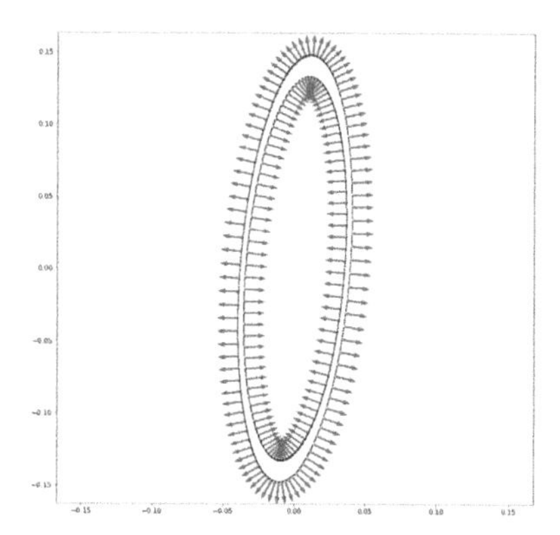

Figure 6. In the figure some upward/downward outgoing gradients are shown: the blue internal ones are downward outgoing gradients calculated on points x on the internal ellipsoid with $N_{f,i}(x) = N_f^{min}$, while the external red ones are upward outgoing gradients calculated on points x on the external ellipsoid with $N_{f,i}(x) = N_f^{max}$.

Theorem 1. *Given N tests with values $I_{f,i}$ and $N_{f,i}$ in the closed intervals $[I_f^{min}, I_f^{max}]$ and $[N_f^{min}, N_f^{max}]$, take the set of all the upward/downward outgoing gradients of functions $N_{f,i}^2(x)$ and $T_{f,i}^2(x)$ calculated in the true solution $\bar{x}_a$, i.e.,*

$$\begin{aligned} &\{\nabla N_{f,i}(\bar{x}_a)\, \text{for } i = 1, \ldots, N \mid N_{f,i}(\bar{x}_a) = N_f^{max}\} \cup \{\nabla N_{f,i}(\bar{x}_a)\, \text{for } i = 1, \ldots, N \mid N_{f,i}(\bar{x}_a) = N_f^{min}\} \cup \\ &\cup \{\nabla T_{f,i}(\bar{x}_a)\, \text{for } i = 1, \ldots, N \mid T_{f,i}(\bar{x}_a) = T_f^{max}\} \cup \{\nabla T_{f,i}(\bar{x}_a)\, \text{for } i = 1, \ldots, N \mid T_{f,i}(\bar{x}_a) = T_f^{min}\}. \end{aligned} \tag{29}$$

If there is at least one outgoing gradient of this set in each orthant of $\mathbb{R}^{n_a}$, then the intersection region I_{zr} of Equation (21) reduces to a point.

Proof. What we want to show is that given any perturbation δ_x of the real solution $\bar{x}_a$, there exists at least one condition among (18) and (19) that is not satisfied by the new perturbed point $\bar{x}_a + \delta_x$.

Any sufficiently small perturbation δ_x in an orthant in which lies an upward/downward outgoing gradient (from now on "Gradient"), determines an increase/decrease in the value of the hyperellipsoid function relative to that Gradient, that makes the relative condition to be unsatisfied.

Hence, if the Gradient in the orthant considered is upward, it satisfies $N_{f,i}(\bar{x}_a) = N_f^{max}$ (or analogously with $T_{f,i}$) and for each perturbation δ_x in the same orthant we obtain

$$N_{f,i}(\bar{x}_a + \delta_x) > N_{f,i}(\bar{x}_a) = N_f^{max}$$

(or analogously with $T_{f,i}$). In the same way, if the Gradient is downward we obtain

$$N_{f,i}(\bar{x}_a + \delta_x) < N_{f,i}(\bar{x}_a) = N_f^{min}$$

(or analogously with $T_{f,i}$).

When in one orthant there are more than one Gradient, it means that more than one condition will be unsatisfied by the perturbed point $\bar{x}_a + \delta_x$ for a sufficiently small δ_x in that orthant. □

4. Problem Solution

The theory previously presented allows us to build a solution algorithm that can deal with different a-priori information. We will start in Section 4.1 with the ideal case, i.e., with exact knowledge of I_f and N_f. Then, we generalize to a more practical setting, where we suppose to know an interval that contains the T_f values of all the experiments considered and an interval for the N_f values. Hence, the estimate solution will satisfy Equations (18) and (19). In this case we describe an algorithm for computing an estimate of the solution, that we will test in Section 5 against a toy model.

4.1. Exact Knowledge of I_f and N_f

When the information about I_f and N_f is exact, with the minimum amount of experiments indicated in Section 3 we can find the unbiased parameter estimate as the intersection I_{zr} of the zero-residual sets Z_{r_i} corresponding to each experiment. In principle this could be done also following the proof of Lemma 4, but the computation of the v_i vectors is quite cumbersome. Since this is an ideal case, we solve it by simply imposing the satisfaction of the various N_f and T_f conditions (Equation (14)) as an optimization problem:

$$\min_x F(x) \quad \text{with} \quad F(x) = \sum_{i=1}^{N} (\|A_{a,i}x\| - N_{f,i})^2 + \sum_{i=1}^{N} (\|A_{a,i}x - f_i^{\|}\| - T_{f,i})^2. \tag{30}$$

The solution of this problem is unique when the tests are in a sufficient number and satisfies the conditions of Lemma 4.

This nonlinear least-squares problem can be solved using a general nonlinear optimization algorithm, like Gauss–Newton method or Levenberg–Marquardt [8].

4.2. Approximate Knowledge of I_f and N_f

In practice, as already pointed out in Section 3.2, it is more realistic to know the two intervals that contain all the $N_{f,i}$ and $I_{f,i}$ values for each test i. Then, we know that within the region I_{zr} there is also the exact unbiased parameter solution $\bar{x}_a$, that we want at least to approximate. We introduce here an Unbiased Least-Squares (ULS) Algorithm 1 for the computation of this estimate.

Algorithm 1 An Unbiased Least-Squares (ULS) algorithm.

1: Given a number n_{tests} of available tests, indexed with a number between 1 and n_{tests}, and two intervals, $\left[I_f^{min}, I_f^{max}\right]$ and $\left[N_f^{min}, N_f^{max}\right]$, containing the I_f and N_f values of all tests.
2: At each iteration we will consider the tests indexed by the interval $[1, i_t]$; set initially $i_t = n_a$.
3: **while** $i_t \leq n_{tests}$ **do**
4: 1) compute a solution with zero residual of the problem (22) with a nonlinear least-squares optimization algorithm,
5: 2) estimate the size of the zero-residual region as described below in (31),
6: 3) increment by one the number i_t of tests.
7: **end while**
8: Accept the final solution if the estimated region diameter is sufficiently small.

In general, the zero-residual region Z_{r_i} of each test contains the true point of the parameters vector, while the estimated iterates with the local optimization usually start from a point outside this region and converge to a point on the boundary of the region.

The ULS estimate can converge to the true solution in two cases:

1. the true solution lies on the border of the region I_{zr} and the estimate reach the border on that point;
2. the region I_{zr} reduces to a dimension smaller than the required accuracy, or reduces to a point.

The size of the intersection set I_{zr}, of the zero-residual regions Z_{r_i}, is estimated in the following way.

Let us define an index, that we call region shrinkage estimate, as follows:

$$\hat{s}(x) = min\{n \mid \sum_{\delta \in \mathcal{P}} \Delta_{I_{zr}}(x + \mu^{-n}\delta) > 0\}, \tag{31}$$

where we used $\mu = 1.5$ in the experiments below, $\mathcal{P} = \{\delta \in \mathbb{R}^{n_a} \mid \delta(i) \in (-1,0,1)\ \forall i = 1,\ldots,n_a\}$ and $\Delta_{I_{zr}}$ is the Dirac function of the set I_{zr}.

5. Numerical Examples

Let us consider a classical application example, the equations of a DC motor with a mechanical load, where the electrical variables are governed by the following ordinary differential equation

$$\begin{cases} L\dot{I}(t) &= -K\omega(t) - RI(t) + V(t) - f_u(t) \\ I(t_0) &= I_0, \end{cases} \tag{32}$$

where I is the motor current, ω the motor angular speed, V the applied voltage, and $f_u(t)$ a possible unmodelled component

$$f_u(t) = -m_{err}cos(n_{poles}\theta(t)), \tag{33}$$

where n_{poles} is the number of poles of the motor, i.e., the number of windings or magnets [9], m_{err} the magnitude of the error model and θ the angle, given by the system

$$\begin{cases} \dot{\omega}(t) &= \theta(t) \\ \omega(t_0) &= \omega_0. \end{cases} \tag{34}$$

Note that the unknown component f_u of this example can be seen as a difference in the potential that is not described by the approximated model. We are interested in the estimation of parameters $[L, K, R]$. In our test the true values were constant values $[L = 0.0035, K = 0.14, R = 0.53]$.

We suppose to know the measurements of I and ω at equally spaced times $t_0, \ldots, t_{\tilde{N}}$ with step h, such that $t_k = t_0 + kh$, and $t_{k+1} = t_k + h$. In Figure 7 we see the plots of the motor speed ω and of the unknown component f_u for this experiment.

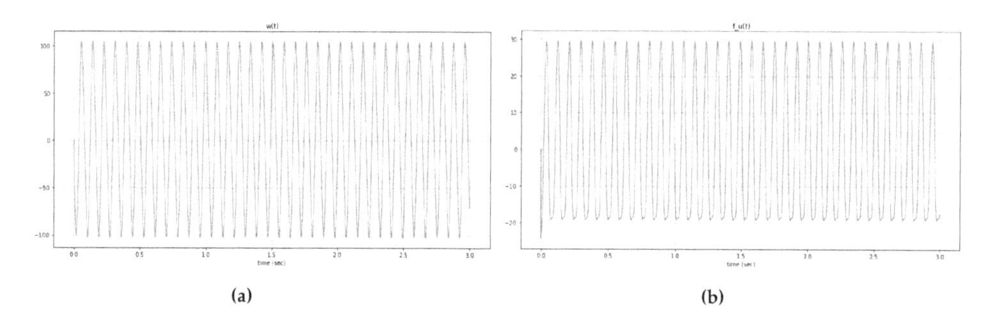

Figure 7. The plots of (**a**) $\omega(t)$ and (**b**) $f_u(t)$ in the experiment.

We compute the approximation of the derivative of the current signal $\hat{\dot{I}}(t_k)$ with the forward finite difference formula of order one

$$\hat{\dot{I}}(t_k) = \frac{I(t_k) - I(t_{k-1})}{h}, \quad \text{for} \quad t_k = t_1, \ldots, t_{\tilde{N}}$$

with a step $h = 4 \times 10^{-4}$. The applied voltage is held constant to the value $V(t) = 30.0$.

To obtain a more accurate estimate, or to allow the possibility of using higher step size values h, finite differences of higher order can be used, for example the fourth order difference formula

$$\hat{I}(t_k) = \frac{I(t_k - 2h) - 8I(t_k - h) + 8I(t_k + h) - I(t_k + 2h)}{12h}, \qquad \text{for} \quad t_k = t_2, \ldots, t_{\bar{N}-2}.$$

With the choice of the finite difference formula, we obtain the discretized equations

$$L\hat{I}(t_k) = -K\omega(t_k) - RI(t_k) + V(t_k) - f_u(t_k), \qquad \text{for} \quad t_k = t_1, \ldots, t_{\bar{N}}. \tag{35}$$

We will show a possible implementation of the method explained in the previous sections, and the results we get with this toy-model example. The comparison is made against the standard least-squares. In particular, we will show that when the information about I_f and N_f is exact, we have an exact removal of the bias. In case this information is only approximate, which is common in a real application, we will show how the bias asymptotically disappears when the number of experiments increases.

We build each test taking the Equation (35) for n samples in the range $t_1, \ldots, t_{\bar{N}}$, obtaining the linear system

$$\begin{bmatrix} \hat{I}(t_k) & \omega(t_k) & I(t_k) \\ \hat{I}(t_{k+1}) & \omega(t_{k+1}) & I(t_{k+1}) \\ \vdots & \vdots & \vdots \\ \hat{I}(t_{k+n}) & \omega(t_{k+n}) & I(t_{k+n}) \end{bmatrix} \begin{bmatrix} L \\ K \\ R \end{bmatrix} + \begin{bmatrix} f_u(t_k) \\ f_u(t_{k+1}) \\ \vdots \\ f_u(t_{k+n}) \end{bmatrix} = \begin{bmatrix} V(t_k) \\ V(t_{k+1}) \\ \vdots \\ V(t_{k+n}) \end{bmatrix} \tag{36}$$

so that the first matrix in the equation is $A_a \in \mathbb{R}^{n \times n_a}$ with $n_a = 3$, the number of parameters to be estimated.

To measure the estimation relative error $\hat{e}_{rel}$ we will use the following formula, where $\hat{x}_a$ is the parameter estimate:

$$\hat{e}_{rel} = \frac{1}{n_a} \sum_{i=1}^{n_a} \frac{||\hat{x}_a(i) - \bar{x}_a(i)||_2}{||\bar{x}_a(i)||_2}. \tag{37}$$

Note that the tests that we built in the numerical experiments below are simply small chunks of consecutive data, taken from one single simulation for each experiment.

The results have been obtained with a Python code developed by the authors, using NumPy for linear algebra computations and `scipy.optimize` for the nonlinear least-squares optimization.

5.1. Exact Knowledge of I_f and N_f

As analyzed in Section 4.1, the solution of the minimization problem (30) is computed with a local optimization algorithm.

Here the obtained results show an error $\hat{e}_{rel}$ with an order of magnitude of 10^{-7} in every test we made. Note that it is also possible to construct geometrically the solution, with exact results.

5.2. Approximate Knowledge of I_f and N_f

When I_f and N_f are known only approximately, i.e., we know only an interval that contains all the I_f values and an interval that contains all the N_f values, we lose the unique intersection of Lemma 4, that would require only n_a tests. Moreover, with a finite number of tests we cannot guarantee in general to satisfy the exact hypotheses of Theorem 1. As a consequence, various issues open up. Let's start by showing in Figure 8 that when all the four conditions of (15) hold with equality, the true solution lies on the boundary of the region I_{zr} as already mentioned in Section 3.2. If this happens, then with the conditions of Theorem 1 on the upward/downward outgoing gradients, the region I_{zr} is a point. When all the four conditions of (15) hold with strict inequalities, the true solution lies inside the region I_{zr} (Figure 8b). From a theoretical point of view this distinction has a big importance, since it means that the zero-residual region can or cannot be reduced to a single point. From a practical point of view it becomes less important, for the moment, since we cannot guarantee that the available tests will reduce I_{zr} exactly to a single point and we will arrive most of the times to an approximate estimate. This can be more or less accurate, but this depends on the specific application, and this is out of the scope of the present work.

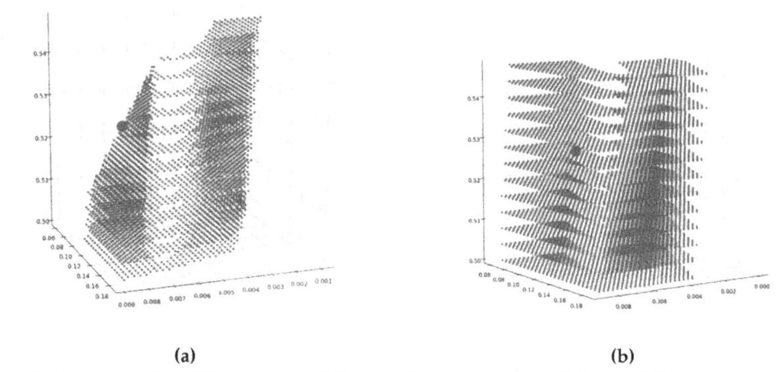

(a) (b)

Figure 8. Two examples of (zero-residual) intersection regions $I_{zr} \subset \mathbb{R}^3$ with different location of the true solution: inside the region or on its border. For graphical reasons the region has been discretized and the dots are the grid nodes; the bigger ball (thick point) is the true solution. (**a**): The true solution (ball) is on the border of I_{zr}; (**b**): The true solution (ball) is internal to I_{zr}.

To be more precise, when the conditions of Theorem 1 are not satisfied, there is an entire region of the parameters space which satisfies exactly problem (30), but only one point of this region is the true solution $\bar{x}_a$. As more tests are added and intersected together, the zero-residual region I_{zr} tends to reduce, simply because it must satisfy an increasing number of inequalities. In Figure 9 we can see four iterations taken from an example, precisely with 3, 5, 9 and 20 tests intersected and $m_{err} = 19$. With only three tests (Figure 9a), there is a big region I_{zr} (described by the mesh of small dots), and here we see that the true solution (thick point) and the current estimate (star) stay on opposite sides of the region, as accidentally happens. With five tests (Figure 9a) the region has shrunk considerably and the estimate is reaching the boundary (in the plot it is still half-way), and even more with nine tests (Figure 9c). The convergence arrives here before the region collapses to a single point, because accidentally the estimate has approached the region boundary at the same point where the true solution is located.

In general, the zero-residual region Z_{r_i} (20) of each test contains the true solution, while the estimate arrives from outside the region and stops when it bumps the border of the intersection region I_{zr} (21). For this reason we have convergence when the region that contains the true solution is reduced to a single point, and the current estimate $\hat{x}_a$ does not lie in a disconnected sub-region of I_{zr} different from the one in which the true solution lies. Figure 10 shows an example of an intersection region I_{zr} which is the union of two closed disconnected regions: this case creates a local minimum in problem (30).

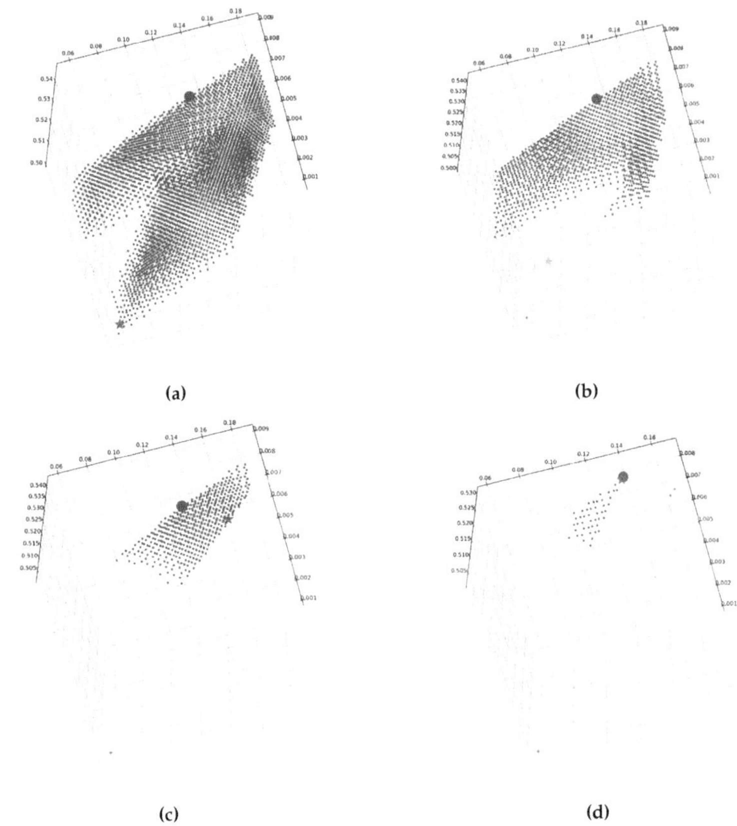

Figure 9. The intersection region $I_{zr} \subset \mathbb{R}^3$ at different number of tests involved. For graphical reasons the region has been discretized and the dots are the grid nodes; the bigger ball is the true solution and the star is the current estimate in the experiment. (**a**) 3 tests; (**b**) 5 tests; (**c**) 9 tests; (**d**) 20 tests.

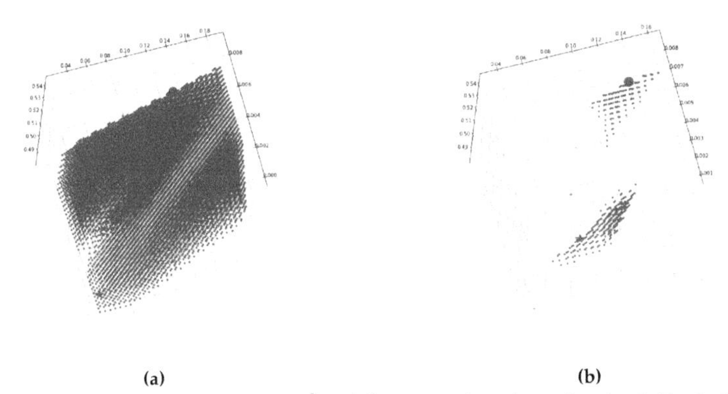

Figure 10. The intersection region $I_{zr} \subset \mathbb{R}^3$ at different number of tests involved. On the left a few tests have created a single connected region while, on the right, adding more tests have splitted it into two subregions. For graphical reasons the region has been discretized and the dots are the grid nodes; the bigger ball is the true solution and the star is the current estimate in the experiment. (**a**) A (portion of a) connected region I_{zr}; (**b**) A region I_{zr} split into two not connected sub regions.

In Figure 11 we see the differences $N_f^{max} - N_f^{min}$ and $T_f^{max} - T_f^{min}$ vs. m_{err}. The differences are bigger for higher values of the model error. It seems that this is the cause of a more frequent creation of local minima.

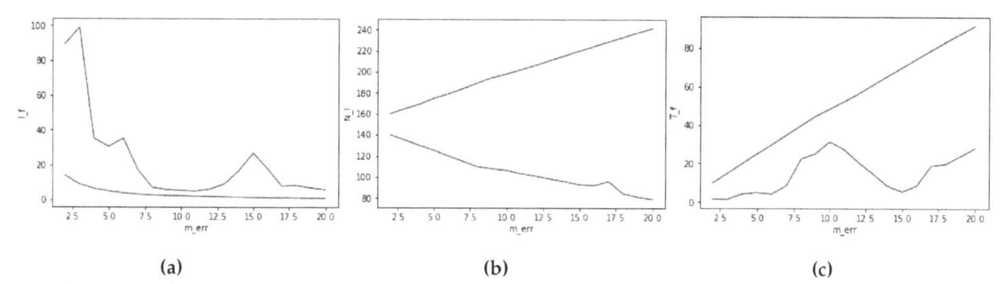

(a) (b) (c)

Figure 11. The three plots show the values assumed by the extreme values (15) as a function of m_{err}. (**a**): $\{I_f^{min}, I_f^{max}\}$ vs. m_{err}; (**b**): $\{N_f^{min}, N_f^{max}\}$ vs. m_{err}; (**c**) $\{T_f^{min}, T_f^{max}\}$ vs. m_{err}.

Figure 12 synthesizes the main results that we have experienced with this new approach. Globally it shows a great reduction of the bias contained in the standard least-squares estimates; indeed, we had to use the logarithmic scale to enhance the differences in the behaviour of the proposed method while varying m_{err}. In particular,

- with considerable levels of modelling error, let us say m_{err} between 2 and 12, the parameter estimation error $\hat{e}_{rel}$ is at least one order of magnitude smaller that that of least-squares; this is accompanied by high levels of shrinkage of the zero-residual region (Figure 12b);
- with higher levels of m_{err}, we see a low shrinkage of the zero-residual region and consequently an estimate whose error is highly oscillating, depending on where the optimization algorithm has brought it to get in contact with the zero-residual region;
- at $m_{err} = 18$ we see the presence of a local minimum, due to the falling to pieces of the zero-residual region as in Figure 10: the shrinkage at the true solution is estimated to be very high, while at the estimated solution it is quite low, since it is attached to a disconnected, wider sub-region.
- the shrinking of the zero-residual region is related to the distribution of the outgoing gradients, as stated by Theorem 1: in Figure 12d we see that in the experiment with $m_{err} = 18$ they occupy only three of eight orthants, while in the best results of the other experiments the gradients distribute themselves in almost all orthants (not shown).

It is evident from these results that for lower values of modelling error m_{err}, it is much easier to produce tests that reduce the zero-residual region to a quite small interval of R^{n_a}, while for high values of m_{err} it is much more difficult and the region I_{zr} can even fall to pieces, thus creating local minima. It is also evident that a simple estimate of the I_{zr} region size, like (31), can reliably assess the quality of the estimate produced by the approach here proposed, as summarized in Figure 12c.

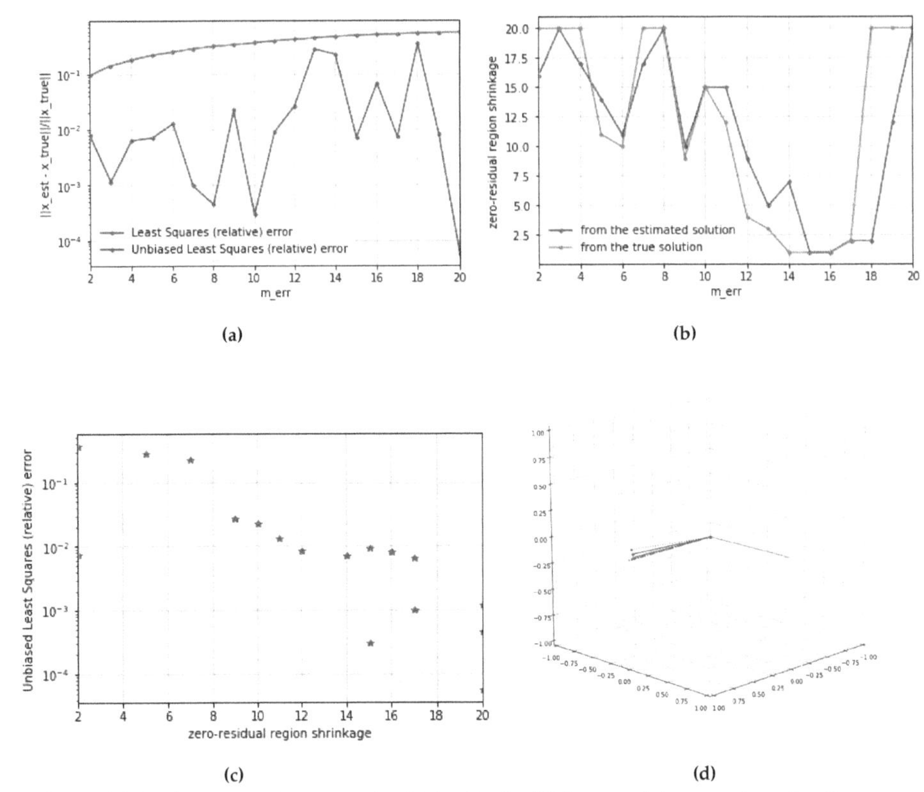

Figure 12. The plots summarize the results obtained by the ULS approach to parameter estimation no the model problem explained at the beginning of this section. (**a**): The relative estimation error (37) vs. m_{err}; (**b**): The I_{zr} region shrinkage estimate (31) vs. m_{err}; (**c**): The relative estimation error (37) vs. the estimate of the I_{zr} region shrinkage, considering the experiments with $m_{err} \in [2, 20]$; (**d**): A three dimensional view of the Outgoing Gradients at the last iteration of the experiment with $m_{err} = 18$.

6. Conclusions

In this paper we have analyzed the bias commonly arising in parameter estimation problems where the model is lacking some deterministic part of the system. This result is useful in applications where an accurate estimation of parameters is important, e.g., in physical (grey-box) modelling typically arising in the model-based design of multi-physical systems, see e.g., the motivations that the authors did experience in the design of digital twins of controlled systems [10–12] for virtual prototyping, among an actually huge literature.

At this point, the method should be tested in a variety of applications, since the ULS approach here proposed is not applicable black-box as Least-Squares are. Indeed, it requires some additional a priori information. Moreover, since the computational complexity of the method here presented is relevant, efficient computational methods must be considered and will be a major issue in future investigations.

Another aspect that is even worth to deepen is also the possibility to design tests that contribute optimally to the reduction of the zero-residual region.

Author Contributions: Conceptualization, methodology, validation, formal analysis, investigation, software, resources, data curation, writing—original draft preparation, writing—review and editing, visualization: M.G. and F.M.; supervision, project administration, funding acquisition: F.M. All authors have read and agreed to the published version of the manuscript.

Funding: This research was funded by the project DOR1983079/19 from the University of Padova and by the doctoral grant "Calcolo ad alte prestazioni per il Model Based Design" from Electrolux Italia s.p.a.

Conflicts of Interest: The authors declare no conflict of interest.

References

1. Björck, A. *Numerical Methods for Least Squares Problems*; Society for Industrial and Applied Mathematics: Philadelphia, PA, USA, 1996. [CrossRef]
2. Huffel, S.V.; Markovsky, I.; Vaccaro, R.J.; Söderström, T. Total least squares and errors-in-variables modeling. *Signal Process.* **2007**, *87*, 2281–2282. [CrossRef]
3. Söderström, T.; Soverini, U.; Mahata, K. Perspectives on errors-in-variables estimation for dynamic systems. *Signal Process.* **2002**, *82*, 1139–1154. [CrossRef]
4. Van Huffel, S.; Vandewalle, J. *The Total Least Squares Problem: Computational Aspects and Analysis*; Frontiers in Applied Mathematics (Book 9); Society for Industrial and Applied Mathematics: Philadelphia, PA, USA, 1991.
5. Peck, C.C.; Beal, S.L.; Sheiner, L.B.; Nichols, A.I. Extended least squares nonlinear regression: A possible solution to the "choice of weights" problem in analysis of individual pharmacokinetic data. *J. Pharmacokinet. Biopharm.* **1984**, *12*, 545–558. [CrossRef] [PubMed]
6. Meyer, C.D. *Matrix Analysis and Applied Linear Algebra*; Society for Industrial and Applied Mathematics: Philadelphia, PA, USA, 2000.
7. Hansen, P.C. Oblique projections and standard-form transformations for discrete inverse problems. *Numer. Linear Algebra Appl.* **2013**, *20*, 250–258. [CrossRef]
8. Nocedal, J.; Wright, S. *Numerical Optimization*; Springer: Berlin, Germany, 1999.
9. Krause, P.C. *Analysis of Electric Machinery*; McGraw Hill: New York, NY, USA, 1986.
10. Beghi, A.; Marcuzzi, F.; Rampazzo, M.; Virgulin, M. Enhancing the Simulation-Centric Design of Cyber-Physical and Multi-physics Systems through Co-simulation. In Proceedings of the 2014 17th Euromicro Conference on Digital System Design, Verona, Italy, 27–29 August 2014; pp. 687–690. [CrossRef]
11. Beghi, A.; Marcuzzi, F.; Rampazzo, M. A Virtual Laboratory for the Prototyping of Cyber-Physical Systems. *IFAC-PapersOnLine* **2016**, *49*, 63–68. [CrossRef]
12. Beghi, A.; Marcuzzi, F.; Martin, P.; Tinazzi, F.; Zigliotto, M. Virtual prototyping of embedded control software in mechatronic systems: A case study. *Mechatronics* **2017**, *43*, 99–111. [CrossRef]

Article

Improved Conditions for Oscillation of Functional Nonlinear Differential Equations

Omar Bazighifan [1,2,†] and Mihai Postolache [3,4,5,*,†]

1 Department of Mathematics, Faculty of Science, Hadhramout University, Hadhramout 50512, Yemen; o.bazighifan@gmail.com
2 Department of Mathematics, Faculty of Education, Seiyun University, Hadhramout 50512, Yemen
3 Center for General Education, China Medical University, Taichung 40402, Taiwan
4 Department of Mathematics and Informatics, University Politehnica of Bucharest, 060042 Bucharest, Romania
5 Romanian Academy, Gh. Mihoc-C. Iacob Institute of Mathematical Statistics and Applied Mathematics, 050711 Bucharest, Romania
* Correspondence: mihai@mathem.pub.ro
† These authors contributed equally to this work.

Received: 17 March 2020; Accepted: 3 April 2020; Published: 9 April 2020

Abstract: The aim of this work is to study oscillatory properties of a class of fourth-order delay differential equations. New oscillation criteria are obtained by using generalized Riccati transformations. This new theorem complements and improves a number of results reported in the literature. Some examples are provided to illustrate the main results.

Keywords: oscillatory solutions; nonoscillatory solutions; fourth-order; delay differential equations; riccati transformation

1. Introduction

In this article, we investigate the asymptotic behavior of solutions of the fourth-order differential equation

$$\left(b(x)\left(w'''(x)\right)^{\kappa}\right)' + \sum_{i=1}^{j} q_i(x) f\left(w\left(\vartheta_i(x)\right)\right) = 0,\ x \geq x_0. \tag{1}$$

Throughout this paper, we assume the following conditions hold:

(Z_1) κ are quotient of odd positive integers;

(Z_2) $b \in C^1([x_0,\infty),\mathbb{R})$, $b(x) > 0,\ b'(x) \geq 0$ and under the condition

$$\int_{x_0}^{\infty} \frac{1}{b^{1/\kappa}(x)} \mathrm{d}x = \infty. \tag{2}$$

(Z_3) $q_i \in C[x_0,\infty),\ q(x) > 0,\ i = 1,2,\ldots,j,$

(Z_4) $\vartheta_i \in C[x_0,\infty),\ \vartheta_i(x) \leq x,\ \lim_{x\to\infty} \vartheta_i(x) = \infty;\ i = 1,2,..,j,$

(Z_5) $f \in C(\mathbb{R},\mathbb{R})$ such that

$$f(x)/x^{\kappa} \geq \ell > 0,\ \text{for } x \neq 0. \tag{3}$$

Definition 1. *The function $y \in C^3[\nu_y,\infty),\ \nu_y \geq \nu_0,$ is called a solution of equation (1), if $b(x)\left(w'''(x)\right)^{\kappa} \in C^1[x_w,\infty)$, and $w(x)$ satisfies (1) on $[x_w,\infty)$.*

Definition 2. *A solution of (1) is called oscillatory if it has arbitrarily large zeros on $[x_w, \infty)$, and otherwise is called to be nonoscillatory.*

Definition 3. *Equation (1) is said to be oscillatory if all its solutions are oscillatory.*

Differential equations arise in modeling situations to describe population growth, biology, economics, chemical reactions, neural networks, and in aeromechanical systems, etc.; see [1].

More and more scholars pay attention to the oscillatory solution of functional differential equations, see [2–5], especially for the second/third-order, see [6–8], or higher-order equations see [9–17]. With the development of the oscillation for the second-order equations, researchers began to study the oscillation for the fourth-order equations, see [18–25].

In the following, we show some previous results in the literature which related to this paper: Moaaz et al. [21] studied the fourth-order nonlinear differential equations with a continuously distributed delay

$$\left(b(x)\left((w(x))'''\right)^{\alpha}\right)' + \int_a^c q(x,\xi) f(w(g(x,\xi)))\,d\xi = 0, \tag{4}$$

by means of the theory of comparison with second-order delay equations, the authors established some oscillation criteria of (4) under the condition

$$\int_{x_0}^{\infty} \frac{1}{b^{1/\kappa}(x)}\mathrm{d}x < \infty. \tag{5}$$

Cesarano and Bazighifan [22] considered Equation (4), and established some new oscillation criteria by means of Riccati transformation technique.

Agarwal et al. [9] and Baculikova et al. [10] studied the equation

$$\left(\left(w^{(n-1)}(x)\right)^{\kappa}\right)' + q(x) f(w(\vartheta(x))) = 0 \tag{6}$$

and established some new sufficient conditions for oscillation.

Theorem 1 (See [9]). *If there exists a positive function $g \in C^1([x_0,\infty),(0,\infty))$, and $\theta > 1$ is a constant such that*

$$\limsup_{x\to\infty} \int_{x_0}^{x} \left(g(s)q(s) - \lambda\theta \frac{(g'(s))^{\kappa+1}}{(g(s)\vartheta^{n-2}(s)\vartheta'(s))^{\kappa}}\right)\mathrm{d}s = \infty, \tag{7}$$

where $\lambda := (1/(\kappa+1))^{\kappa+1}(2(n-1)!)^{\kappa}$, then every solution of (6) is oscillatory.

Theorem 2 (See [10]). *Let $f\left(x^{1/\kappa}\right)/x \ge 1$ for $0 < x \le 1$ such that*

$$\liminf_{x\to\infty} \int_{\vartheta_i(x)}^{x} q(s) f\left(\frac{\varsigma}{(n-1)!}\frac{\vartheta^{n-1}(s)}{b^{1/\kappa}(\vartheta(s))}\right)\mathrm{d}s > \frac{1}{\mathrm{e}} \tag{8}$$

for some $\varsigma \in (0,1)$, then every solution of (6) is oscillatory.

To prove this, we apply the previous results to the equation

$$w^{(4)}(x) + \frac{c_0}{x^4} w\left(\frac{9}{10}x\right) = 0,\ x \ge 1, \tag{9}$$

then we get that (9) is oscillatory if

The condition	(7)	(8)
The criterion	$c_0 > 60$	$c_0 > 28.7$

From above, we see that [10] improved the results in [9].

The motivation in studying this paper is complementary and improves the results in [9,10].

The paper is organized as follows. In Section 2, we state some lemmas, which will be useful in the proof of our results. In Section 3, by using generalized Riccati transformations, we obtain a new oscillation criteria for (1). Finally, some examples are considered to illustrate the main results.

For convenience, we denote

$$\delta(x) := \int_x^\infty \frac{1}{b^{1/\kappa}(s)} \mathrm{d}s, \; F_+(x) := \max\{0, F(x)\},$$

$$\psi(x) := g(x)\left(\ell \sum_{i=1}^{j} q_i(x)\left(\frac{\vartheta_i^3(x)}{x^3}\right)^\kappa + \frac{\varepsilon \beta_1^{(1+\kappa)/\kappa} x^2 - 2\beta_1 \kappa}{2b^{\frac{1}{\kappa}}(x)\,\delta^{\kappa+1}(x)}\right),$$

$$\phi(x) := \frac{g'_+(x)}{g(x)} + \frac{(\kappa+1)\beta_1^{1/\kappa}\varepsilon x^2}{2b^{\frac{1}{\kappa}}(x)\,\delta(x)}, \; \phi^*(x) := \frac{\xi'_+(x)}{\xi(x)} + \frac{2\beta_2}{\delta(x)},$$

and

$$\psi^*(x) := \xi(x)\left(\int_x^\infty \left(\frac{\ell}{b(v)} \int_v^\infty \sum_{i=1}^{j} q_i(s) \frac{\vartheta_i^\kappa(s)}{s^\kappa} \mathrm{d}s\right)^{1/\kappa} \mathrm{d}v + \frac{\beta_2^2 - \beta_2 b^{\frac{-1}{\kappa}}(x)}{\delta^2(x)}\right),$$

where β_1, β_2 are constants and $g, \xi \in C^1([x_0, \infty), (0, \infty))$.

Remark 1. *We define the generalized Riccati substitutions*

$$\pi(x) := g(x)\left(\frac{b(x)(w''')^\kappa(x)}{w^\kappa(x)} + \frac{\beta_1}{\delta^\kappa(x)}\right), \tag{10}$$

and

$$\varpi(x) := \xi(x)\left(\frac{w'(x)}{w(x)} + \frac{\beta_2}{\delta(x)}\right). \tag{11}$$

2. Some Auxiliary Lemmas

Next, we begin with the following lemmas.

Lemma 1 ([8]). *Let β be a ratio of two odd numbers, $V > 0$ and U are constants. Then,*

$$P^{(\beta+1)/\beta} - (P-Q)^{(\beta+1)/\beta} \leq \frac{1}{\beta} Q^{1/\beta}\left[(1+\beta)P - Q\right], \; PQ \geq 0, \; \beta \geq 1$$

and

$$Uw - Vw^{(\beta+1)/\beta} \leq \frac{\beta^\beta}{(\beta+1)^{\beta+1}} \frac{U^{\beta+1}}{V^\beta}.$$

Lemma 2 ([15]). *Suppose that $h \in C^n([x_0, \infty), (0, \infty))$, $h^{(n)}$ is of a fixed sign on $[x_0, \infty)$, $h^{(n)}$ not identically zero, and there exists a $x_1 \geq x_0$ such that*

$$h^{(n-1)}(x)\, h^{(n)}(x) \leq 0,$$

for all $x \geq x_1$. *If we have* $\lim_{x\to\infty} h(x) \neq 0$, *then there exists* $x_\beta \geq x_1$ *such that*

$$h(x) \geq \frac{\beta}{(n-1)!} x^{n-1} \left| h^{(n-1)}(x) \right|,$$

for every $\beta \in (0,1)$ *and* $x \geq x_\beta$.

Lemma 3 ([19]). *If the function* u *satisfies* $u^{(j)} > 0$ *for all* $j = 0, 1, ..., n$, *and* $u^{(n+1)} < 0$, *then*

$$\frac{n!}{x^n} u(x) - \frac{(n-1)!}{x^{n-1}} \frac{d}{dx} u(x) \geq 0.$$

3. Oscillation Criteria

In this section, we shall establish some oscillation criteria for Equation (1).

Upon studying the asymptotic behavior of the positive solutions of (1), there are only two cases:

$$\begin{array}{llll} \text{Case (1)}: & w^{(r)}(x) > 0 & \text{for} & r = 0,1,2,3. \\ \text{Case (2)}: & w^{(r)}(x) > 0 & \text{for} & r = 0,1,3 \text{ and } w''(x) < 0. \end{array}$$

Moreover, from Equation (1) and condition (3), we have that $\left(b(x)\left(w'''(x)\right)^\kappa\right)'$. In the following, we will first study each case separately.

Lemma 4. *Assume that* w *be an eventually positive solution of (1) and* $w^{(r)}(x) > 0$ *for all* $r = 1, 2, 3$. *If we have the function* $\pi \in C^1[x, \infty)$ *defined as (10), where* $g \in C^1([x_0, \infty), (0, \infty))$, *then*

$$\pi'(x) \leq -\psi(x) + \phi(x)\pi(x) - \frac{\kappa \varepsilon x^2}{2\left(b(x) g(x)\right)^{1/\kappa}} \pi^{\frac{\kappa+1}{\kappa}}(x), \tag{12}$$

for all $x > x_1$, *where* x_1 *is large enough.*

Proof. Let w be an eventually positive solution of (1) and $w^{(r)}(x) > 0$ for all $r = 1, 2, 3$. Thus, from Lemma 2, we get

$$w'(x) \geq \frac{\varepsilon}{2} x^2 w'''(x), \tag{13}$$

for every $\varepsilon \in (0,1)$ and for all large x. From (10), we see that $\pi(x) > 0$ for $x \geq x_1$, and

$$\begin{aligned} \pi'(x) &= g'(x)\left(\frac{b(x)\left(w'''\right)^\kappa(x)}{w^\kappa(x)} + \frac{\beta_1}{\delta^\kappa(x)}\right) + g(x)\frac{\left(b\left(w'''\right)^\kappa\right)'(x)}{w^\kappa(x)} \\ &\quad -\kappa g(x)\frac{w^{\kappa-1}(x)\, w'(x)\, b(x)\left(w'''\right)^\kappa(x)}{w^{2\kappa}(x)} + \frac{\kappa\beta_1 g(x)}{b^{\frac{1}{\kappa}}(x)\,\delta^{\kappa+1}(x)}. \end{aligned}$$

Using (13) and (10), we obtain

$$\begin{aligned} \pi'(x) &\leq \frac{g'_+(x)}{g(x)}\pi(x) + g(x)\frac{\left(b(x)\left(w'''(x)\right)^\kappa\right)'}{w^\kappa(x)} \\ &\quad -\kappa g(x)\frac{\varepsilon}{2}x^2\frac{b(x)\left(w'''(x)\right)^{\kappa+1}}{w^{\kappa+1}(x)} + \frac{\kappa\beta_1 g(x)}{b^{\frac{1}{\kappa}}(x)\,\delta^{\kappa+1}(x)} \\ &\leq \frac{g'(x)}{g(x)}\pi(x) + g(x)\frac{\left(b(x)\left(w'''(x)\right)^\kappa\right)'}{w^\kappa(x)} \\ &\quad -\kappa g(x)\frac{\varepsilon}{2}x^2 b(x)\left(\frac{\pi(x)}{g(x)\,b(x)} - \frac{\beta_1}{b(x)\,\delta^\kappa(x)}\right)^{\frac{\kappa+1}{\kappa}} + \frac{\kappa\beta_1 g(x)}{b^{\frac{1}{\kappa}}(x)\,\delta^{\kappa+1}(x)}. \end{aligned} \tag{14}$$

Using Lemma 1 with $P = \pi(x) / (g(x) b(x))$, $Q = \beta_1 / (b(x) \delta^\kappa(x))$ and $\beta = \kappa$, we get

$$\begin{aligned}\left(\frac{\pi(x)}{g(x)b(x)} - \frac{\beta_1}{b(x)\delta^\kappa(x)}\right)^{\frac{\kappa+1}{\kappa}} \geq & \left(\frac{\pi(x)}{g(x)b(x)}\right)^{\frac{\kappa+1}{\kappa}} \\ & - \frac{\beta_1^{1/\kappa}}{\kappa b^{\frac{1}{\kappa}}(x)\delta(x)}\left((\kappa+1)\frac{\pi(x)}{g(x)b(x)} - \frac{\beta_1}{b(x)\delta^\kappa(x)}\right). \quad (15)\end{aligned}$$

From Lemma 3, we have that $w(x) \geq \frac{x}{3} w'(x)$ and hence

$$\frac{w(\vartheta_i(x))}{w(x)} \geq \frac{\vartheta_i^3(x)}{x^3}. \quad (16)$$

From (1), (14), and (15), we obtain

$$\begin{aligned}\pi'(x) \leq & \frac{g'_+(x)}{g(x)}\pi(x) - \ell g(x)\sum_{i=1}^{j} q_i(x)\left(\frac{\vartheta_i^3(x)}{x^3}\right)^\kappa - \kappa g(x)\frac{\varepsilon}{2}x^2 b(x)\left(\frac{\pi(x)}{g(x)b(x)}\right)^{\frac{\kappa+1}{\kappa}} \\ & -\kappa g(x)\frac{\varepsilon}{2}x^2 b(x)\left(\frac{-\beta_1^{1/\kappa}}{\kappa b^{\frac{1}{\kappa}}(x)\delta(x)}\left((\kappa+1)\frac{\pi(x)}{g(x)b(x)} - \frac{\beta_1}{b(x)\delta^\kappa(x)}\right)\right) + \frac{\kappa\beta_1 g(x)}{b^{\frac{1}{\kappa}}(x)\delta^{\kappa+1}(x)}.\end{aligned}$$

This implies that

$$\begin{aligned}\pi'(x) \leq & \left(\frac{g'_+(x)}{g(x)} + \frac{(\kappa+1)\beta_1^{1/\kappa}\varepsilon x^2}{2b^{\frac{1}{\kappa}}(x)\delta(x)}\right)\pi(x) - \frac{\kappa\varepsilon x^2}{2b^{1/\kappa}(x)g^{1/\kappa}(x)}\pi^{\frac{\kappa+1}{\kappa}}(x) \\ & -g(x)\left(\ell\sum_{i=1}^{j} q_i(x)\left(\frac{\vartheta_i^3(x)}{x^3}\right)^\kappa + \frac{\varepsilon\beta_1^{(1+\kappa)/\kappa}x^2 - 2\beta_1\kappa}{2b^{\frac{1}{\kappa}}(x)\delta^{\kappa+1}(x)}\right).\end{aligned}$$

Thus,

$$\pi'(x) \leq -\psi(x) + \phi(x)\pi(x) - \frac{\kappa\varepsilon x^2}{2(b(x)g(x))^{1/\kappa}}\pi^{\frac{\kappa+1}{\kappa}}(x).$$

The proof is complete. □

Lemma 5. *Assume that w is an eventually positive solution of (1), $w^{(r)}(x) > 0$ for $r = 1,3$ and $w''(x) < 0$. If we have the function $\varpi \in C^1[x,\infty)$ defined as (11), where $\xi \in C^1([x_0,\infty),(0,\infty))$, then*

$$\varpi'(x) \leq -\psi^*(x) + \phi^*(x)\varpi(x) - \frac{1}{\xi(x)}\varpi^2(x), \quad (17)$$

for all $x > x_1$, where x_1 is large enough.

Proof. Let w be an eventually positive solution of (1), $w^{(r)} > 0$ for $r = 1,3$ and $w''(x) < 0$. From Lemma 3, we get that $w(x) \geq x w'(x)$. By integrating this inequality from $\vartheta_i(x)$ to x, we get

$$w(\vartheta_i(x)) \geq \frac{\vartheta_i(x)}{x}w(x).$$

Hence, from (3), we have

$$f(w(\vartheta_i(x))) \geq \ell\frac{\vartheta_i^\kappa(x)}{x^\kappa}w^\kappa(x). \quad (18)$$

Integrating (1) from x to u and using $w'(x) > 0$, we obtain

$$\begin{aligned} b(u)\left(w'''(u)\right)^{\kappa} - b(x)\left(w'''(x)\right)^{\kappa} &= -\int_x^u \sum_{i=1}^{j} q_i(s) f\left(w\left(\vartheta_i(s)\right)\right) ds \\ &\leq -\ell w^{\kappa}(x) \int_x^u \sum_{i=1}^{j} q_i(s) \frac{\vartheta_i^{\kappa}(s)}{s^{\kappa}} \mathrm{d}s. \end{aligned}$$

Letting $u \to \infty$, we see that

$$b(x)\left(w'''(x)\right)^{\kappa} \geq \ell w^{\kappa}(x) \int_x^{\infty} \sum_{i=1}^{j} q_i(s) \frac{\vartheta_i^{\kappa}(s)}{s^{\kappa}} \mathrm{d}s$$

and so

$$w'''(x) \geq w(x) \left(\frac{\ell}{b(x)} \int_x^{\infty} \sum_{i=1}^{j} q_i(s) \frac{\vartheta_i^{\kappa}(s)}{s^{\kappa}} \mathrm{d}s \right)^{1/\kappa}.$$

Integrating again from x to ∞, we get

$$w''(x) \leq -w(x) \int_x^{\infty} \left(\frac{\ell}{b(v)} \int_v^{\infty} \sum_{i=1}^{j} q_i(s) \frac{\vartheta_i^{\kappa}(s)}{s^{\kappa}} \mathrm{d}s \right)^{1/\kappa} \mathrm{d}v. \tag{19}$$

From the definition of $\varpi(x)$, we see that $\varpi(x) > 0$ for $x \geq x_1$. By differentiating, we find

$$\varpi'(x) = \frac{\xi'(x)}{\xi(x)} \varpi(x) + \xi(x) \frac{w''(x)}{w(x)} - \xi(x) \left(\frac{\varpi(x)}{\xi(x)} - \frac{\beta_2}{\delta(x)} \right)^2 + \frac{\xi(x)\beta_2}{b^{1/\kappa}(x)\delta^2(x)}. \tag{20}$$

Using Lemma 1 with $P = \varpi(x)/\xi(x), Q = \beta_2/\delta(x)$ and $\beta = 1$, we get

$$\left(\frac{\varpi(x)}{\xi(x)} - \frac{\beta_2}{\delta(x)} \right)^2 \geq \left(\frac{\varpi(x)}{\xi(x)} \right)^2 - \frac{\beta_2}{\delta(x)} \left(\frac{2\varpi(x)}{\xi(x)} - \frac{\beta_2}{\delta(x)} \right). \tag{21}$$

From (1), (20), and (21), we obtain

$$\begin{aligned} \varpi'(x) \leq\ & \frac{\xi'(x)}{\xi(x)} \varpi(x) - \xi(x) \int_x^{\infty} \left(\frac{\ell}{b(v)} \int_v^{\infty} \sum_{i=1}^{j} q_i(s) \frac{\vartheta_i^{\kappa}(s)}{s^{\kappa}} \mathrm{d}s \right)^{1/\kappa} \mathrm{d}v \\ & - \xi(x) \left(\left(\frac{\varpi(x)}{\xi(x)} \right)^2 - \frac{\beta_2}{\delta(x)} \left(\frac{2\varpi(x)}{\xi(x)} - \frac{\beta_2}{\delta(x)} \right) \right) + \frac{\beta_2 \xi(x)}{b^{\frac{1}{\kappa}}(x)\delta^2(x)}. \end{aligned}$$

This implies that

$$\begin{aligned} \varpi'(x) \leq\ & \left(\frac{\xi'_+(x)}{\xi(x)} + \frac{2\beta_2}{\delta(x)} \right) \varpi(x) - \frac{1}{\xi(x)} \varpi^2(x) \\ & - \xi(x) \left(\int_x^{\infty} \left(\frac{\ell}{b(v)} \int_v^{\infty} \sum_{i=1}^{j} q_i(s) \frac{\vartheta_i^{\kappa}(s)}{s^{\kappa}} \mathrm{d}s \right)^{1/\kappa} \mathrm{d}v + \frac{\beta_2^2 - \beta_2 b^{\frac{-1}{\kappa}}(x)}{\delta^2(x)} \right). \end{aligned}$$

Thus,

$$\varpi'(x) \leq -\psi^*(x) + \phi^*(x)\varpi(x) - \frac{1}{\xi(x)} \varpi^2(x).$$

The proof is complete. □

Lemma 6. *Assume that w is an eventually positive solution of (1). If there exists a positive function $g \in C([x_0,\infty))$ such that*

$$\int_{x_0}^{\infty} \left(\psi(s) - \left(\frac{2}{\varepsilon s^2} \right)^{\kappa} \frac{b(s)\, g(s)\, (\phi(s))^{\kappa+1}}{(\kappa+1)^{\kappa+1}} \right) \mathrm{d}s = \infty, \tag{22}$$

for some $\varepsilon \in (0,1)$, then w does not fulfill Case (1).

Proof. Assume that w is an eventually positive solution of (1). From Lemma 4, we get that (12) holds. Using Lemma 1 with

$$U = \phi(x), \; V = \kappa \varepsilon x^2 / \left(2 (b(x)\, g(x))^{1/\kappa} \right) \text{ and } x = \pi,$$

we get

$$\pi'(x) \leq -\psi(x) + \left(\frac{2}{\varepsilon x^2} \right)^{\kappa} \frac{b(x)\, g(x)\, (\phi(x))^{\kappa+1}}{(\kappa+1)^{\kappa+1}}. \tag{23}$$

Integrating from x_1 to x, we get

$$\int_{x_1}^{x} \left(\psi(s) - \left(\frac{2}{\varepsilon s^2} \right)^{\kappa} \frac{b(s)\, g(s)\, (\phi(s))^{\kappa+1}}{(\kappa+1)^{\kappa+1}} \right) \mathrm{d}s \leq \pi(x_1),$$

for every $\varepsilon \in (0,\ 1)$, which contradicts (22). The proof is complete. □

Lemma 7. *Assume that w is an eventually positive solution of (1), $w^{(r)}(x) > 0$ for $r = 1,3$ and $w''(x) < 0$. If there exists a positive function $\xi \in C([x_0,\infty))$ such that*

$$\int_{x_0}^{\infty} \left(\psi^*(s) - \frac{1}{4} \xi(s) (\phi^*(s))^2 \right) \mathrm{d}s = \infty, \tag{24}$$

then w does not fulfill Case (2).

Proof. Assume that w is an eventually positive solution of (1). From Lemma 5, we get that (17) holds. Using Lemma 1 with

$$U = \phi^*(x), \; V = 1/\xi(x), \kappa = 1 \text{ and } x = \varpi,$$

we get

$$\pi'(x) \leq -\psi^*(x) + \frac{1}{4} \xi(x) (\phi^*(x))^2. \tag{25}$$

Integrating from x_1 to x, we get

$$\int_{x_1}^{x} \left(\psi^*(s) - \frac{1}{4} \xi(s) (\phi^*(s))^2 \right) \mathrm{d}s \leq \pi(x_1),$$

which contradicts (24). The proof is complete. □

Theorem 3. *Assume that there exist positive functions $g, \xi \in C([x_0,\infty))$ such that (22) and (24) hold, for some $\varepsilon \in (0,1)$. Then, every solution of (1) is oscillatory.*

When putting $g(x) = x^3$ and $\xi(x) = x$ into Theorem 3, we get the following oscillation criteria:

Corollary 1. *Let (2) hold. Assume that*

$$\limsup_{x\to\infty}\int_{x_1}^{x}\left(\varphi(s)-\left(\frac{2}{\varepsilon s^2}\right)^{\kappa}\frac{b(s)\,g(s)\,(\tilde{\varphi}(s))^{\kappa+1}}{(\kappa+1)^{\kappa+1}}\right)\mathrm{d}s=\infty, \tag{26}$$

for some $\varepsilon\in(0,1)$. *If*

$$\limsup_{x\to\infty}\int_{x_1}^{x}\left(\varphi_1(s)-\frac{1}{4}\xi(s)\,(\tilde{\varphi}_1(s))^2\right)\mathrm{d}s=\infty, \tag{27}$$

where

$$\begin{aligned}\varphi(x) &:= x^3\left(\ell\sum_{i=1}^{j}q_i(x)\left(\frac{\vartheta_i^3(x)}{x^3}\right)^{\kappa}+\frac{\varepsilon\beta_1^{(1+\kappa)/\kappa}x^2-2\beta_1\kappa}{2b^{\frac{1}{\kappa}}(x)\,\delta^{\kappa+1}(x)}\right)\\ \tilde{\varphi}(x) &:= \frac{3}{x}+\frac{(\kappa+1)\,\beta_1^{1/\kappa}\varepsilon x^2}{2b^{\frac{1}{\kappa}}(x)\,\delta(x)},\quad \tilde{\varphi}_1(x):=\frac{1}{x}+\frac{2\beta_2}{\delta(x)}\end{aligned}$$

and

$$\varphi_1(x):=x\left(\int_x^{\infty}\left(\frac{\ell}{b(v)}\int_v^{\infty}\sum_{i=1}^{j}q_i(s)\frac{\vartheta_i^{\kappa}(s)}{s^{\kappa}}\mathrm{d}s\right)^{1/\kappa}\mathrm{d}v+\frac{\beta_2^2-\beta_2 b^{\frac{-1}{\kappa}}(x)}{\delta^2(x)}\right),$$

then every solution of (1) is oscillatory.

Example 1. *Consider a differential equation*

$$w^{(4)}(x)+\frac{c_0}{x^4}w\left(\frac{1}{2}x\right)=0,\ x\geq 1, \tag{28}$$

where $c_0>0$ *is a constant. Note that* $\kappa=b(x)=1$, $q(x)=c_0/x^4$ *and* $\vartheta(x)=x/2$. *Hence, we have*

$$\delta(x_0)=\infty,\ \varphi(s)=\frac{c_0}{8s}.$$

If we set $\ell=\beta_1=1$, *then condition (26) becomes*

$$\begin{aligned}\limsup_{x\to\infty}\int_{x_1}^{x}\left(\varphi(s)-\left(\frac{2}{\varepsilon s^2}\right)^{\kappa}\frac{b(s)\,g(s)\,(\tilde{\varphi}(s))^{\kappa+1}}{(\kappa+1)^{\kappa+1}}\right)\mathrm{d}s &= \limsup_{x\to\infty}\int_{x_1}^{x}\left(\frac{c_0}{8s}-\frac{9}{2s}\right)ds\\ &= \infty\ \ if\ \ c_0>36.\end{aligned}$$

Therefore, from Corollary 1, the solutions of Equation (28) are all oscillatory if $c_0>36$.

Remark 2. *We compare our result with the known related criteria for oscillations of this equation as follows:*

1. *By applying Condition (7) in [9] on Equation (28) where* $\theta=2$, *we get*

$$c_0>432.$$

2. *By applying Condition (8) in [10] on Equation (28) where* $\varsigma=1/2$, *we get*

$$c_0>51.$$

Therefore, our result improves results [9,10].

Remark 3. *By applying Condition (26) in Equation (9), we find*

$$c_0 > 6.17.$$

Therefore, our result improves results [9,10].

4. Conclusions

In this article, we study the oscillatory behavior of a class of nonlinear fourth-order differential equations and establish sufficient conditions for oscillation of a fourth-order differential equation by using Riccati transformation. Furthermore, in future work, we get some Hille and Nehari type and Philos type oscillation criteria of (1).

Author Contributions: O.B.: Writing original draft, and writing review and editing. M.P.: Formal analysis, writing review and editing, funding and supervision. All authors have read and agreed to the published version of the manuscript.

Funding: The authors received no direct funding for this work.

Acknowledgments: The authors thank the reviewers for for their useful comments, which led to the improvement of the content of the paper.

Conflicts of Interest: The authors declare no conflict of interest.

References

1. Hale, J.K. *Theory of Functional Differential Equations*; Springer: New York, NY, USA, 1977.
2. Agarwal, R.; Grace, S.; O'Regan, D. *Oscillation Theory for Difference and Functional Differential Equations*; Kluwer Academic Publishers: Dordrecht, The Netherlands, 2000.
3. Alzabut, J.; Tunc, C. Existence of Periodic solutions for a type of Rayleigh equation with state-dependent delay. *Electron. J. Differ. Equ.* **2012**, *2012*, 1–8. [CrossRef]
4. Philos, C.G. A new criterion for the oscillatory and asymptotic behavior of delay differential equations. *Bull. Acad. Pol. Sci. Sér. Sci. Math.* **1981**, *39*, 61–64.
5. Philos, C.G. On the existence of non-oscillatory solutions tending to zero at ∞ for differential equations with positive delays. *Arch. Math.* **1981**, *36*, 168–178. [CrossRef]
6. Bazighifan, O.; Cesarano, C. Some New Oscillation Criteria for Second-Order Neutral Differential Equations with Delayed Arguments. *Mathematics* **2019**, *7*, 619. [CrossRef]
7. Cesarano, C.; Bazighifan, O. Qualitative behavior of solutions of second order differential equations. *Symmetry* **2019**, *11*, 777. [CrossRef]
8. Agarwal, R.P.; Zhang, C.; Li, T. Some remarks on oscillation of second order neutral differential equations. *Appl. Math. Compt.* **2016**, *274*, 178–181. [CrossRef]
9. Agarwal, R.P.; Grace, S.R.; O'Regan, D. Oscillation criteria for certain nth order differential equations with deviating arguments. *J. Math. Appl. Anal.* **2001**, *262*, 601–622. [CrossRef]
10. Baculikova, B.; Dzurina, J.; Graef, J.R. On the oscillation of higher-order delay differential equations. *J. Math.* **2012**, *187*, 387–400. [CrossRef]
11. Grace, S.R. Oscillation theorems for nth-order differential equations with deviating arguments. *J. Math. Appl. Anal.* **1984**, *101*, 268–296. [CrossRef]
12. Xu, Z.; Xia, Y. Integral averaging technique and oscillation of certain even order delay differential equations. *J. Math. Appl. Anal.* **2004**, *292*, 238–246. [CrossRef]
13. Bazighifan, O.; Elabbasy, E.M.; Moaaz, O. Oscillation of higher-order differential equations with distributed delay. *J. Inequal. Appl.* **2019**, *55*, 1–9. [CrossRef]
14. Zhang, C.; Agarwal, R.P.; Bohner, M.; Li, T. New results for oscillatory behavior of even-order half-linear delay differential equations. *Appl. Math. Lett.* **2013**, *26*, 179–183. [CrossRef]
15. Zhang, C.; Li, T.; Sun, B.; Thandapani, E. On the oscillation of higher-order half-linear delay differential equations. *Appl. Math. Lett.* **2011**, *24*, 1618–1621. [CrossRef]
16. Moaaz, O.; Park, C.; Muhib, A.; Bazighifan, O. Oscillation criteria for a class of even-order neutral delay differential equations. *J. Appl. Math. Comput.* **2020**, *2020*, 1–11. [CrossRef]

17. Moaaz, O.; Jan, A.; Omar, B. A New Approach in the Study of Oscillation Criteria of Even-Order Neutral Differential Equations. *Mathematics* **2020**, *8*, 197. [CrossRef]
18. Bazighifan, O.; Cesarano, C. A Philos-Type Oscillation Criteria for Fourth-Order Neutral Differential Equations. *Symmetry* **2020**, *12*, 379. [CrossRef]
19. Chatzarakis, G.E.; Elabbasy, E.M.; Bazighifan, O. An oscillation criterion in 4th-order neutral differential equations with a continuously distributed delay. *Adv. Differ. Equ.* **2019**, *336*, 1–9.
20. Cesarano, C.; Pinelas, S.; Al-Showaikh, F.; Bazighifan, O. Asymptotic Properties of Solutions of Fourth-Order Delay Differential Equations. *Symmetry* **2019**, *11*, 628. [CrossRef]
21. Moaaz, O.; Elabbasy, E.M.; Bazighifan, O. On the asymptotic behavior of fourth-order functional differential equations. *Adv. Differ. Equ.* **2017**, *2017*, 261. [CrossRef]
22. Cesarano, C.; Bazighifan, O. Oscillation of fourth-order functional differential equations with distributed delay. *Axioms* **2019**, *8*, 61. [CrossRef]
23. Moaaz, O.; El-Nabulsi, R.; Bazighifan, O. Oscillatory behavior of fourth-order differential equations with neutral delay. *Symmetry* **2020**, *12*, 371. [CrossRef]
24. Parhi, N.; Tripathy, A. On oscillatory fourth order linear neutral differential equations-I. *Math. Slovaca* **2004**, *54*, 389–410.
25. Zhang, C.; Li, T.; Saker, S. Oscillation of fourth-order delay differential equations. *J. Math. Sci.* **2014**, *201*, 296–308. [CrossRef]

 *mathematics*

Article

Approximation of Finite Hilbert and Hadamard Transforms by Using Equally Spaced Nodes

Frank Filbir [1,2], Donatella Occorsio [3,4,*] and Woula Themistoclakis [4]

[1] Department of Scientific Computing, Helmholtz Zentrum München German Research Center for Environmental Health, Ingolstädter Landstrasse 1, 85764 Neuherberg, Germany; filbir@helmholtz-muenchen.de

[2] Applied Numerical Analysis, Fakultät für Mathematik, Technische Universität München, Boltzmannstrasse 3 85748 Garching bei München. Research Center, Ingolstädter Landstrasse 1, 85764 Neuherberg, Germany

[3] Department of Mathematics, Computer Science and Economics, University of Basilicata, viale dell'Ateneo Lucano 10, 85100 Potenza, Italy

[4] C.N.R. National Research Council of Italy, IAC Institute for Applied Computing "Mauro Picone", via P. Castellino, 111, 80131 Napoli, Italy; woula.themistoclakis@cnr.it

* Correspondence: donatella.occorsio@unibas.it

Received: 6 March 2020; Accepted: 1 April 2020; Published: 7 April 2020

Abstract: In the present paper, we propose a numerical method for the simultaneous approximation of the finite Hilbert and Hadamard transforms of a given function f, supposing to know only the samples of f at equidistant points. As reference interval we consider $[-1,1]$ and as approximation tool we use iterated Boolean sums of Bernstein polynomials, also known as generalized Bernstein polynomials. Pointwise estimates of the errors are proved, and some numerical tests are given to show the performance of the procedures and the theoretical results.

Keywords: Hilbert transform; Hadamard transform; hypersingular integral; Bernstein polynomials; Boolean sum; simultaneous approximation; equidistant nodes

---

1. Introduction

The Hilbert transform in its original form is an integral transform given by

$$H(f,t) = \fint_{-\infty}^{\infty} \frac{f(x)}{x-t}\, dx, \qquad t \in \mathbb{R}. \tag{1}$$

Alongside this form there are different variants defining Hilbert transforms on a finite interval, on the torus, or discrete groups. Objects of our studies are the finite Hilbert transform and its derivative, namely the Hadamard transform, both defined on the finite (standard) interval $[-1,1]$. They are given by

$$\mathcal{H}(f,t) = \fint_{-1}^{1} \frac{f(x)}{x-t} dx, \quad \mathcal{H}^1(f,t) = \fint\!\!\!\!\!-_{-1}^{1} \frac{f(x)}{(x-t)^2} dx, \qquad -1 < t < 1, \tag{2}$$

where the single and double bar-integral notation indicate that the involved integrals have to be understood as the Cauchy principal value and the Hadamard finite-part integrals, respectively.

The interest in integrals of this kind is due to their wide use to formulate boundary-value problems in many areas of mathematical physics (potential theory, fracture mechanics, aerodynamics, elasticity, etc...) in terms of singular integral equations in $[-1,1]$ involving such integrals (see e.g., [1–5] and the references therein).

In fact, the Hilbert transform in its aforementioned form (1) and all its relatives appear in various fields in mathematical analysis, signal processing, physics and other fields in science. Among them are partial differential equations, optics (X-ray crystallography, electron-atom scattering), electrodynamics and quantum mechanics (Kramers–Kronig relation), signal processing (phase retrieval, transfer functions of linear systems, spectral factorization). We will not go into details here but instead refer to the comprehensive two volume treatise by F. King [6] on many aspects of the Hilbert transform and its various variants. Due to its outstanding relevance it is of great importance to possess procedures which allow computation of the Hilbert transform numerically with high degree of accuracy. This problem was studied by many authors for all the different variants of the Hilbert transform and under different assumptions. We limit the citation here to only a few interesting papers [7–9].

Our focus in the present paper lies on the numerical computation of the finite Hilbert and Hadamard transforms (2). There is an extensive literature on numerical methods for these transforms. We only mention here [5,10] and the references therein. Many of these methods produce a high degree of approximation, especially when the smoothness of f increases (see e.g., [11–15]). Since they are based on Gaussian quadrature rules and its modified versions or product rules, they require the values of f to be given at the zeros of Jacobi polynomials which often is not the case. For example, in many applications the measurements of f are produced by devices which sample the function on equidistant knots. Other procedures which pay attention to this fact and which are frequently used in applications involve composite quadrature rules on equally spaced points. However, this type of quadrature rules suffers from a low degree of approximation or show saturation phenomena. Hence there is a need to establish a new approach which combines the advantages of both the aforementioned methods.

To move towards this goal, we propose some quadrature rules obtained by means of the sequence $\{B_{m,s}f\}_m$ of the so-called *generalized Bernstein polynomials*, defined as iterated Boolean sums of the classical Bernstein polynomials $\{B_m f\}_m$ ([16–18]). These types of formulas are based on equally spaced knots in the interval $[-1,1]$ and their convergence order increases with increasing smoothness of the function, in contrast to various popular rules based on piecewise polynomial approximation. Moreover, there exists a numerical evidence showing that the speed of convergence of the formula increases for higher values of the parameter s and for fixed m (see [19], Remark 4.1).

Concerning the numerical computation of the Hilbert transform $\mathcal{H}(f)$, we revisit the method introduced in [20] from both the theoretical and computational point of view. Indeed, here, according to a more recent result obtained in [21], we estimate the quadrature error in terms of the more refined kth φ-modulus of Ditzian and Totik, instead of the ordinary modulus of smoothness. As consequence, we get error estimates in Sobolev and Hölder Zygmund spaces and we are able to state the maximum rate of convergence for functions in such spaces. The second improvement of the method in [20] regards the computation of the quadrature weights that is performed in a more stable way. It is based on a recurrence relation which does not require the transformation to the canonical bases $\{1, x, \dots, x^m\}$, but it preserves the fundamental Bernstein polynomials $\{p_{m,k}(x)\}_{k=0}^m$.

As regards the Hadamard transform $\mathcal{H}^1(f,t)$, before introducing the numerical procedure for its computation, we prove that $\mathcal{H}^1(f,t)$ presents algebraic singularities at the endpoints of the interval, when the density function f satisfies a Dini-type condition. Successively, we introduce a quadrature rule for approximating $\mathcal{H}^1(f,t)$ always based on the polynomials $B_{m,s}f$ and useful also for the simultaneous approximation of $\mathcal{H}(f,t)$ and $\mathcal{H}^1(f,t)$, since the samples of the function f at the equidistant nodes employed in the computation of $\mathcal{H}(f,t)$ have been reused to approximate $\mathcal{H}^1(f,t)$ too. The convergence of such a quadrature rule is proved by using the simultaneous approximation property of the generalized Bernstein polynomials, and similarly to the Hilbert transform case, for the quadrature error we state weighted pointwise estimates.

It comes out that the additional integer parameter s introduced by the $B_{m,s}f$ can be suitable chosen to accelerate the convergence of the quadrature rules for both the transforms $\mathcal{H}$ and $\mathcal{H}^1$. Moreover, the coefficients of both the quadrature rules are given in a simple compact vectorial form and can be efficiently computed by recurrence.

The outline of the paper is as follows. Section 2 contains some notation and preliminary results concerning the generalized Bernstein polynomials and the Hilbert and Hadamard transforms. The quadrature rules with the corresponding pointwise error estimates can be found in Section 3 where details about the recurrence relations for their coefficients are also given. Section 4 contains additional numerical details for computing the quadrature weights and some numerical tests which show the performance of our procedures and confirm the theoretical estimates. Finally, in Section 5 the proofs are given.

2. Notation and Preliminary Results

In the sequel $\mathcal{C}$ will denote a generic positive constant which may differ at different occurrences. We will write $\mathcal{C} \neq \mathcal{C}(a, b, ..)$ to indicate that $\mathcal{C}$ is independent of $a, b, ...$ Moreover, if $A, B > 0$ depend on some parameters the notation $A \sim B$ means that there are fixed constants $\mathcal{C}_1, \mathcal{C}_2 > 0$ (independent of the parameters in A, B) such that $\mathcal{C}_1 A \leq B \leq \mathcal{C}_2 A$. For $m \in \mathbb{N}$, we set $N_0^m = \{0, 1, 2, \dots, m\}$ and denote by $\mathbb{P}_m$ the space of all algebraic polynomials of degree at most m. C^m will denote the space of functions with m continuous derivatives on $[-1, 1]$ and C^0 is the space of the continuous functions on $[-1, 1]$ equipped with the uniform norm $\|f\| := \max_{x \in [-1,1]} |f(x)|$. In C^0, setting $\varphi(x) := \sqrt{1 - x^2}$, it is possible to define the following φ-modulus of smoothness by Ditzian and Totik ([22], Theorem 2.1.2)

$$\omega_\varphi^r(f, t) = \sup_{0 < h \leq t} \|\Delta_{h\varphi}^r f\|, \qquad r \in \mathbb{N}$$

where

$$\Delta_{h\varphi(x)}^r f(x) = \sum_{k=0}^{r} (-1)^k \binom{r}{k} f\left(x + (r - 2k)\frac{h}{2}\varphi(x)\right).$$

We recall that ([22], Theorem 2.1.1)

$$\omega_\varphi^r(f, t) \sim K_{r,\varphi}(f, t^r) := \inf\{\|f - g\| + t^r \|g^{(r)} \varphi^r\| : g^{(r-1)} \in \mathcal{AC}\}, \tag{3}$$

where $\mathcal{AC}$ denotes the space of the absolutely continuous functions on $[-1, 1]$.

By means of this modulus of continuity, we define the subspace $DT \subset C^0$ of all functions satisfying a Dini-type condition, namely

$$DT = \left\{ f \in C^0 : \int_0^1 \frac{\omega_\varphi(f, u)}{u} du < \infty \right\}, \tag{4}$$

where we set $\omega_\varphi(f, u) = \omega_\varphi^1(f, u)$.

Moreover, the Hölder–Zygmund space of order $\lambda > 0$ is defined by

$$Z_\lambda = \left\{ f \in C^0 : \sup_{t > 0} \frac{\omega_\varphi^r(f, t)}{t^\lambda} < \infty, \quad r > \lambda \right\}, \qquad \lambda > 0, \tag{5}$$

and equipped with the norm

$$\|f\|_{Z_\lambda} = \|f\| + \sup_{t > 0} \frac{\omega_\varphi^r(f, t)}{t^\lambda}, \qquad r > \lambda.$$

The space Z_λ constitutes a particular case of the Besov-type spaces studied in [23] where it has been proved that ([23], Theorem 2.1)

$$\|f\|_{Z_\lambda} \sim \sup_{n \geq 0} (n + 1)^\lambda E_n(f), \qquad E_n(f) := \inf_{P \in \mathbb{P}_n} \|f - P\|. \tag{6}$$

Such norms' equivalence ensures that the previous definitions are indeed independent of the integer $r > \lambda$ we choose. Moreover, by (6) we get an interesting characterization of the continuous functions $f \in Z_\lambda$ in terms of the rate of convergence to zero of the errors of best uniform polynomial approximation of f, which in turn is closely related to the smoothness of f (see e.g., Corollary 8.2.2 and Theorem 6.2.2 of [22]). More precisely, for any continuous function f and any $\lambda > 0$ we have

$$f \in Z_\lambda \iff E_n(f) = \mathcal{O}(n^{-\lambda}) \iff \omega_\varphi^r(f,t) = \mathcal{O}(t^\lambda),\ \forall r > \lambda. \tag{7}$$

Furthermore, by the previous definitions, for any $r > \lambda > 0$ we get

$$\omega_\varphi^r(f,t) \le C t^\lambda \|f\|_{Z_\lambda}, \qquad \forall f \in Z_\lambda, \qquad C \ne C(f,t). \tag{8}$$

In the case that $\lambda = k \in \mathbb{N}$, by virtue of (3), we have that the space Z_λ is equivalent to the Sobolev space

$$W_k = \left\{ f^{(k-1)} \in \mathcal{AC} : \|f^{(k)}\varphi^k\| < \infty \right\}, \qquad k \in \mathbb{N},$$

equipped with the norm $\|f\|_{W_k} = \|f\| + \|f^{(k)}\varphi^k\|$, and we recall that ([22], Theorem 4.2.1)

$$\omega_\varphi^r(f,t) = \mathcal{O}(t^r) \iff f \in W_r, \qquad \forall r \in \mathbb{N}, \tag{9}$$

$$\omega_\varphi^r(f,t) = o(t^r) \implies f \in \mathbb{P}_{r-1}, \qquad \forall r \in \mathbb{N}. \tag{10}$$

Finally, since we are going to use a result of [24] based also on the ordinary moduli of smoothness (cf. Theorem 2), we conclude the subsection by recalling their definition and some properties.

Set

$$\Delta_h f(x) := f\left(x + \frac{h}{2}\right) - f\left(x - \frac{h}{2}\right), \qquad \Delta_h^r := \Delta_h(\Delta_h^{r-1}), \qquad r > 1,$$

the ordinary r-th modulus of smoothness of f is defined as

$$\omega^r(f,t) := \sup_{0<h\le t} \|\Delta_h^r f\|, \qquad r \in \mathbb{N}.$$

It is related with the φ modulus by

$$\omega_\varphi^r(f,t) \le C\omega^r(f,t), \qquad C \ne C(f,t).$$

Moreover, set

$$\tilde{W}_k := \left\{ f^{k-1} \in \mathcal{AC} : \|f^{(k)}\| < \infty \right\}, \qquad k \in \mathbb{N}$$

we have the following analogues of (9) and (10) (see e.g., [22], p. 40)

$$\omega^r(f,t) = \mathcal{O}(t^r) \iff f \in \tilde{W}_r \subseteq W_r, \qquad \forall r \in \mathbb{N} \tag{11}$$

$$\omega^r(f,t) = o(t^r) \implies f \in \mathbb{P}_{r-1}, \qquad \forall r \in \mathbb{N} \tag{12}$$

2.1. Generalized Bernstein Polynomials in $[-1,1]$

For any $f \in C^0$ the m-th Bernstein polynomial $B_m f$ is defined as

$$B_m f(x) := \sum_{k=0}^{m} f(t_k) p_{m,k}(x), \qquad t_k := \frac{2k}{m} - 1, \qquad x \in [-1,1], \tag{13}$$

where

$$p_{m,k}(x) := \frac{1}{2^m}\binom{m}{k}(1+x)^k(1-x)^{m-k}, \qquad k = 0,1,\ldots,m, \tag{14}$$

are the so-called fundamental Bernstein polynomials. They satisfy the following recurrence relation

$$p_{m,k}(x) = \frac{(1-x)}{2} p_{m-1,k}(x) + \frac{(1+x)}{2} p_{m-1,k-1}(x), \quad m = 1,2,\ldots, \tag{15}$$

with $p_{0,0}(x) = 1$ and $p_{m,k}(x) = 0$ if $k < 0$ or $k > m$.

The computation of $B_m f(x)$ can be efficiently performed by the de Casteljau algorithm (see e.g., [25]).

Based on the polynomial $B_m f$, the generalized Bernstein polynomial $B_{m,s} f$ were introduced separately in [16–18]. They are defined as the following Boolean sums

$$B_{m,s} f = f - (f - B_m f)^s, \qquad s \in \mathbb{N}, \quad B_{m,1} f = B_m f.$$

Please note that $B_{m,s} f \in \mathbb{P}_m$ and it can be expressed as

$$B_{m,s} f(x) = \sum_{j=0}^{m} p_{m,j}^{(s)}(x) f(t_j), \qquad t_j := \frac{2j}{m} - 1, \qquad x \in [-1,1], \tag{16}$$

where

$$p_{m,j}^{(s)}(x) = \sum_{i=1}^{s} \binom{s}{i} (-1)^{i-1} B_m^{i-1} p_{m,j}(x) \qquad B_m^i = B_m(B_m^{i-1}), \quad i = 1,\ldots,s. \tag{17}$$

An estimate of the error $R_{m,s} f := f - B_{m,s} f$ in uniform norm is given by the following theorem

Theorem 1. *[21] Let $s \in \mathbb{N}$ be fixed. Then for all $m \in \mathbb{N}$ and any $f \in C^0$ we have*

$$\|f - B_{m,s} f\| \le C \left\{ \omega_\varphi^{2s}\left(f, \frac{1}{\sqrt{m}}\right) + \frac{\|f\|}{m^s} \right\}, \qquad C \neq C(m,f).$$

Moreover, for any $0 < \lambda \le 2s$ we obtain

$$\|f - B_{m,s} f\| = \mathcal{O}(m^{-\frac{\lambda}{2}}),\ m \to \infty \iff \omega_\varphi^{2s}(f,t) = \mathcal{O}(t^\lambda)$$

and the o-saturation class is characterized by

$$\|f - B_{m,s} f\| = o(m^{-s}) \iff f \text{ is a linear function.}$$

Remark 1. *Please note that unlike the basic Bernstein operator B_m, the Boolean sums $B_{m,s}$ may accelerate the speed of convergence as the smoothness of f increases. In particular, taking into account (7)–(9), from Theorem 1 we deduce*

$$\|f - B_{m,s} f\| \le C \frac{\|f\|_{Z_\lambda}}{\sqrt{m^\lambda}}, \qquad \forall f \in Z_\lambda \text{ with } 0 < \lambda \le 2s,\ C \neq C(m,f). \tag{18}$$

About the simultaneous approximation of the derivatives of f by means of the sequence $\{B_{m,s} f\}_m$, the following estimate holds.

Theorem 2 ([24], Corollary 1.6). *Let $s \in \mathbb{N}$ be fixed. Then for all $m,k \in \mathbb{N}$ and any $f \in C^k$ we have*

$$\|(f - B_{m,s} f)^{(k)}\| \le C \begin{cases} \omega_\varphi^{2s}\left(f', \frac{1}{\sqrt{m}}\right) + \omega^s\left(f', \frac{1}{m}\right) + \omega\left(f', \frac{1}{m^s}\right), & k = 1, \\ \omega_\varphi^{2s}\left(f^{(k)}, \frac{1}{\sqrt{m}}\right) + \omega^s\left(f^{(k)}, \frac{1}{m}\right) + \frac{\|f^{(k)}\|}{m^s}, & k \ge 2, \end{cases}$$

where $\omega := \omega^1$ and $C \neq C(m,f)$.

Remark 2. *From Theorem 2 and (9), (11) we deduce the following maximum rate of convergence*

$$\|f^{(k)} - (B_{m,s}f)^{(k)}\| = \mathcal{O}\left(\frac{1}{m^s}\right) \quad (m \to \infty) \qquad \forall f \in C^k \cap \tilde{W}_{2s+k}, \quad k \in \mathbb{N}. \tag{19}$$

Finally, we give some details on the computation of $B_{m,s}f$ and its first derivative.

Observe that a more convenient representation of the fundamental polynomials $\{p_{m,i}^{(s)}\}_{i=0}^m$ is given by [26] (see also [27])

$$\mathbf{p}_m^{(s)}(x) = \mathbf{p}_m(x)C_{m,s}, \qquad \forall x \in [-1,1], \tag{20}$$

where we set

$$\begin{aligned} \mathbf{p}_m^{(s)}(x) &:= [p_{m,0}^{(s)}(x), p_{m,1}^{(s)}(x), \ldots, p_{m,m}^{(s)}(x)], \\ \mathbf{p}_m(x) &:= [p_{m,0}(x), \ldots, p_{m,m}(x)], \end{aligned}$$

and $C_{m,s} \in \mathbb{R}^{(m+1)\times(m+1)}$ is the changing basis matrix given by

$$C_{m,s} = \mathcal{I} + (\mathcal{I} - \mathcal{A}) + \ldots + (\mathcal{I} - \mathcal{A})^{s-1}, \quad C_{m,1} = \mathcal{I}, \tag{21}$$

where $\mathcal{I}$ denotes the identity matrix and $\mathcal{A}$ is the matrix with entries

$$\mathcal{A} := (\mathcal{A}_{i,j}) \qquad \mathcal{A}_{i,j} := p_{m,j}(t_i), \qquad i,j \in N_0^m. \tag{22}$$

Let $c_{i,j}^{(m,s)}$ be the entry (i,j) of $C_{m,s}$, then in view of (20) we get

$$p_{m,j}^{(s)}(x) = \sum_{i=0}^{m} p_{m,i}(x)c_{i,j}^{(m,s)}, \qquad \forall x \in [-1,1], \tag{23}$$

and consequently

$$B_{m,s}f(x) = \sum_{i=0}^{m}\left(\sum_{j=0}^{m} c_{i,j}^{(m,s)} f(t_j)\right) p_{m,i}(x). \tag{24}$$

In matrix-vector notation this reads as

$$B_{m,s}f(x) = \mathbf{p}_m(x)C_{m,s}\mathbf{f}, \tag{25}$$

with

$$\mathbf{f} := [f(t_0), f(t_1), \ldots, f(t_m)]^T.$$

As regards the derivatives of the Bernstein polynomials $B_{m,s}f$, we obtain from (25) the following useful representation

$$(B_{m,s}f)'(x) = \mathbf{p}_m^1(x)C_{m,s}\mathbf{f}, \tag{26}$$

where

$$\mathbf{p}_m^1(x) := [p'_{m,0}(x), \ldots, p'_{m,m}(x)],$$

Finally, concerning the entries of the vector $\mathbf{p}_m^1(x)$, i.e., the derivatives of the fundamental Bernstein polynomials at $x \in [-1,1]$, starting from the definition (14), easy computations yield the expression

$$p'_{m,k}(x) = \frac{m}{2}\left(p_{m-1,k-1}(x) - p_{m-1,k}(x)\right), \qquad k = 0, \ldots, m, \tag{27}$$

with the usual convention $p_{m,j}(x) = 0$ if $j \notin \mathbb{N}_0^m$.

2.2. Hilbert and Hadamard Transforms

First, we recall the finite Hilbert transform $\mathcal{H}(f,t)$ is defined by

$$\mathcal{H}(f,t) = \fint_{-1}^{1} \frac{f(x)}{x-t} dx = \lim_{\epsilon \to 0^+} \left[\int_{-1}^{t-\epsilon} \frac{f(x)}{x-t} dx + \int_{t+\epsilon}^{1} \frac{f(x)}{x-t} dx \right]. \tag{28}$$

The following theorem provides a sufficient condition for the existence of $\mathcal{H}(f,t)$ in $(-1,1)$ when the density function f satisfies a Dini-type condition. It also shows the behavior of $\mathcal{H}(f,t)$ as t approaches the endpoints of the interval $[-1,1]$.

Theorem 3 ([28], Theorem 2.1). *For any $f \in DT$ and $|t| < 1$, we have*

$$\log^{-1}\left(\frac{e}{1-t^2}\right) |\mathcal{H}(f,t)| \le \mathcal{C}\left(\|f\| + \int_0^1 \frac{\omega_\varphi(f,u)}{u} du \right), \qquad \mathcal{C} \ne \mathcal{C}(f,t).$$

Consider now $\mathcal{H}^1(f,t)$, which is the finite part of the divergent integral in the Hadamard sense (see for instance [5,10,14]), i.e., defined for $|t| < 1$ as (cf. [5], Equation (1.3))

$$\mathcal{H}^1(f,t) = \neq\!\!\!\!\!\!\int_{-1}^{1} \frac{f(x)}{(x-t)^2} dx = \lim_{\varepsilon \to 0^+} \left[\int_{-1}^{t-\varepsilon} \frac{f(x)}{(x-t)^2} dx + \int_{t+\varepsilon}^{1} \frac{f(x)}{(x-t)^2} dx - \frac{2f(t)}{\varepsilon} \right]. \tag{29}$$

An alternative definition interprets $\mathcal{H}^1(f,t)$ as the first derivative of $\mathcal{H}(f)$ at t, i.e.,

$$\mathcal{H}^1(f,t) = \frac{d}{dt} \fint_{-1}^{1} \frac{f(x)}{x-t} dx, \quad |t| < 1, \tag{30}$$

being (30) and (29) equivalent when f' is an Hölder continuous function (see [5]).

By the following theorem, we are going to state that for all functions f with $f' \in DT$, we have that $\mathcal{H}^1(f,t)$ exists finite for any $|t| < 1$, while it algebraically diverges at the endpoints of the interval $[-1,1]$.

Theorem 4. *Let the function $f \in C^1$ be s.t. $f' \in DT$. Then, for any $-1 < t < 1$, we have*

$$\varphi^2(t) |\mathcal{H}^1(f,t)| \le \mathcal{C}\left(\|f\| + \int_0^1 \frac{\omega_\varphi(f',\tau)}{\tau} d\tau \right), \qquad \mathcal{C} \ne \mathcal{C}(f,t). \tag{31}$$

3. The Quadrature Rules

3.1. On the Computation of $\mathcal{H}(f,t)$

The numerical method for computing $\mathcal{H}(f,t)$ is based on the following proposition

Proposition 1. *For any $f \in DT$ and for any $|t| < 1$, we have*

$$\mathcal{H}(f,t) = \int_{-1}^{1} \frac{f(x) - f(t)}{x-t} dx + f(t) \log\left(\frac{1-t}{1+t}\right), \tag{32}$$

In view of (32), we mainly must approximate the function

$$\mathcal{F}(f,t) := \int_{-1}^{1} \frac{f(x) - f(t)}{x-t} dx, \qquad -1 < t < 1. \tag{33}$$

For any given $s \in \mathbb{N}$, by means of the polynomial sequence $\{B_{m,s}f\}_m$, we define the following approximation of $\mathcal{F}(f,t)$

$$\mathcal{F}_{m,s}(f,t) := \int_{-1}^{1} \frac{B_{m,s}f(x) - B_{m,s}f(t)}{x-t} dx \tag{34}$$

and let

$$\Phi_{m,s}(f,t) := \mathcal{F}(f,t) - \mathcal{F}_{m,s}(f,t), \qquad -1 < t < 1. \tag{35}$$

Please note that

$$\mathcal{F}_{m,s}(f,t) = \sum_{j=0}^{m} f(t_j) \int_{-1}^{1} \frac{p_{m,j}^{(s)}(x) - p_{m,j}^{(s)}(t)}{x-t} dx =: \sum_{j=0}^{m} f(t_j) D_{m,j}^{(s)}(t), \tag{36}$$

and taking into account the relation in (20) between the bases $\{p_{m,i}(x)\}_{i\in\mathbb{N}_0^m}$ and $\{p_{m,i}^{(s)}(x)\}_{i\in\mathbb{N}_0^m}$, we have

$$D_{m,j}^{(s)}(t) = \sum_{i=0}^{m} c_{i,j}^{(m,s)} \int_{-1}^{1} \frac{p_{m,i}(x) - p_{m,i}(t)}{x-t} dx =: \sum_{i=0}^{m} c_{i,j}^{(m,s)} q_{m,i}(t). \tag{37}$$

About the computation of $\{q_{m,i}(t)\}_{i\in\mathbb{N}_0^m}$ we can prove the following

Proposition 2. *For the sequence $\{q_{m,i}(t)\}$ the following recurrence relation holds*

$$\begin{aligned}
q_{0,0}(t) &= 0, \quad q_{1,0}(t) = -1, \quad q_{1,1}(t) = 1 \\
q_{m,0}(t) &= \frac{(1-t)}{2} q_{m-1,0}(t) - \frac{1}{m} \\
q_{m,k}(t) &= \frac{(1-t)}{2} q_{m-1,k}(t) + \frac{(1+t)}{2} q_{m-1,k-1}(t), \quad 1 \le k \le m-1 \\
q_{m,m}(t) &= \frac{(1+t)}{2} q_{m-1,m-1}(t) + \frac{1}{m}.
\end{aligned}$$

Setting

$$\mathbf{q}_m(t) = [q_{m,0}(t), q_{m,1}(t), \ldots, q_{m,m}(t)], \tag{38}$$

the quadrature rule (34) takes the form

$$\mathcal{F}_{m,s}(f,t) = \mathbf{q}_m(t) C_{m,s} \mathbf{f}. \tag{39}$$

This formula can be directly applied to approximate $\mathcal{H}(f,t)$ in the form given in (32), i.e., supposed to know $f(t)$, we can approximate

$$\mathcal{H}(f,t) = \mathcal{F}(f,t) + \log\left(\frac{1-t}{1+t}\right) f(t) \approx \mathcal{F}_{m,s}(f,t) + \log\left(\frac{1-t}{1+t}\right) f(t).$$

In the case only the samples $f(t_j) \neq f(t)$ are given, we propose to approximate $\mathcal{H}(f,t)$ by

$$\mathcal{H}_{m,s}(f,t) := \mathcal{F}_{m,s}(f,t) + \log\left(\frac{1-t}{1+t}\right) B_{m,s} f(t). \tag{40}$$

Using matrix-vector notation as in (39) and (25) we arrive at

$$\mathcal{H}_{m,s}(f,t) = \left[\mathbf{q}_m(t) + \log\left(\frac{1-t}{1+t}\right) \mathbf{p}_m(t)\right] C_{m,s} \mathbf{f}. \tag{41}$$

The quadrature error can then be expressed as

$$\begin{aligned}
\mathcal{E}_{m,s}(f,t) &:= \mathcal{H}(f,t) - \mathcal{H}_{m,s}(f,t) \\
&= \Phi_{m,s}(f,t) + \log\left(\frac{1-t}{1+t}\right) [f(t) - B_{m,s} f(t)]
\end{aligned}$$

About the convergence of both the previous quadrature rules $\mathcal{F}_{m,s}$ and $\mathcal{H}_{m,s}$, the following theorem estimates the associate errors, $\Phi_{m,s}$ and $\mathcal{E}_{m,s}$ respectively.

Theorem 5. *Let be $-1 < t < 1$. Then for any $f \in DT$, we have*

$$\log^{-1}\left(\frac{e}{1-t^2}\right) |\, \mathcal{E}_{m,s}(f,t)| \le \mathcal{C} \log m \left[\omega_\varphi^{2s}\left(f, \frac{1}{\sqrt{m}}\right) + \frac{\|f\|}{m^s}\right] + \mathcal{C}\int_0^{\frac{1}{m}} \frac{\omega_\varphi^r(f,u)}{u} du, \tag{42}$$

with $r < m$ and $\mathcal{C} \neq \mathcal{C}(m,f,t)$.

The same estimate continues to hold for $\Phi_{m,s}(f,t)$, which satisfies also

$$|\Phi_{m,s}(f,t)| \le \mathcal{C}\left[\omega_\varphi^{2s}\left(f', \frac{1}{\sqrt{m}}\right) + \omega^s\left(f', \frac{1}{m}\right) + \omega\left(f', \frac{1}{m^s}\right)\right], \qquad \forall f \in C^1, \tag{43}$$

with $\mathcal{C} \neq \mathcal{C}(m,f,t)$.

In case of smoother functions, from the previous estimates and (7), (8), (9) and (11), we easily get

Corollary 1. *Let be $-1 < t < 1$. Then for all $f \in Z_\lambda$, with $0 < \lambda \le 2s$, we have*

$$|\mathcal{E}_{m,s}(f,t)| \le \mathcal{C} \log\left(\frac{e}{1-t^2}\right) \frac{\|f\|_{Z_\lambda}}{m^{\lambda/2}} \log m, \qquad \mathcal{C} \neq \mathcal{C}(m,f,t),$$

and the same holds for $|\Phi_{m,s}(f,t)|$. Moreover, for all $f \in C^{k+1}$, with $1 \le k \le 2s$, we have

$$|\Phi_{m,s}(f,t)| \le \frac{\mathcal{C}}{m^{k/2}}, \qquad \mathcal{C} \neq \mathcal{C}(m,t).$$

In conclusion, we remark that in proving Theorem 5 we also stated the following relations between the quadrature errors and the approximation errors by generalized Bernstein polynomials

$$\begin{aligned} |\mathcal{E}_{m,s}(f,t)| &\le \mathcal{C} \log\left(\frac{e}{1-t^2}\right)\left[\log m \|f - B_{m,s}f\| + \int_0^{\frac{1}{m}} \frac{\omega_\varphi^r(f,u)}{u} du\right], \qquad \forall f \in DT, \\ |\Phi_{m,s}(f,t)| &\le \mathcal{C}\|(f - B_{m,s}f)'\|, \qquad \forall f \in C^1. \end{aligned}$$

3.2. On the Computation of $\mathcal{H}^1(f,t)$

We are going to use the following proposition

Proposition 3. *For any $f \in C^1$ s.t. $f' \in DT$ and for all $|t| < 1$, we have*

$$\mathcal{H}^1(f,t) = \int_{-1}^1 \frac{f(x) - f(t) - f'(t)(x-t)}{(x-t)^2} dx + f'(t) \log\left(\frac{1-t}{1+t}\right) - f(t)\left[\frac{2}{1-t^2}\right]. \tag{44}$$

Let

$$\mathcal{F}^1(f,t) := \int_{-1}^1 \frac{f(x) - f(t) - f'(t)(x-t)}{(x-t)^2} dx, \qquad -1 < t < 1.$$

Supposed both $f'(t)$ and $f(t)$ are known, then we can get the exact value of the non-integral part at the right-hand side of (44). In this case, the numerical computation of $\mathcal{H}^1(f,t)$ can be performed by the following quadrature rule

$$\mathcal{F}^1(f,t) = \mathcal{F}^1_{m,s}(f,t) + \Phi^1_{m,s}(f,t), \tag{45}$$

where

$$\mathcal{F}^1_{m,s}(f,t) := \int_{-1}^{1} \frac{B_{m,s}f(x) - B_{m,s}f(t) - (B_{m,s}f)'(t)(x-t)}{(x-t)^2} dx = \frac{d}{dt}\mathcal{F}_{m,s}(f,t). \tag{46}$$

Using (36), (37) and (46), we get

$$\begin{aligned} \mathcal{F}^1_{m,s}(f,t) &= \sum_{j=0}^{m} f(t_j) \sum_{j=0}^{m} \frac{d}{dt} D^{(s)}_{m,j}(t), \\ \frac{d}{dt} D^{(s)}_{m,j}(t) &= \sum_{i=0}^{m} c^{(m,s)}_{i,j} d_{m,i}(t), \qquad d_{m,i}(t) := q'_{m,i}(t), \end{aligned} \tag{47}$$

where the polynomials $d_{m,i}(t), i = 0, \dots, m$, can be computed recursively, according to

Proposition 4. *The sequence $d_{m,i}(t), i = 0, \dots, m$, satisfies the following recurrence relation*

$$\begin{aligned} d_{1,0}(t) &= 0, \quad d_{1,1}(t) = 0, \\ d_{m,0}(t) &= \frac{(1-t)}{2} d_{m-1,0}(t) - \frac{1}{2} q_{m-1,0}(t), \\ d_{m,k}(t) &= \frac{(1-t)}{2} d_{m-1,k}(t) - \frac{1}{2} q_{m-1,k}(t) + \frac{(1+t)}{2} d_{m-1,k-1}(t) + \frac{1}{2} q_{m-1,k-1}(t), \\ & \qquad\qquad 1 \le k \le m-1, \\ d_{m,m}(t) &= \frac{(1+t)}{2} d_{m-1,m-1}(t) + \frac{1}{2} q_{m-1,m-1}(t). \end{aligned}$$

The previous recurrence relation can be easily deduced by Proposition 2.

Let

$$\mathbf{d}_m(t) = [d_{m,0}(t), d_{m,1}(t), \dots, d_{m,m}(t)], \tag{48}$$

then the quadrature rule (46) takes the following form

$$\mathcal{F}^1_{m,s}(f,t) = \mathbf{d}_m(t) C_{m,s} \mathbf{f}. \tag{49}$$

In the case that only the vector $\mathbf{f}$ is known, we have to approximate also the non-integral part in (44) and we propose the following quadrature rule

$$\mathcal{H}^1(f,t) = \mathcal{H}^1_{m,s}(f,t) + \mathcal{E}^1_{m,s}(f,t), \tag{50}$$

where $\mathcal{E}^1_{m,s}(f,t)$ denotes the error and

$$\mathcal{H}^1_{m,s}(f,t) := \mathcal{F}^1_{m,s}(f,t) + \log\left(\frac{1-t}{1+t}\right)(B_{m,s}f)'(t) - \frac{2}{1-t^2} B_{m,s}f(t). \tag{51}$$

By (49), (25) and (26), the rule in vector form is given by

$$\mathcal{H}^1_{m,s}(f,t) = \left[\mathbf{d}_m(t) + \log\left(\frac{1-t}{1+t}\right)\mathbf{p}^1_m(t) - \frac{2}{1-t^2}\mathbf{p}_m(t)\right] C_{m,s}\mathbf{f}. \tag{52}$$

We point out that both the rules (49) and (52) are based on the same data vector $\mathbf{f}$ used in the rules (39) and (41). We see that our method allows simultaneous approximation of the Hilbert transform $\mathcal{H}(f,t)$ and its first derivative $\mathcal{H}^1(f,t)$ for $|t| < 1$ by using the same samples of the function f.

About the convergence of the quadrature rules $\mathcal{F}^1_{m,s}$ and $\mathcal{H}^1_{m,s}$, the following theorem estimates the associate errors $\Phi^1_{m,s}$ and $\mathcal{E}^1_{m,s}$ by means of the error of approximation when f and f' are approximated by generalized Bernstein polynomials.

Theorem 6. *Let be $-1 < t < 1$. Then for any $f \in C^1$ s.t. $f' \in DT$, we have*

$$(1-t^2)|\mathcal{E}^1_{m,s}(f,t)| \leq \mathcal{C}\left[\|f - B_{m,s}f\| + \log m\|(f - B_{m,s}f)'\| + \int_0^{\frac{1}{m}} \frac{\omega^r_\varphi(f',u)}{u}du\right] \tag{53}$$

with $r < m$ and $\mathcal{C} \neq \mathcal{C}(m,f,t)$.

The same estimate can also be applied to $\Phi^1_{m,s}(f,t)$, which in the case of continuously differentiable functions in C^2 satisfies also

$$|\Phi^1_{m,s}(f,t)| \leq \mathcal{C}\|(f - B_{m,s}f)''\|, \qquad \forall f \in C^2, \tag{54}$$

with $\mathcal{C} \neq \mathcal{C}(m,f,t)$.

Thanks to this theorem, by Theorem 1 and Theorem 2 we can easily get estimates of the quadrature errors $\mathcal{E}^1_{m,s}$ and $\Phi^1_{m,s}$ based on several moduli of smoothness of f and f'. For brevity we omit the details and only state the following result, which easily follows by using (9) and (11) in the estimates of Theorems 1 and 2, which in turn are used in Theorem 6.

Corollary 2. *Let $-1 < t < 1$ and $s \in \mathbb{N}$. For all functions $f \in C^{k+1}$, with $1 \leq k \leq 2s$, and for sufficiently large $m \in \mathbb{N}$, we have*

$$(1-t^2)|\mathcal{E}^1_{m,s}(f,t)| \leq \frac{\mathcal{C}}{m^{k/2}}\log m, \qquad \mathcal{C} \neq \mathcal{C}(m,t).$$

The same estimate holds for $\Phi^1_{m,s}(f,t)$, which also satisfies

$$|\Phi^1_{m,s}(f,t)| \leq \frac{\mathcal{C}}{m^{k/2}}, \qquad \mathcal{C} \neq \mathcal{C}(m,t), \qquad \forall f \in C^{k+2},\ 1 \leq k \leq 2s.$$

4. Numerical Details and Some Experiments

First, we recall some details given in [19] about the computation of the matrix $C_{m,s}$ in (21). We start from the matrix $\mathcal{A}$ defined in (22). It will be constructed by rows by making use of the triangular scheme in (15) and thus for each row m^2 long operations are required. On the other hand, since $\mathcal{A}$ is centrosymmetric, i.e., $\mathcal{A} = \mathcal{J}\mathcal{A}\mathcal{J}$, where $\mathcal{J}$ is the counter-identity matrix of order $m+1$ ($\mathcal{J}_{i,j} = \delta_{i,m-j}$, $i,j \in N_0^m$, being $\delta_{h,k}$ the Kronecker delta), it will be enough to compute only the first $\left(\frac{m+1}{2}\right)$ or $\left(\frac{m+2}{2}\right)$ rows, according to m is odd or even, respectively. Therefore, the construction of $\mathcal{A}$ requires about $\frac{m^3}{2}$ long operations. Furthermore, since the product of two centrosymmetric matrices can be performed in almost $\frac{m^3}{4}$ long operations [29], the matrix $C_{m,s}$ in (21) can be constructed in almost $(s-2)m^3/4$ long operations, instead of $(s-2)m^3$ ones, i.e., with a saving of about the 75%. A more significant reduction is achieved when the parameter $s = 2^p$, $p \in N, p \geq 1$. Indeed, by using ([30], (14))

$$C_{m,2^p} = C_{m,2^{p-1}} + (\mathcal{I} - \mathcal{A})^{2^{p-1}} C_{m,2^{p-1}}, \tag{55}$$

the matrix $C_{m,s}$ can be determined by $2(\log_2 s - 1)$ products of centrosymmetric matrices and therefore requiring almost $\frac{m^3}{2}(\log_2 s - 1)$ long operations. For instance, for $s = 256$, if we use Equation (21), 255 products of centrosymmetric matrices require about $255\frac{m^3}{4} \sim 63.7m^3$ long operations. On the contrary, if we use (55) then approximatively only $3.5m^3$ long operations are needed.

Now we propose some numerical tests obtained by approximating $\mathcal{H}(f,t)$ and $\mathcal{H}^1(f,t)$ by means of the quadrature rules $\{\mathcal{F}_{m,s}(f,t)\}_m$ and $\{\mathcal{F}^1_{m,s}(f,t)\}_m$, respectively, namely for a given $t \in (-1,1)$, we compute

$$\begin{aligned} \mathcal{H}(f,t) &\sim \mathcal{F}_{m,s}(f,t) + \log\left(\frac{1-t}{1+t}\right) f(t), \\ \mathcal{H}^1(f,t) &\sim \mathcal{F}^1_{m,s}(f,t) + \log\left(\frac{1-t}{1+t}\right) f'(t) - \frac{2}{1-t^2} f(t). \end{aligned}$$

For any choice of m we consider different values of s. In the tables we report the approximating values of the integrals. All the computations have been performed in double-machine precision ($eps \sim 2.22044e-16$).

Example 1.

$$\mathcal{H}(f,t) = \fint_{-1}^{1} \frac{\sin x}{x-t} dx, \quad \mathcal{H}^1(f,t) = \fint_{-1}^{1} \frac{\sin x}{(x-t)^2} dx, \quad t = 0.1.$$

Here $f \in C^\infty$ and as we can see the performance of the quadrature rules improves keeping m fixed and increasing the values of s. An empty cell means that there is no improvement in the computation. In particular as we can see in Tables 1–2, the machine precision is attained for $m = 128$ and $s = 16$ as well as for $m = 64$ and $s = 32$.

Table 1. Example 1a: $\fint_{-1}^{1} \frac{\sin x}{x-0.1} dx$.

m	$s = 8$	$s = 16$	$s = 32$	$s = 64$
8	1.868	1.8688	1.86885	1.86885
16	1.8688	1.868855	1.86885558	1.868855589
32	1.868855	1.868855589	1.868855589128	**1.86885558912878**
64	1.868855589	1.8688555891287	**1.86885558912878**	
128	1.86885558912	**1.86885558912878**		
256	1.8688555891287			

Table 2. Example 1b: $\fint_{-1}^{1} \frac{\sin x}{(x-0.1)^2} dx$.

m	$s = 8$	$s = 16$	$s = 32$	$s = 64$
8	−0.466	−0.4668	−0.4668	−0.46685
16	−0.4668	−0.46685	−0.466857	−0.466857
32	−0.46685	−0.466857	−0.46685700178	**−0.46685700178498**
64	−0.466857	−0.466857001784	**−0.46685700178498**	
128	−0.4668570017	−0.4668570017849		
256	−0.466857001784	**−0.46685700178498**		

Example 2.

$$\mathcal{H}(f,t) = \fint_{-1}^{1} \frac{|x-0.5|^{\frac{15}{2}}}{x-t} dx, \quad \mathcal{H}^1(f,t) = \fint_{-1}^{1} \frac{|x-0.5|^{\frac{15}{2}}}{(x-t)^2} dx, \quad t = 0.3.$$

In this case, $f \in Z_{\frac{15}{2}}$, and as the results in Tables 3–4 show, the numerical errors agree with the theoretical estimates.

Table 3. Example 2a: $-\!\!\!\!\!\!\int_{-1}^{1} \frac{|x-0.5|^{\frac{15}{2}}}{x-0.3} dx$. Exact value −3.29987610310676.

m	$s = 8$	$s = 16$	$s = 32$	$s = 64$
16	−3	−3.298	−3.299	−3.2998
32	−3.299	−3.29987	−3.29987	−3.299876
64	−3.299876	−3.299876	−3.299876	−3.299876
128	−3.29987610	−3.2998761	−3.29987610	−3.29987610
256	−3.29987610	−3.299876103	−3.299876103	−3.2998761031
e 512	−3.2998761031	−3.2998761031	−3.29987610310	−3.2998761031
1024	−3.299876103106	−3.299876103106	−3.2998761031066	−3.2998761031067

Table 4. Example 2b: $=\!\!\!\!\!\!\int_{-1}^{1} \frac{|x-0.5|^{\frac{15}{2}}}{(x-0.3)^2} dx$.

m	$s = 8$	$s = 16$	$s = 32$	$s = 64$
32	3.0	3.03	3.038	3.0383
64	3.038	3.03838	3.03838	3.038388
128	3.03838	3.038388	3.038388	3.0383888
256	3.0383888	3.0383888	3.03838883	3.03838883
512	3.03838883	3.03838883	3.038388835	3.03838883525
1024	3.038388835	3.03838883528	3.03838883525	3.03838883525

Example 3.

$$\mathcal{H}(f,t) = -\!\!\!\!\!\!\int_{-1}^{1} \frac{\exp(x)\sin(x)}{1+x^2} \frac{dx}{x-t}, \qquad t = -0.7.$$

Here $f \in C^{\infty}$. In this test (see Table 5), we want to show the performance of the quadrature rule when m is fixed and s increases, highlighting how we get an improvement, but it seems till to a certain threshold. This behavior will be the subject of future investigations.

Table 5. Example 3: $⨍_{-1}^{1} \frac{\exp(x)\sin(x)}{1+x^2} \frac{dx}{x+0.7}$.

	$m = 8$	$m = 16$	$m = 32$	$m = 64$	$m = 128$	$m = 516$	$m = 1024$	$m = 2048$
$s = 4$	2.03	2.00	2.00	2.0067	2.00674	2.006741	2.006741	2.00674110
$s = 8$	2.023	2.006	2.006	2.0067	2.0067412	2.00674121	2.00674121192	2.0067412119231
$s = 16$	2.004	2.006	2.00674	2.006741	2.00674121	2.00674121192	2.0067412119231	2.00674121192318
$s = 32$	2.000	2.006	2.00674	2.006741	2.0067412119	2.006741211923	2.0067412119231	2.00674121192318
$s = 64$	2.002	2.006	2.00674	2.00674121	2.0067412119	2.006741211923	2.0067412119231	2.0067412119231
$s = 128$	2.006	2.006	2.00674	2.00674121	2.006741211923	2.006741211923	2.0067412119231	2.0067412119231
$s = 256$	2.008	2.0067	2.00674	2.006741211	2.006741211923	2.006741211923	2.006741211923	2.00674121192318
$s = 512$	2.010	2.0067	2.0067412	2.006741211	2.006741211923	2.006741211923	2.006741211923	2.006741211923
$s = 1024$	2.010	2.0067	2.0067412	2.0067412119	2.006741211923	2.006741211923	2.006741211923	2.006741211923
$s = 2048$	2.011	2.0067	2.0067412	2.0067412119	2.006741211923	2.006741211923	2.006741211923	2.006741211923
$s = 4096$	2.011	2.0067	2.0067412	2.0067412119	2.006741211923	2.006741211923	2.006741211923	2.0067412119231

5. Proofs

The following three lemmas will be useful in the sequel.

Lemma 1. *Let $f \in DT$ and $P_m \in \mathbb{P}_m$, $m \geq 2$. Then*

$$\int_0^{\frac{1}{m}} \frac{\omega_\varphi(f-P_m,t)}{t}dt \leq \mathcal{C}\left(\|(f-P_m)\|_\infty + \int_0^{\frac{1}{m}} \frac{\omega_\varphi^r(f,t)}{t}dt\right),$$

where $r \in \mathbb{N}$ with $r < m$ and $0 < \mathcal{C} \neq \mathcal{C}(m,f)$.

Proof. Taking into account that $\omega_\varphi(f,t)$ is a non-decreasing function of t, we have

$$\int_0^{\frac{1}{m}} \frac{\omega_\varphi(f-P_m,t)}{t}dt = \sum_{j=m}^{\infty}\int_{\frac{1}{j+1}}^{\frac{1}{j}} \frac{\omega_\varphi(f-P_m,t)}{t}dt \leq \mathcal{C}\sum_{j=m}^{\infty}\frac{\omega_\varphi\left(f-P_m,\frac{1}{j}\right)}{j}.$$

Then, by applying the following Stechkin type inequality ([22], Theorem 7.2.4)

$$\omega_\varphi(f,t) \leq \mathcal{C}t\sum_{i=0}^{\lfloor\frac{1}{t}\rfloor} E_i(f), \quad 0 < \mathcal{C} \neq \mathcal{C}(f,t),$$

we get

$$\begin{aligned}
\int_0^{\frac{1}{m}} \frac{\omega_\varphi(f-P_m,t)}{t}dt &\leq \mathcal{C}\sum_{j=m}^{\infty}\frac{1}{j^2}\sum_{i=0}^{j}E_i(f-P_m)\\
&= \mathcal{C}\sum_{j=m}^{\infty}\frac{1}{j^2}\left[\sum_{i=0}^{m-1}E_i(f-P_m)+\sum_{i=m}^{j}E_i(f-P_m)\right]\\
&\leq \mathcal{C}\|(f-P_m)\|_\infty\left(\sum_{j=m}^{\infty}\frac{m}{j^2}\right)+\mathcal{C}\sum_{j=m}^{\infty}\frac{1}{j^2}\sum_{i=m}^{j}E_i(f),
\end{aligned}$$

and taking into account that $\sum_{j=n}^{\infty}\frac{1}{j^2} \leq \frac{\mathcal{C}}{n}$ holds for all $n \in \mathbb{N}$, with $\mathcal{C} \neq \mathcal{C}(n)$, we obtain

$$\begin{aligned}
\int_0^{\frac{1}{m}} \frac{\omega_\varphi(f-P_m,t)}{t}dt &\leq \mathcal{C}\|(f-P_m)\|_\infty+\mathcal{C}\sum_{i=m}^{\infty}E_i(f)\sum_{j=i}^{\infty}\frac{1}{j^2}\\
&\leq \mathcal{C}\|(f-P_m)\|_\infty+\mathcal{C}\sum_{i=m}^{\infty}\frac{E_i(f)}{i}.
\end{aligned}$$

Finally, by applying the Jackson type inequality ([22], Theorem 7.2.1) (see also [31], Section 2.5.2),

$$E_m(f) \leq \mathcal{C}\omega_\varphi^r\left(f,\frac{1}{m}\right), \quad r < m, \quad \mathcal{C} \neq \mathcal{C}(m,f),$$

and recalling that ([22], (4.1.3))

$$\omega_\varphi(g,\alpha t) \leq \mathcal{C}\alpha\omega_\varphi(g,t), \qquad \forall\alpha \geq 1, \quad \mathcal{C} \neq \mathcal{C}(g,t,\alpha), \tag{56}$$

we deduce

$$\begin{aligned}
\sum_{i=m}^{\infty} \frac{E_i(f)}{i} &\le C \sum_{i=m}^{\infty} \frac{\omega_\varphi^r\left(f, \frac{1}{i}\right)}{i} = \sum_{i=m}^{\infty} \omega_\varphi^r\left(f, \frac{1}{i}\right)(i-1)\int_{\frac{1}{i}}^{\frac{1}{i-1}} du \\
&\le C \sum_{i=m}^{\infty} \int_{\frac{1}{i}}^{\frac{1}{i-1}} \frac{\omega_\varphi^r(f,u)}{u} du = C \int_0^{\frac{1}{m-1}} \frac{\omega_\varphi^r(f,u)}{u} du \\
&= C \int_0^{\frac{1}{m}} \frac{\omega_\varphi^r\left(f, \frac{m}{m-1}t\right)}{t} dt \le C \int_0^{\frac{1}{m}} \frac{\omega_\varphi^r(f,t)}{t} dt,
\end{aligned}$$

which completes the proof. □

Lemma 2. *For any $-1 < t \le -\frac{1}{2}$, and for any f s.t. $f' \in DT$, we have*

$$⨍_{-1}^{2t+1} \frac{f(x)}{(x-t)^2} dx \le C\left(\int_0^1 \frac{\omega_\varphi(f',\sigma)}{\sigma} d\sigma + \frac{\|f\|}{1+t}\right),$$

where $C \ne C(f,t)$.

Proof. Since $⨍_{-1}^{2t+1} \frac{dx}{x-t} = 0$, we write

$$\begin{aligned}
⨍_{-1}^{2t+1} \frac{f(x)}{(x-t)^2} dx &= ⨍_{-1}^{2t+1} \frac{f(x)-f(t)-f'(t)(x-t)}{(x-t)^2} dx + f(t) ⨍_{-1}^{2t+1} \frac{dx}{(x-t)^2} \\
&=: A_1(t) + A_2(t). \qquad (57)
\end{aligned}$$

Concerning A_1, by reasoning as done in proving Proposition 3 we have that $f' \in DT$ implies

$$A_1(t) = \int_{-1}^{2t+1} \frac{f(x)-f(t)-f'(t)(x-t)}{(x-t)^2} dx$$

and using

$$f(x) - f(t) - f'(t)(x-t) = \int_t^x [f'(\tau) - f'(t)] d\tau, \qquad (58)$$

we obtain the form

$$A_1(t) = \int_{-1}^{t} \left[\int_x^t [f'(t) - f'(\tau)] d\tau\right] \frac{dx}{(x-t)^2} + \int_t^{2t+1} \left[\int_t^x [f'(\tau) - f'(t)] d\tau\right] \frac{dx}{(x-t)^2}.$$

Hence, changing the variables $x = t - \frac{\sigma}{2}\sqrt{1-t^2}$, $\tau = t - \frac{h}{2}\sqrt{1-t^2}$ in the first addendum and $x = t + \frac{\sigma}{2}\sqrt{1-t^2}$, $\tau = t + \frac{h}{2}\sqrt{1-t^2}$ in the second one, we get

$$\begin{aligned}
A_1(t) &= \int_0^{2\sqrt{\frac{1+t}{1-t}}} \left[\int_0^\sigma \left[f'\left(t + \frac{h}{2}\sqrt{1-t^2}\right) - f'\left(t - \frac{h}{2}\sqrt{1-t^2}\right)\right] dh\right] \frac{d\sigma}{\sigma^2} \\
&= \int_0^{2\sqrt{\frac{1+t}{1-t}}} \left(\int_0^\sigma \Delta_{h\varphi(t)} f'(t) dh\right) \frac{d\sigma}{\sigma^2}.
\end{aligned}$$

Consequently, for any $-1 < t \le -\frac{1}{2}$ we obtain

$$\begin{aligned}
|A_1(t)| &\le \int_0^{2\sqrt{\frac{1+t}{1-t}}} \left(\int_0^\sigma \|\Delta_{h\varphi} f'\| dh\right) \frac{d\sigma}{\sigma^2} \le \int_0^{2\sqrt{\frac{1+t}{1-t}}} \sup_{h \le \sigma} \|\Delta_{h\varphi} f'\| \frac{d\sigma}{\sigma} \\
&= \int_0^{2\sqrt{\frac{1+t}{1-t}}} \frac{\omega_\varphi(f',\sigma)}{\sigma} d\sigma \le \int_0^{\frac{2}{\sqrt{3}}} \frac{\omega_\varphi(f',\sigma)}{\sigma} d\sigma,
\end{aligned}$$

and using (56), we conclude that

$$|A_1(t)| \leq \int_0^{\frac{2}{\sqrt{3}}} \frac{\omega_\varphi(f',\sigma)}{\sigma} d\sigma = \int_0^1 \omega_\varphi\left(f', \frac{2}{\sqrt{3}}u\right) \frac{du}{u} \leq \mathcal{C} \int_0^1 \frac{\omega_\varphi(f',u)}{u} du. \tag{59}$$

Finally, since

$$\fint_{-1}^{2t+1} \frac{dx}{(x-t)^2} = \lim_{\varepsilon \to 0^+} \left[\int_{-1}^{t-\varepsilon} \frac{1}{(x-t)^2} dx + \int_{t+\varepsilon}^{2t+1} \frac{1}{(x-t)^2} dx - \frac{2}{\varepsilon}\right] = -\frac{2}{1+t},$$

we have

$$|A_2(t)| = \frac{2}{1+t}|f(t)| \leq 2\frac{\|f\|}{1+t},$$

and the statement follows by collecting this last inequality, (59) and (57). □

Similarly, we can prove the following

Lemma 3. *For any $\frac{1}{2} \leq t < 1$, and for any f s.t. $f' \in DT$, we have*

$$\fint_{2t-1}^{1} \frac{f(x)}{(x-t)^2} dx \leq \mathcal{C}\left(\int_0^1 \frac{\omega_\varphi(f',\sigma)}{\sigma} d\sigma + \frac{\|f\|}{1-t}\right),$$

where $\mathcal{C} \neq \mathcal{C}(f,t)$.

Proof of Theorem 4. Assume first that $-1 < t \leq -\frac{1}{2}$. In this case, $\varphi^2(t) \sim (1+t)$ and we have

$$\varphi^2(t)\left|\mathcal{H}^1(f,t)\right| \sim (1+t)\left|\fint_{-1}^{2t+1} \frac{f(x)}{(x-t)^2} dx + \int_{2t+1}^1 \frac{f(x)}{(x-t)^2} dx\right|. \tag{60}$$

Since

$$(1+t)\left|\int_{2t+1}^1 \frac{f(x)}{(x-t)^2} dx\right| \leq \mathcal{C}\|f\|,$$

the statement follows from Lemma 2 for any $-1 < t \leq -\frac{1}{2}$.

Assume now $\frac{1}{2} \leq t < 1$, so that $\varphi^2(t) \sim (1-t)$. By using the decomposition

$$\varphi^2(t)\left|\mathcal{H}^1(f,t)\right| \sim (1-t)\left|\int_{-1}^{2t-1} \frac{f(x)}{(x-t)^2} dx + \fint_{2t-1}^1 \frac{f(x)}{(x-t)^2} dx\right|, \tag{61}$$

and taking into account that

$$(1-t)\left|\int_{-1}^{2t-1} \frac{f(x)}{(x-t)^2} dx\right| \leq \mathcal{C}\|f\|,$$

the statement follows from Lemma 3 for any $\frac{1}{2} \leq t < 1$.

Finally, suppose $|t| < \frac{1}{2}$ and fix $\frac{1}{4} < a < \frac{1}{2}$. In this case, $\varphi(t) \sim 1$ and we consider the following decomposition

$$\begin{aligned}\varphi^2(t)\left|\mathcal{H}^1(f,t)\right| \sim \; & \left|\int_{|x-t|\geq a} \frac{f(x)}{(x-t)^2} dx + \fint_{t-a}^{t+a} \frac{f(x)-f(t)-f'(t)(x-t)}{(x-t)^2} dx +\right. \\ & \left. +f(t)\fint_{t-a}^{t+a} \frac{dx}{(x-t)^2}\right|.\end{aligned} \tag{62}$$

For the first term at the right-hand side of (62) we get

$$\left|\int_{|x-t|\geq a} \frac{f(x)}{(x-t)^2} dx\right| \leq \mathcal{C}\|f\|.$$

Concerning the second addendum of (62), we proceed analogously to the estimate of $A_1(t)$ in Lemma 2. More precisely, by using $f' \in DT$ and (58) we obtain

$$\begin{aligned}
\fint_{t-a}^{t+a} \frac{f(x)-f(t)-f'(t)(x-t)}{(x-t)^2}dx &= \int_{t-a}^{t+a} \frac{f(x)-f(t)-f'(t)(x-t)}{(x-t)^2}dx \\
&= \left(\int_{t-a}^{t} + \int_{t}^{t+a}\right)\left(\int_t^x [f'(\tau)-f'(t)]\,d\tau\right)\frac{dx}{(x-t)^2},
\end{aligned}$$

and by changing the variables $x = t \pm \frac{\sigma}{2}\varphi(t)$ and $\tau = t \pm \frac{h}{2}\varphi(t)$, we get

$$\left|\fint_{t-a}^{t+a} \frac{f(x)-f(t)-f'(t)(x-t)}{(x-t)^2}dx\right| \le \int_0^{\frac{2a}{\varphi(t)}} \int_0^{\sigma} \left|\Delta_{h\varphi(t)} f'(t)\right| dh \frac{d\sigma}{\sigma^2} \le C \int_0^1 \frac{\omega_\varphi(f',u)}{u}du.$$

Finally, as regards the third term at the right-hand side of (62), since $\fint_{t-a}^{t+a} \frac{dx}{(x-t)^2} = -\frac{2}{a}$, we have

$$\left| f(t) \fint_{t-a}^{t+a} \frac{dx}{(x-t)^2} \right| \le \frac{2}{a}\|f\|,$$

and the theorem is completely proven. □

Proof of Proposition 1. Start from the standard decomposition

$$\mathcal{H}(f,t) = \fint_{-1}^{1} \frac{f(x)-f(t)}{x-t}dx + f(t)\mathcal{H}(\mathbf{1},t), \tag{63}$$

and taking into account

$$\mathcal{H}(\mathbf{1},t) := \fint_{-1}^{1} \frac{dx}{x-t} = \log\left(\frac{1-t}{1+t}\right),$$

we must prove that the principal value integral in (63) is indeed an improper integral. To this aim, let us first prove that

$$\int_t^1 \frac{f(x)-f(t)}{x-t}dx = \lim_{\epsilon\to 0^+} \int_{t+\epsilon}^1 \frac{f(x)-f(t)}{x-t}dx < \infty. \tag{64}$$

Please note that for any $\epsilon > 0$,

$$\int_{t+\epsilon}^1 \frac{f(x)-f(t)}{x-t}dx = \int_\epsilon^{1-t} \frac{f(u+t)-f(t)}{u}du.$$

Moreover, for any $g \in \mathcal{AC}$, we note that

$$\begin{aligned}
f(u+t)-f(t) &= f(u+t) - g(u+t) - f(t) + g(t) + g(u+t) - g(t) \\
&\le 2\|f-g\| + \int_t^{u+t} g'(\sigma)d\sigma \\
&\le 2\|f-g\| + \|g'\varphi\| \int_t^{u+t} \frac{d\sigma}{\varphi(\sigma)} \\
&= 2\|f-g\| + u\|g'\varphi\| \left[\frac{\arcsin(u+t)-\arcsin(t)}{u}\right].
\end{aligned}$$

On the other hand, recalling that

$$\arcsin y = y + \frac{y^3}{6} + \frac{3}{40}y^5 + \frac{5}{112}y^7 + \frac{35}{1152}y^9 + \ldots, \qquad |y| < 1,$$

we easily get

$$\frac{\arcsin(u+t)-\arcsin(t)}{u} \le C \ne C(t,u), \qquad |t| < 1, \quad 0 < u \le 2,$$

and therefore, the previous estimate and (3) yield

$$f(u+t)-f(t)\le \mathcal{C}\left(\inf_{g\in AC}\{\|f-g\|+u\|g'\varphi\|\right)=\mathcal{C}K_{1,\varphi}(f,u)\sim\omega_\varphi(f,u).$$

Hence, for all $|t|<1$ it follows

$$\lim_{\epsilon\to 0^+}\int_\epsilon^{1-t}\frac{f(u+t)-f(t)}{u}du\le \mathcal{C}\lim_{\epsilon\to 0^+}\int_\epsilon^2\frac{\omega_\varphi(f,u)}{u}du,\qquad \mathcal{C}\ne\mathcal{C}(t),$$

i.e., under the assumption $f\in DT$, (64) holds.

Similarly proceeding, we can prove that

$$\int_{-1}^t\frac{f(x)-f(t)}{x-t}dx=\lim_{\varepsilon\to 0^+}\int_\epsilon^{1+t}\frac{f(t)-f(t-u)}{u}du<\infty$$

and the statement follows. □

Proof of Proposition 2. For $1\le k\le m-1$, by using the recurrence relation (15) and taking into account that $\int_{-1}^1 p_{m,h}(x)dx=\frac{2}{m+1}$ holds $\forall h\in\mathbb{N}_0^m$, we get

$$\begin{aligned}
q_{m,k}(t) = &\ \frac{1}{2}\int_{-1}^1\frac{(1-x)p_{m-1,k}(x)-(1-t)p_{m-1,k}(t)}{x-t}dx\\
&+\frac{1}{2}\int_{-1}^1\frac{(1+x)p_{m-1,k-1}(x)-(1+t)p_{m-1,k-1}(t)}{x-t}dx\\
= &\ \frac{1}{2}\left(q_{m-1,k}(t)-\int_{-1}^1\frac{xp_{m-1,k}(x)-tp_{m-1,k}(t)}{x-t}dx\right)\\
&+\frac{1}{2}\left(q_{m-1,k-1}(t)+\int_{-1}^1\frac{xp_{m-1,k-1}(x)-tp_{m-1,k-1}(t)}{x-t}dx\right)\\
= &\ \frac{1}{2}\left(q_{m-1,k}(t)-\frac{2}{m}-tq_{m-1,k}(t)\right)+\frac{1}{2}\left(q_{m-1,k-1}(t)+\frac{2}{m}+tq_{m-1,k-1}(t)\right)\\
= &\ \frac{(1-t)}{2}q_{m-1,k}(t)+\frac{(1+t)}{2}q_{m-1,k-1}(t).
\end{aligned}$$

For $k=0$, we have

$$\begin{aligned}
q_{m,0}(t) &= \frac{1}{2}\int_{-1}^1\frac{(1-x)p_{m-1,0}(x)-(1-t)p_{m-1,0}(t)}{x-t}dx=\frac{1}{2}\left(q_{m-1,k}(t)-\frac{2}{m}-tq_{m-1,k}(t)\right)\\
&= \frac{(1-t)}{2}q_{m-1,k}(t)-\frac{1}{m}.
\end{aligned}$$

For $k=m$ we proceed analogously. □

Proof of Theorem 5. Set $R_{m,s}f=f-B_{m,s}f$, we have

$$\mathcal{E}_{m,s}(f,t)=\mathcal{H}(R_{m,s}f,t),\qquad\text{and}\qquad\Phi_{m,s}(f,t)=\mathcal{F}(R_{m,s}f,t).$$

Applying Theorem 3, $\mathcal{E}_{m,s}(f,t)$ can be estimated as follows

$$|\mathcal{E}_{m,s}(f,t)|\le\mathcal{C}\log\left(\frac{e}{1-t^2}\right)\left[\|R_{m,s}f\|+\int_0^1\frac{\omega_\varphi(R_{m,s}f,u)}{u}du\right],\qquad\mathcal{C}\ne\mathcal{C}(m,f,t),\tag{65}$$

and by Theorem 1 we further obtain

$$\|R_{m,s}f\| \leq \mathcal{C}\left[\omega_\varphi^{2s}\left(f,\frac{1}{\sqrt{m}}\right)+\frac{\|f\|}{m^s}\right], \qquad \mathcal{C}\neq \mathcal{C}(m,f). \tag{66}$$

Moreover, by Lemma 1 we get

$$\begin{aligned}\int_0^1 \frac{\omega_\varphi(R_{m,s}f,u)}{u}du &= \int_0^{\frac{1}{m}} \frac{\omega_\varphi(R_{m,s}f,u)}{u}du + \int_{\frac{1}{m}}^1 \frac{\omega_\varphi(R_{m,s}f,u)}{u}du \\ &\leq \mathcal{C}\left(\int_0^{\frac{1}{m}} \frac{\omega_\varphi^r(f,u)}{u}du + \|R_{m,s}f\|\log m\right),\end{aligned}$$

and (42) follows from this last estimate, (65) and (66).

Regarding the quadrature error $\Phi_{m,s}(f,t)$, we observe that

$$\Phi_{m,s}(f,t)=\mathcal{F}(R_{m,s}f,t)=\mathcal{H}(R_{m,s}f,t)-\log\left(\frac{1-t}{1+t}\right)R_{m,s}f(t),$$

which leads to

$$\begin{aligned}\log^{-1}\left(\frac{e}{1-t^2}\right)|\Phi_{m,s}(f,t)| &\leq \log^{-1}\left(\frac{e}{1-t^2}\right)|\mathcal{H}(R_{m,s}f,t)|+\mathcal{C}|R_{m,s}f(t)| \\ &\leq \mathcal{C}\log^{-1}\left(\frac{e}{1-t^2}\right)|\mathcal{E}_{m,s}(f,t)|+\mathcal{C}\|R_{m,s}f\|.\end{aligned}$$

Hence, in the case that $f\in DT$, the estimate (42) holds for $\Phi_{m,s}(f,t)$ as well.

Finally, if $f\in C^1$ then, by applying the mean value theorem, we get

$$|\Phi_{m,s}(f,t)|=\left|\int_{-1}^1 \frac{R_{m,s}f(x)-R_{m,s}f(t)}{x-t}dx\right|\leq \mathcal{C}\|(f-B_{m,s}f)'\|$$

and (43) follows from Theorem 2. □

Proof of Proposition 3. We start from the standard decomposition

$$\mathcal{H}^1(f,t)=\neq\!\!\!\!\!\!\int_{-1}^1 \frac{f(x)-f(t)-f'(t)(x-t)}{(x-t)^2}dx+\neq\!\!\!\!\!\!\int_{-1}^1 \frac{f(t)+f'(t)(x-t)}{(x-t)^2}dx, \tag{67}$$

and recalling the definitions

$$\begin{aligned}\neq\!\!\!\!\!\!\int_{-1}^1 \frac{g(x)}{(x-t)^2}dx &= \lim_{\varepsilon\to 0^+}\left[\int_{-1}^{t-\varepsilon}\frac{g(x)}{(x-t)^2}dx+\int_{t+\varepsilon}^1\frac{g(x)}{(x-t)^2}dx-\frac{2g(t)}{\varepsilon}\right], \\ -\!\!\!\!\!\!\int_{-1}^1 \frac{g(x)}{x-t}dx &= \lim_{\epsilon\to 0^+}\left[\int_{-1}^{t-\epsilon}\frac{g(x)}{x-t}dx+\int_{t+\epsilon}^1\frac{g(x)}{x-t}dx\right],\end{aligned}$$

we note that

$$\neq\!\!\!\!\!\!\int_{-1}^1 \frac{dx}{(x-t)^2}=-\frac{2}{1-t^2}, \qquad \neq\!\!\!\!\!\!\int_{-1}^1 \frac{(x-t)}{(x-t)^2}dx=-\!\!\!\!\!\!\int_{-1}^1 \frac{dx}{(x-t)}=\log\left(\frac{1-t}{1+t}\right).$$

Moreover, taking into account that

$$f(x)-f(t)=f'(\xi_{x,t})(x-t), \qquad \min\{x,t\}<\xi_{x,t}<\max\{x,t\},$$

we have

$$\fint_{-1}^{1}\frac{f(x)-f(t)-f'(t)(x-t)}{(x-t)^2}dx=\fint_{-1}^{1}\frac{f'(\xi_{x,t})-f'(t)}{(x-t)}dx.$$

Hence to complete the proof, we have to prove that this last principal value integral is indeed an improper integral if $f'\in DT$.

We are going to prove that

$$\int_{t}^{1}\frac{f'(\xi_{x,t})-f'(t)}{(x-t)}dx=\lim_{\epsilon\to 0^+}\int_{t+\epsilon}^{1}\frac{f'(\xi_{x,t})-f'(t)}{(x-t)}dx<\infty, \tag{68}$$

being the proof of

$$\int_{-1}^{t}\frac{f'(\xi_{x,t})-f'(t)}{(x-t)}dx=\lim_{\epsilon\to 0^+}\int_{-1}^{t-\epsilon}\frac{f'(\xi_{x,t})-f'(t)}{(x-t)}dx<\infty$$

analogous.
Set $\xi_{x,t}=(x-t)\theta+t$, with $0<\theta<1$, for any $\epsilon>0$, we have

$$\int_{t+\epsilon}^{1}\frac{f'(\xi_{x,t})-f'(t)}{(x-t)}dx=\int_{t+\epsilon}^{1}\frac{f'((x-t)\theta+t)-f'(t)}{(x-t)}dx=\int_{\epsilon}^{1-t}\frac{f'(u\theta+t)-f'(t)}{u}du.$$

On the other hand, for any $g\in\mathcal{AC}$, $|t|<1$, $0<\theta<1$ and $0<u\le 2$, similarly to the proof of Proposition 1, we have

$$\begin{aligned}
f'(u\theta+t)-f'(t) &= f'(u\theta+t)-g(u\theta+t)-f'(t)+g(t)+g(u\theta+t)-g(t)\\
&\le 2\|f'-g\|+\int_{t}^{u\theta+t}g'(\sigma)d\sigma\\
&\le 2\|f'-g\|+u\|g'\varphi\|\left[\frac{\arcsin(u\theta+t)-\arcsin(t)}{u}\right]\\
&\le \mathcal{C}\left(\|f'-g\|+u\|g'\varphi\|\right), \qquad \mathcal{C}\neq\mathcal{C}(g,u,\theta,t).
\end{aligned}$$

Hence, by means of (3), we get

$$\lim_{\epsilon\to 0^+}\int_{\epsilon}^{1-t}\frac{f'(u\theta+t)-f'(t)}{u}du\le\mathcal{C}\lim_{\epsilon\to 0^+}\int_{\epsilon}^{2}\frac{\omega_\varphi(f',u)}{u}du$$

and under the assumption $f'\in DT$, (68) follows. □

Proof of Theorem 6. We start from

$$\mathcal{E}^1_{m,s}(f,t)=\mathcal{H}^1(R_{m,s}f,t), \qquad R_{m,s}f(t)=f(t)-B_{m,s}f(t).$$

By Theorem 4, we have

$$(1-t^2)|\mathcal{H}^1(R_{m,s}f,t)|\le\mathcal{C}\left(\|R_{m,s}f\|+\int_0^1\frac{\omega_\varphi((R_{m,s}f)',\tau)}{\tau}d\tau\right).$$

Since

$$\int_0^1 \frac{\omega_\varphi((R_{m,s}f)',\tau)}{\tau}d\tau = \left\{\int_0^{\frac{1}{m}} + \int_{\frac{1}{m}}^1\right\} \frac{\omega_\varphi((R_{m,s}f)',\tau)}{\tau}d\tau$$
$$\leq \int_0^{\frac{1}{m}} \frac{\omega_\varphi((R_{m,s}f)',\tau)}{\tau}d\tau + 2\|(R_{m,s}f)'\| \int_{\frac{1}{m}}^1 \frac{d\tau}{\tau}$$
$$= \int_0^{\frac{1}{m}} \frac{\omega_\varphi((R_{m,s}f)',\tau)}{\tau}d\tau + 2\|(R_{m,s}f)'\| \log m,$$

by Lemma 1 we get

$$(1-t^2)|\mathcal{H}^1(R_{m,s}f,t)| \leq \mathcal{C}\left(\|R_{m,s}f\| + \|(R_{m,s}f)'\| \log m + \int_0^{\frac{1}{m}} \frac{\omega_\varphi^r(f',\tau)}{\tau}d\tau \right),$$

i.e., (53) holds.

The same estimate (53) also holds for $\Phi^1_{m,s}$, since by (44) we have

$$\Phi^1_{m,s}(f,t) = \mathcal{H}^1(R_{m,s}f,t) - \log\left(\frac{1-t}{1+t}\right)(R_{m,s}f)'(t) + \frac{2}{1-t^2}R_{m,s}f(t),$$

and we note that

$$(1-t^2)\left|\log\left(\frac{1-t}{1+t}\right)(R_{m,s}f)'(t)\right| \leq \mathcal{C}\|(R_{m,s}f)'\|, \qquad \mathcal{C} \neq \mathcal{C}(t,f,m),$$
$$(1-t^2)\left|\frac{2}{1-t^2}R_{m,s}f(t)\right| \leq 2\|R_{m,s}f\|.$$

Finally, (54) follows from the Peano form of the Taylor's remainder term, namely

$$g(x) = g(t) + g'(t)(x-t) + g''(\xi)\frac{(x-t)^2}{2}, \qquad min\{x,t\} \leq \xi \leq \max\{x,t\},$$

which for $g = R_{m,s}f$, yields

$$|\Phi^1_{m,s}(f,t)| = |\mathcal{F}^1(R_{m,s}f,t)|$$
$$\leq \int_{-1}^1 \frac{|R_{m,s}f(x) - R_{m,s}f(t) - (R_{m,s}f)'(t)(x-t)|}{(x-t)^2}dx$$
$$\leq \|(R_{m,s}f)''\|.$$

□

Author Contributions: All authors equally contributed to the paper. Conceptualization, F.F., D.O. and W.T.; methodology, F.F., D.O. and W.T.; software, F.F., D.O. and W.T.; validation, F.F., D.O. and W.T.; analysis, F.F., D.O. and W.T.; investigation, F.F., D.O. and W.T.; resources, F.F., D.O. and W.T.; data curation, F.F., D.O. and W.T.; writing–original draft preparation, writing–review and editing, F.F., D.O. and W.T.; visualization, F.F., D.O. and W.T.; supervision F.F., D.O. and W.T. All authors have read and agreed to the published version of the manuscript.

Funding: This research was partially supported by INdAM - GNCS Project 2019 "Discretizzazione di misure, approssimazione di operatori integrali ed applicazioni". The research of the first author was partially supported by the Helmholtz Association under the project Ptychography4.0.

Acknowledgments: The authors thank the anonymous referees for their suggestions and remarks, which allowed to improve the paper. This research has been accomplished within the RITA "Research ITalian network on Approximation".

Conflicts of Interest: The authors declare no conflict of interest.

References

1. Kalandiya, A.I. *Mathematical Methods of Two-Dimensional Elasticity*; Publ. Nauka: Moscow, Russia, 1973.
2. Mastroianni, G.; Russo, M.G.; Themistoclakis, W. Numerical Methods for Cauchy Singular Integral Equations in Spaces of Weighted Continuous Functions. In *Operator Theory Advances and Applications*; Birkäuser Verlag: Basel, Switzerland, 2005; Volume 160, pp. 311–336.
3. Mastroianni, G.; Russo, M.G.; Themistoclakis, W. The boundedness of the Cauchy singular integral operator in weighted Besov type spaces with uniform norms. *Integr. Equ. Oper. Theory* **2002**, *42*, 57–89. [CrossRef]
4. Mastroianni, G.; Themistoclakis, W. A numerical method for the generalized airfoil equation based on the de la Vallée Poussin interpolation. *J. Comput. Appl. Math.* **2005**, *180*, 71–105. [CrossRef]
5. Sun, W.; Wu, J. Interpolatory quadrature rules for Hadamard finite-part integrals and their superconvergence. *IMA J. Numer. Anal.* **2008**, *28*, 580–597. [CrossRef]
6. King, F. *Hilbert Transforms I & II*; Cambridge University Press: Cambridge, UK, 2009.
7. Boche, H.; Pohl, V. On the calculation of the Hilbert transform from interpolated data. *IEEE Trans. Inform. Theory* **2008**, *54*, 2358–2366. [CrossRef]
8. Boche, H.; Pohl, V. Limits of calculating the finite Hilbert transform from discrete samples. *Appl. Comp. Harm. Anal.* **2019**, *46*, 66–93. [CrossRef]
9. Parker, P.J.; Anderson, B.D.O Hilbert transform from interpolation data. *Math. Control Signals Syst.* **1990**, *3*, 97–124. [CrossRef]
10. Monegato, G. Definitions, properties and applications of finite-part integrals. *J. Comp. Appl. Math.* **2009**, *229*, 425–439. [CrossRef]
11. Davis, P.J.; Rabinowitz, P. *Methods of Numerical Integration*, 2nd ed.; Academic Press: New York, NY, USA, 1984.
12. De Bonis, M.C.; Occorsio, D. On the simultaneous approximation of a Hilbert transform and its derivatives on the real semiaxis. *Appl. Numer. Math.* **2017**, *114*, 132–153. [CrossRef]
13. De Bonis, M.C.; Occorsio, D. Error bounds for a Gauss-type quadrature rule to evaluate hypersingular integrals. *Filomat* **2018**, *32*, 2525–2543.
14. Monegato, G. Numerical evaluation of hypersingular integrals. *J. Comp. Appl. Math.* **1994**, *50*, 9–31. [CrossRef]
15. Monegato, G. The numerical evaluation of one-dimensional Cauchy principal value integrals. *Computing* **1982**, *29*, 337–354. [CrossRef]
16. Felbecker, G. Linearkombinationen von iterierten Bernsteinoperatoren. *Manuscripta Math.* **1979**, *29*, 229–246. [CrossRef]
17. Mastroianni, G.; Occorsio, M.R. Una generalizzazione dell'operatore di Bernstein. *Rend. Accad. Sci. Fis. Mat. Napoli* **1977**, *44*, 151–169.
18. Micchelli, C. The saturation class and iterates of the Bernstein polynomials. *J. Approx. Theory* **1973**, *8*, 1–18. [CrossRef]
19. Occorsio, D.; Russo, M.G. *Bivariate Generalized Bernstein Operators and Their Application to Fredholm Integral Equations*; Nouvelle serie, (**114**), tome **100**; Publications de l'Institut Matthématique: Belgrade, Serbia, 2016; pp. 141–162.
20. Mastroianni, G.; Occorsio, M.R. *Alcuni Algoritmi Per il Calcolo Numerico di Integrali A Valor Principale Secondo Cauchy*; Technical Report CNR IAM n. 3/84; Institute for Applications of Mathematics of National Research Council of Italy: Naples, Italy, 1984.
21. Gonska, H.H.; Zhou, X.-L. Approximation theorems for the iterated Boolean sums of Bernstein operators. *J. Comput. Appl. Math.* **1994**, *53*, 21–31. [CrossRef]
22. Ditzian, Z.; Totik, V. *Moduli of Smoothness*; SCMG Springer: New York, NY, USA, 1987.
23. Ditzian, Z.; Totik, V. Remarks on Besov spaces and best polynomial approximation. *Proc. Am. Math. Soc.* **1988**, *104*, 1059–1066. [CrossRef]
24. Draganov, B.R. Strong estimates of the weighted simultaneous approximation by the Bernstein and Kantorovich operators and their Boolean sums. *J. Approx. Theory* **2015**, *200*, 92–135. [CrossRef]
25. Farin, G.E. *Curves and Surfaces for Computer Aided Geometric Design: A Practical Guide*; Academic Press: Cambridge, MA, USA, 1993; ISBN 0122490525.

26. Occorsio, D.; Simoncelli, A.C. How to go from Bézierto Lagrange curves by means of generalized Bézier curves. *Facta Univ. Ser. Math. Inform. (Niš)* **1996**, *11*, 101–111.
27. Occorsio, D. Some new properties of Generalized Bernstein polynomials. *Stud. Univ. Babes Bolyai Math.* **2011**, *56*, 147–160.
28. Capobianco, M.R.; Mastroianni, G.; Russo, M.G. Pointwise and uniform approximation of the finite Hilbert transform. *Approx. Optim.* **1997**, *1*, 45–66.
29. Abu-Jeib, I.T. Algorithms for Centrosymmetric and Skew-Centrosymmetric Matrices. *Missouri J. Math. Sci.* **2006**, *18*, 1–8.
30. Occorsio, D.; Russo, M.G. Nyström methods for Fredholm integral equations using equispaced points. *Filomat* **2014**, *28*, 49–63. [CrossRef]
31. Mastroianni, G.; Milovanovic, G.V. *Interpolation Processes. Basic Theory and Applications*; Springer: Berlin, Germany, 2008.

Article

Oscillation Criteria of Higher-order Neutral Differential Equations with Several Deviating Arguments

Osama Moaaz [1,†], Ioannis Dassios [2,*,†] and Omar Bazighifan [3,4,†]

[1] Department of Mathematics, Faculty of Science, Mansoura University, Mansoura 35516, Egypt; o_moaaz@mans.edu.eg
[2] AMPSAS, University College Dublin, D4 Dublin, Ireland
[3] Department of Mathematics, Faculty of Science, Hadhramout University, Hadhramout 50512, Yemen; o.bazighifan@gmail.com
[4] Department of Mathematics, Faculty of Education, Seiyun University, Hadhramout 50512, Yemen
* Correspondence: ioannis.dassios@ucd.ie
† These authors contributed equally to this work.

Received: 19 February 2020; Accepted: 11 March 2020; Published: 13 March 2020

Abstract: This work is concerned with the oscillatory behavior of solutions of even-order neutral differential equations. By using the technique of Riccati transformation and comparison principles with the second-order differential equations, we obtain a new Philos-type criterion. Our results extend and improve some known results in the literature. An example is given to illustrate our main results.

Keywords: even-order differential equations; neutral delay; oscillation

---

1. Introduction

In this article, we investigate the asymptotic behavior of solutions of even-order neutral differential equation of the form

$$\left(b(t)\left(z^{(n-1)}(t)\right)^{\gamma}\right)' + \sum_{i=1}^{k} q_i(t)\, u^{\gamma}(\delta_i(t)) = 0, \tag{1}$$

where $t \geq t_0$, $n \geq 4$ is an even natural number, $k \geq 1$ is an integer and $z(t) := u(t) + p(t)\, u(\sigma(t))$. Throughout this paper, we assume the following conditions to hold:

(P_1) γ is a quotient of odd positive integers;
(P_2) $b \in C[t_0,\infty)$, $b(t) > 0$, $b'(t) \geq 0$;
(P_3) $\sigma \in C^1[t_0,\infty)$, $\delta_i \in C[t_0,\infty)$, $\sigma'(t) > 0$, $\delta(t) \leq \delta_i(t)$, $\sigma(t) \leq t$ and $\lim_{t\to\infty}\sigma(t) = \lim_{t\to\infty}\delta_i(t) = \infty$, $i = 1,2,...,k$;
(P_4) $p, q_i \in C[t_0,\infty)$, $q_i(t) > 0$, $0 \leq p(t) < p_0 < \infty$ and

$$\int_{t_0}^{\infty} b^{-1/\gamma}(s)\, ds = \infty \tag{2}$$

Definition 1. *The function $u \in C^3[t_u,\infty)$, $t_u \geq t_0$, is called a solution of (1), if $b(t)\left(z^{(n-1)}(t)\right)^{\gamma} \in C^1[t_u,\infty)$, and $u(t)$ satisfies (1) on $[t_u,\infty)$. Moreover, a solution of (1) is called oscillatory if it has arbitrarily large zeros on $[t_u,\infty)$, and otherwise is called to be nonoscillatory.*

Definition 2. *Let*

$$D = \{(t,s) \in \mathbb{R}^2 : t \geq s \geq t_0\} \text{ and } D_0 = \{(t,s) \in \mathbb{R}^2 : t > s \geq t_0\}.$$

A kernel function $H_i \in p(D, \mathbb{R})$ is said to belong to the function class $\Im$, written by $H \in \Im$, if, for $i = 1, 2$,

(i) $H_i(t,s) = 0$ for $t \geq t_0$, $H_i(t,s) > 0$, $(t,s) \in D_0$;
(ii) $H_i(t,s)$ has a continuous and nonpositive partial derivative $\partial H_i/\partial s$ on D_0 and there exist functions $\sigma, \vartheta \in C^1([t_0,\infty),(0,\infty))$ and $h_i \in C(D_0, \mathbb{R})$ such that

$$\frac{\partial}{\partial s} H_1(t,s) + \frac{\theta'(s)}{\theta(s)} H_1(t,s) = h_1(t,s) H_1^{\gamma/(\gamma+1)}(t,s) \tag{3}$$

and

$$\frac{\partial}{\partial s} H_2(t,s) + \frac{v'(s)}{v(s)} H_2(t,s) = h_2(t,s) \sqrt{H_2(t,s)}. \tag{4}$$

The oscillation theory of differential equations with deviating arguments was initiated in a pioneering paper [1] of Fite, which appeared in the first quarter of the twentieth century. Delay equations play an important role in applications of real life. One area of active research in recent times is to study the sufficient criteria for oscillation of differential equations, see [1–11], and oscillation of neutral differential equations has become an important area of research, see [12–30]. Having in mind such applications, for instance, in electrical engineering, we cite models that describe electrical power systems, see [18]. Neutral differential equations also have wide applications in applied mathematics [31,32], physics [33], ecology [34] and engineering [35].

In the following, we show some previous results in the literature related to this paper: Moaaz et al. [23] proved that if there exist positive functions η, $\zeta \in C^1([t_0,\infty), \mathbb{R})$ such that the differential equations

$$\psi'(t) + \left(\frac{\mu \left(\delta^{-1}(\eta(t))\right)^{n-1}}{(n-1)! r^{1/\alpha}\left(\delta^{-1}(\eta(t))\right)} \right)^{\alpha} q(t) P_n^{\alpha}(\sigma(t)) \psi\left(\delta^{-1}(\eta(t))\right) = 0$$

and

$$\phi'(t) + \delta^{-1}(\zeta(t)) R_{n-3}(t) \phi\left(\delta^{-1}(\zeta(t))\right) = 0$$

are oscillatory, then (1) is oscillatory.

Zafer [29] proved that the even-order differential equation

$$z^{(n)}(t) + q(t) x(\sigma(t)) = 0 \tag{5}$$

is oscillatory if

$$\liminf_{t\to\infty} \int_{\sigma(t)}^{t} Q(s) \, ds > \frac{(n-1) 2^{(n-1)(n-2)}}{e}, \tag{6}$$

or

$$\limsup_{t\to\infty} \int_{\sigma(t)}^{t} Q(s) \, ds > (n-1) 2^{(n-1)(n-2)}, \quad \sigma'(t) \geq 0.$$

where $Q(t) := \sigma^{n-1}(t)(1 - p(\sigma(t))) q(t)$.

Zhang and Yan [30] proved that (5) is oscillatory if either

$$\liminf_{t\to\infty} \int_{\sigma(t)}^{t} Q(s) \, ds > \frac{(n-1)!}{e}, \tag{7}$$

or

$$\limsup_{t\to\infty}\int_{\sigma(t)}^{t} Q(s)\,\mathrm{d}s > (n-1)!,\ \ \sigma(t)\geq 0.$$

It's easy to note that $(n-1)! < (n-1)\,2^{(n-1)(n-2)}$ for $n>3$, and hence results in [30] improved results of Zafer in [29].

Xing et al. [28] proved that (1) is oscillatory if

$$\left(\delta^{-1}(t)\right)' \geq \delta_0 > 0,\ \sigma'(t)\geq\sigma_0>0,\ \sigma^{-1}(\delta(t))<t$$

and

$$\liminf_{t\to\infty}\int_{\sigma^{-1}(\delta(t))}^{t}\frac{\widehat{q}(s)}{b(s)}\left(s^{n-1}\right)^{\gamma}\mathrm{d}s > \left(\frac{1}{\delta_0}+\frac{p_0^{\gamma}}{\delta_0\sigma_0}\right)\frac{((n-1)!)^{\gamma}}{\mathrm{e}}, \tag{8}$$

where $\widehat{q}(t) := \min\left\{q\left(\delta^{-1}(t)\right), q\left(\delta^{-1}(\sigma(t))\right)\right\}$.

Hence, [28] improved the results in [29,30].

In our paper, by carefully observing and employing some inequalities of different type, we provide a new criterion for oscillation of differential Equation (1). Here, we provide different criteria for oscillation, which can cover a larger area of different models of fourth order differential equations. We introduce a Riccati substitution and comparison principles with the second-order differential equations to obtain a new Philos-type criteria. Finally, we apply the main results to one example.

2. Some Auxiliary Lemmas

We shall employ the following lemmas:

Lemma 1 ([5]). *Let β be a ratio of two odd numbers, $V>0$ and U are constants. Then*

$$Uu - Vu^{(\beta+1)/\beta} \leq \frac{\beta^{\beta}}{(\beta+1)^{\beta+1}}\frac{U^{\beta+1}}{V^{\beta}}.$$

Lemma 2 ([6]). *If the function u satisfies $u^{(i)}(t)>0$, $i=0,1,...,n$, and $u^{(n+1)}(t)<0$, then*

$$\frac{u(t)}{t^n/n!} \geq \frac{u'(t)}{t^{n-1}/(n-1)!}.$$

Lemma 3 ([4]). *The equation*

$$\left(b(t)\left(u'(t)^{\gamma}\right)\right)' + q(t)\,u^{\gamma}(t) = 0, \tag{9}$$

where $b\in C[t_0,\infty)$, $b(t)>0$ and $q(t)>0$, is non-oscillatory if and only if there exist a $t\geq t_0$ and a function $v\in C^1[\ell,\infty)$ such that

$$v'(t) + \frac{\gamma}{b^{1/\gamma}(t)}v^{1+1/\gamma}(t) + q(t) \leq 0,$$

for $t\geq t_0$.

Lemma 4 ([2], Lemma 2.2.3). *Let $u\in C^n([t_0,\infty),(0,\infty))$. Assume that $u^{(n)}(t)$ is of fixed sign and not identically zero on $[t_0,\infty)$ and that there exists a $t_1\geq t_0$ such that $u^{(n-1)}(t)\,u^{(n)}(t)\leq 0$ for all $t\geq t_1$. If $\lim_{t\to\infty}u(t)\neq 0$, then for every $\mu\in(0,1)$ there exists $t_{\mu}\geq t_1$ such that*

$$u(t) \geq \frac{\mu}{(n-1)!}t^{n-1}\left|u^{(n-1)}(t)\right| \text{ for } t\geq t_{\mu}.$$

3. Main Results

In this section, we give the main results of the article. Here, we define the next notation:

$$\begin{aligned}
P_k(t) &= \frac{1}{p(\sigma^{-1}(t))}\left(1-\frac{(\sigma^{-1}(\sigma^{-1}(t)))^{k-1}}{(\sigma^{-1}(t))^{k-1}p(\sigma^{-1}(\sigma^{-1}(t)))}\right), \text{ for } k=2,n,\\
R_0(t) &= \left(\frac{1}{b(t)}\int_t^\infty \sum_{i=1}^k q_i(s)P_2^\gamma(\delta_i(s))\,ds\right)^{1/\gamma},\\
\Theta(t) &= \gamma\frac{\mu_1}{(n-2)!}\left(\frac{b(t)}{b(\sigma^{-1}(\delta_i(t)))}\right)^{1/\gamma}\frac{(\sigma^{-1}(\delta_i(t)))'(\delta_i(t))'(\sigma^{-1}(\delta_i(t)))^{n-2}}{(b\theta)^{1/\gamma}(t)},\\
\tilde{\Theta}(t) &= \frac{h_1^{\gamma+1}(t,s)H_1^\gamma(t,s)}{(\gamma+1)^{\gamma+1}}\frac{((n-2)!)^\gamma b(\sigma^{-1}(\delta_i(t)))\theta(t)}{\left(\mu_1(\sigma^{-1}(\delta_i(t)))'(\delta_i(t))'(\sigma^{-1}(\delta_i(t)))^{n-2}\right)^\gamma}
\end{aligned}$$

and

$$R_m(t)=\int_t^\infty R_{m-1}(s)\,ds,\quad m=1,2,...,n-3.$$

Lemma 5 ([8], Lemma 1.2). *Assume that u is an eventually positive solution of (1). Then, there exist two possible cases:*

$$\begin{aligned}
&(\mathbf{S}_1)\quad z(t)>0,\ z'(t)>0,\ z''(t)>0,\ z^{(n-1)}(t)>0,\ z^{(n)}(t)<0,\\
&(\mathbf{S}_2)\quad z(t)>0,\ z^{(j)}(t)>0,\ z^{(j+1)}(t)<0 \text{ for all odd integer}\\
&\qquad\quad j\in\{1,3,...,n-3\},\ z^{(n-1)}(t)>0,\ z^{(n)}(t)<0,
\end{aligned}$$

for $t\ge t_1$, where $t_1\ge t_0$ is sufficiently large.

Lemma 6. *Let u be an eventually positive solution of (1) and*

$$\left(\sigma^{-1}\left(\sigma^{-1}(t)\right)\right)^{n-1}<\left(\sigma^{-1}(t)\right)^{n-1}p\left(\sigma^{-1}\left(\sigma^{-1}(t)\right)\right). \tag{10}$$

Then

$$u(t)\ge\frac{z(\sigma^{-1}(t))}{p(\sigma^{-1}(t))}-\frac{1}{p(\sigma^{-1}(t))}\frac{z(\sigma^{-1}(\sigma^{-1}(t)))}{p(\sigma^{-1}(\sigma^{-1}(t)))}. \tag{11}$$

Proof. Let u be an eventually positive solution of (1) on $[t_0,\infty)$. From the definition of $z(t)$, we see that

$$p(t)u(\sigma(t))=z(t)-u(t)$$

and so

$$p\left(\sigma^{-1}(t)\right)u(t)=z\left(\sigma^{-1}(t)\right)-z\left(\sigma^{-1}(t)\right).$$

Repeating the same process, we obtain

$$u(t)=\frac{1}{p(\sigma^{-1}(t))}\left(z\left(\sigma^{-1}(t)\right)-\left(\frac{z(\sigma^{-1}(\sigma^{-1}(t)))}{p(\sigma^{-1}(\sigma^{-1}(t)))}-\frac{u(\sigma^{-1}(\sigma^{-1}(t)))}{p(\sigma^{-1}(\sigma^{-1}(t)))}\right)\right),$$

which yields

$$u(t)\ge\frac{z(\sigma^{-1}(t))}{p(\sigma^{-1}(t))}-\frac{1}{p(\sigma^{-1}(t))}\frac{z(\sigma^{-1}(\sigma^{-1}(t)))}{p(\sigma^{-1}(\sigma^{-1}(t)))}.$$

Thus, (11) holds. This completes the proof. □

Lemma 7. *Assume that u is an eventually positive solution of (1) and*

$$\left(b(t)\left(z^{(n-1)}(t)\right)^{\gamma}\right)' \leq -z^{\gamma}\left(\sigma^{-1}(\delta(t))\right)\sum_{i=1}^{k} q_i(t) P_n^{\gamma}(\delta_i(t)), \text{ if } z \text{ satisfies } (\mathbf{S}_1) \tag{12}$$

and

$$z''(t) + R_{n-3}(t) z\left(\sigma^{-1}(\delta(t))\right) \leq 0, \text{ if } z \text{ satisfies } (\mathbf{S}_2). \tag{13}$$

Proof. Let u be an eventually positive solution of (1) on $[t_0, \infty)$. It follows from Lemma 5 that there exist two possible cases $(\mathbf{S}_1)$ and $(\mathbf{S}_2)$.

Suppose that Case $(\mathbf{S}_1)$ holds. From Lemma 2, we obtain $z(t) \geq \frac{1}{(n-1)} t z'(t)$ and hence the function $t^{1-n} z(t)$ is nonincreasing, which with the fact that $\sigma(t) \leq t$ gives

$$\left(\sigma^{-1}(t)\right)^{n-1} z\left(\sigma^{-1}\left(\sigma^{-1}(t)\right)\right) \leq \left(\sigma^{-1}\left(\sigma^{-1}(t)\right)\right)^{n-1} z\left(\sigma^{-1}(t)\right). \tag{14}$$

Combining (11) and (14), we conclude that

$$\begin{aligned} u(t) &\geq \frac{1}{p(\sigma^{-1}(t))}\left(1 - \frac{(\sigma^{-1}(\sigma^{-1}(t)))^{n-1}}{(\sigma^{-1}(t))^{n-1} p(\sigma^{-1}(\sigma^{-1}(t)))}\right) z\left(\sigma^{-1}(t)\right) \\ &= P_n(t) z\left(\sigma^{-1}(t)\right). \end{aligned} \tag{15}$$

From (1) and (15), we obtain

$$\begin{aligned} \left(b(t)\left(z^{(n-1)}(t)\right)^{\gamma}\right)' &\leq -\sum_{i=1}^{k} q_i(t) P_n^{\gamma}(\delta_i(t)) z^{\gamma}\left(\sigma^{-1}(\delta_i(t))\right) \\ &\leq -z^{\gamma}\left(\sigma^{-1}(\delta(t))\right)\sum_{i=1}^{k} q_i(t) P_n^{\gamma}(\delta_i(t)). \end{aligned}$$

Thus, (12) holds.

Suppose that Case $(\mathbf{S}_2)$ holds. From Lemma 2, we find

$$z(t) \geq t z'(t) \tag{16}$$

and thus the function $t^{-1} z(t)$ is nonincreasing, eventually. Since $\sigma^{-1}(t) \leq \sigma^{-1}\left(\sigma^{-1}(t)\right)$, we obtain

$$\sigma^{-1}(t) z\left(\sigma^{-1}\left(\sigma^{-1}(t)\right)\right) \leq \sigma^{-1}\left(\sigma^{-1}(t)\right) z\left(\sigma^{-1}(t)\right). \tag{17}$$

Combining (11) and (17), we find

$$\begin{aligned} u(t) &\geq \frac{1}{p(\sigma^{-1}(t))}\left(1 - \frac{(\sigma^{-1}(\sigma^{-1}(t)))}{(\sigma^{-1}(t)) p(\sigma^{-1}(\sigma^{-1}(t)))}\right) z\left(\sigma^{-1}(t)\right) \\ &= P_2(t) z\left(\sigma^{-1}(t)\right), \end{aligned}$$

which with (1) yields

$$\left(b(t)\left(z^{(n-1)}(t)\right)^{\gamma}\right)' + \sum_{i=1}^{k} q_i(t) P_2^{\gamma}(\delta_i(t)) z^{\gamma}\left(\sigma^{-1}(\delta_i(t))\right) \leq 0. \tag{18}$$

Integrating the (18) from t to ∞, we obtain

$$z^{(n-1)}(t) \geq b_0(t) z\left(\sigma^{-1}(\delta(t))\right).$$

Integrating this inequality from t to ∞ a total of $n-3$ times, we obtain

$$z''(t) + R_{n-3}(t) z\left(\sigma^{-1}(\delta(t))\right) \leq 0.$$

Thus, (13) holds. This completes the proof. □

Theorem 1. *Let (2) and (10) hold. If there exist positive functions $\theta, v \in C^1([t_0,\infty),\mathbb{R})$ such that*

$$\limsup_{t\to\infty} \frac{1}{H_1(t,t_1)} \int_{t_1}^{t} \left(H_1(t,s)\psi(s) - \tilde{\Theta}(s)\right) ds = \infty \tag{19}$$

and

$$\limsup_{t\to\infty} \frac{1}{H_2(t,t_1)} \int_{t_1}^{t} \left(H_2(t,s)\psi^*(s) - \frac{v(s) h_2^2(t,s)}{4}\right) ds = \infty, \tag{20}$$

where

$$\psi(s) = \theta(t) \sum_{i=1}^{k} q_i(t) P_n^{\gamma}(\delta_i(t)), \; \psi^*(s) = v(t) b_{n-3}(t) \left(\frac{\sigma^{-1}(\delta(t))}{t}\right)$$

and

$$\tilde{\Theta}(s) = \frac{h_1^{\gamma+1}(t,s) H_1^{\gamma}(t,s)}{(\gamma+1)^{\gamma+1}} \frac{((n-2)!)^{\gamma} b(\sigma^{-1}(\delta(t)))\theta(t)}{\left(\mu_1 (\sigma^{-1}(\delta(t)))'(\delta(t))'(\sigma^{-1}(\delta(t)))^{n-2}\right)^{\gamma}},$$

then (1) is oscillatory.

Proof. Let u be a non-oscillatory solution of (1) on $[t_0,\infty)$. Without loss of generality, we can assume that u is eventually positive. It follows from Lemma 5 that there exist two possible cases $(\mathbf{S}_1)$ and $(\mathbf{S}_2)$.

Let $(\mathbf{S}_1)$ hold. From Lemma 7, we arrive at (12). Next, we define a function ξ by

$$\xi(t) := \theta(t) \frac{b(t)\left(z^{(n-1)}(t)\right)^{\gamma}}{z^{\gamma}(\sigma^{-1}(\delta(t)))} > 0.$$

Differentiating and using (12), we obtain

$$\begin{aligned} \xi'(t) \leq\; & \frac{\theta'(t)}{\theta(t)}\xi(t) - \theta(t)\sum_{i=1}^{k} q_i(t) P_n^{\gamma}(\delta_i(t)) \\ & -\gamma\theta(t) \frac{b(t)\left(z^{(n-1)}(t)\right)^{\gamma}(\sigma^{-1}(\delta(t)))'(\delta(t))' z_u'(\sigma^{-1}(\delta(t)))}{z_u^{\gamma+1}(\sigma^{-1}(\delta(t)))}. \end{aligned} \tag{21}$$

Recalling that $b(t)\left(z^{(n-1)}(t)\right)^{\gamma}$ is decreasing, we get

$$b\left(\sigma^{-1}(\delta(t))\right)\left(z^{(n-1)}\left(\sigma^{-1}(\delta(t))\right)\right)^{\gamma} \geq b(t)\left(z^{(n-1)}(t)\right)^{\gamma}.$$

This yields

$$\left(z^{(n-1)}\left(\sigma^{-1}(\delta(t))\right)\right)^{\gamma} \geq \frac{b(t)}{b(\sigma^{-1}(\delta(t)))}\left(z^{(n-1)}(t)\right)^{\gamma}. \tag{22}$$

It follows from Lemma 4 that

$$z'\left(\sigma^{-1}(\delta(t))\right) \geq \frac{\mu_1}{(n-2)!}\left(\sigma^{-1}(\delta(t))\right)^{n-2} z^{(n-1)}\left(\sigma^{-1}(\delta(t))\right), \tag{23}$$

for all $\mu_1 \in (0,1)$ and every sufficiently large t. Thus, by (21), (22) and (23), we get

$$\begin{aligned}\xi'(t) \leq\ & \frac{\theta'(t)}{\theta(t)}\xi(t) - \theta(t)\sum_{i=1}^{k} q_i(t) P_n^{\gamma}(\delta_i(t)) \\ & -\gamma\theta(t)\frac{\mu_1}{(n-2)!}\left(\frac{b(t)}{b(\sigma^{-1}(\delta(t)))}\right)^{1/\gamma}\frac{b(t)\left(z^{(n-1)}(t)\right)^{\gamma+1}(\sigma^{-1}(\delta(t)))'(\delta(t))'(\sigma^{-1}(\delta(t)))^{n-2}}{z^{\gamma+1}(\sigma^{-1}(\delta(t)))}.\end{aligned}$$

Hence,

$$\begin{aligned}\xi'(t) \leq\ & \frac{\theta'(t)}{\theta(t)}\xi(t) - \theta(t)\sum_{i=1}^{k} q_i(t) P_n^{\gamma}(\delta_i(t)) \\ & -\Theta(t)\xi^{\frac{\gamma+1}{\gamma}}(t).\end{aligned} \tag{24}$$

Multiplying (24) by $H_1(t,s)$ and integrating the resulting inequality from t_1 to t; we find that

$$\begin{aligned}\int_{t_1}^{t} H_1(t,s)\psi(s)\,\mathrm{d}s \leq\ & \xi(t_1)H_1(t,t_1) + \int_{t_1}^{t}\left(\frac{\partial}{\partial s}H_1(t,s) + \frac{\theta'(s)}{\theta(s)}H_1(t,s)\right)\xi(s)\,\mathrm{d}s \\ & -\int_{t_1}^{t}\Theta(s)H_1(t,s)\xi^{\frac{\gamma+1}{\gamma}}(s)\,\mathrm{d}s.\end{aligned}$$

From (3), we get

$$\begin{aligned}\int_{t_1}^{t} H_1(t,s)\psi(s)\,\mathrm{d}s \leq\ & \xi(t_1)H_1(t,t_1) + \int_{t_1}^{t} h_1(t,s)H_1^{\gamma/(\gamma+1)}(t,s)\xi(s)\,\mathrm{d}s \\ & -\int_{t_1}^{t}\Theta(s)H_1(t,s)\xi^{\frac{\gamma+1}{\gamma}}(s)\,\mathrm{d}s.\end{aligned} \tag{25}$$

Using Lemma 1 with $V = \Theta(s)H_1(t,s)$, $U = h_1(t,s)H_1^{\gamma/(\gamma+1)}(t,s)$ and $u = \xi(s)$, we get

$$\begin{aligned}& h_1(t,s)H_1^{\gamma/(\gamma+1)}(t,s)\xi(s) - \Theta(s)H_1(t,s)\xi^{\frac{\gamma+1}{\gamma}}(s) \\ \leq\ & \frac{h_1^{\gamma+1}(t,s)H_1^{\gamma}(t,s)}{(\gamma+1)^{\gamma+1}}\frac{((n-2)!)^{\gamma}b(\sigma^{-1}(\delta(t)))\theta(t)}{\left(\mu_1(\sigma^{-1}(\delta(t)))'(\delta(t))'(\sigma^{-1}(\delta(t)))^{n-2}\right)^{\gamma}},\end{aligned}$$

which with (25) gives

$$\frac{1}{H_1(t,t_1)}\int_{t_1}^{t}\left(H_1(t,s)\psi(s) - \tilde{\Theta}(s)\right)\mathrm{d}s \leq \xi(t_1),$$

which contradicts (19).

On the other hand, let $(\mathbf{S}_2)$ hold. Using Lemma 7, we get that (13) holds. Now, we define

$$\varphi(t) = v(t)\frac{z'(t)}{z(t)}. \tag{26}$$

Then $\varphi(t) > 0$ for $t \geq t_1$. By differentiating φ and using (13), we find

$$\begin{aligned}\varphi'(t) &= \frac{v'(t)}{v(t)}\varphi(t) + v(t)\frac{z''(t)}{z(t)} - v(t)\left(\frac{z'(t)}{z(t)}\right)^2 \\ &\leq \frac{v'(t)}{v(t)}\varphi(t) - v(t)\, b_{n-3}(t)\frac{z\left(\sigma^{-1}(\delta(t))\right)}{z(t)} - \frac{1}{v(t)}\varphi^2(t). \end{aligned} \tag{27}$$

By using Lemma 2, we find that

$$z(t) \geq t z'(t). \tag{28}$$

From (28), we get that

$$z\left(\sigma^{-1}(\delta(t))\right) \geq \frac{\sigma^{-1}(\delta(t))}{t} z(t). \tag{29}$$

Thus, from (27) and (29), we obtain

$$\varphi'(t) \leq \frac{v'(t)}{v(t)}\varphi(t) - v(t)\, R_{n-3}(t)\left(\frac{\sigma^{-1}(\delta(t))}{t}\right) - \frac{1}{v(t)}\varphi^2(t). \tag{30}$$

Multiplying (30) by $H_2(t,s)$ and integrating the resulting from t_1 to t, we obtain

$$\begin{aligned}\int_{t_1}^{t} H_2(t,s)\,\psi^*(s)\,ds \leq\ & \varphi(t_1) H_2(t,t_1) \\ & + \int_{t_1}^{t}\left(\frac{\partial}{\partial s}H_2(t,s) + \frac{v'(s)}{v(s)}H_2(t,s)\right)\varphi(s)\,ds \\ & - \int_{t_1}^{t}\frac{1}{v(s)}H_2(t,s)\,\varphi^2(s)\,ds.\end{aligned}$$

Thus,

$$\begin{aligned}\int_{t_1}^{t} H_2(t,s)\,\psi^*(s)\,ds &\leq \varphi(t_1) H_2(t,t_1) + \int_{t_1}^{t} h_2(t,s)\sqrt{H_2(t,s)}\varphi(s)\,ds \\ &\quad - \int_{t_1}^{t}\frac{1}{v(s)}H_2(t,s)\,\varphi^2(s)\,ds \\ &\leq \varphi(t_1) H_2(t,t_1) + \int_{t_1}^{t}\frac{v(s)\,h_2^2(t,s)}{4}ds\end{aligned}$$

and so

$$\frac{1}{H_2(t,t_1)}\int_{t_1}^{t}\left(H_2(t,s)\,\psi^*(s) - \frac{v(s)\,h_2^2(t,s)}{4}\right)ds \leq \varphi(t_1),$$

which contradicts (20). This completes the proof. □

In the next theorem, we establish new oscillation results for (1) by using the theory of comparison with a second order differential equation.

Theorem 2. *Assume that the equation*

$$y''(t) + y(t)\sum_{i=1}^{k} q_i(t)\, P_n^{\gamma}(\delta_i(t)) = 0 \tag{31}$$

and

$$\left[b(t)\left(y'(t)\right)^{\gamma}\right]' + R_{n-3}(t)\left(\frac{\sigma^{-1}(\delta(t))}{t}\right) y^{\gamma}(t) = 0, \tag{32}$$

are oscillatory, then every solution of (1) is oscillatory.

Proof. Suppose to the contrary that (1) has a eventually positive solution u and by virtue of Lemma 3. From Theorem 1, we set $\theta(t) = 1$ in (24), then we get

$$\xi'(\ell) + \Theta(t)\,\xi^{\frac{\gamma+1}{\gamma}} + \sum_{i=1}^{k} q_i(t)\, P_n^{\gamma}(\delta_i(t)) \leq 0.$$

Thus, we can see that Equation (31) is nonoscillatory, which is a contradiction. If we now set $v(t) = 1$ in (30), then we obtain

$$\varphi'(t) + R_{n-3}(t)\left(\frac{\sigma^{-1}(\delta(t))}{t}\right) + \varphi^2(t) \leq 0.$$

Hence, Equation (32) is nonoscillatory, which is a contradiction.
Theorem 2 is proved. □

Corollary 1. *If conditions (19) and (20) in Theorem 1 are replaced by the following conditions:*

$$\limsup_{t\to\infty} \frac{1}{H_1(t,t_1)} \int_{t_1}^{t} H_1(t,s)\,\psi(s)\,\mathrm{d}s = \infty$$

and

$$\limsup_{t\to\infty} \frac{1}{H_1(t,t_1)} \int_{t_1}^{t} \tilde{\Theta}(s)\,\mathrm{d}s < \infty.$$

Moreover,

$$\limsup_{t\to\infty} \frac{1}{H_2(t,t_1)} \int_{t_1}^{t} H_2(t,s)\,\psi^*(s)\,\mathrm{d}s = \infty$$

and

$$\limsup_{t\to\infty} \frac{1}{H_2(t,t_1)} \int_{t_1}^{t} v(s)\, h_2^2(t,s)\,\mathrm{d}s < \infty,$$

then (1) is oscillatory.

Corollary 2. *Let (10) holds. If there exist positive functions $v, \theta \in^1([t_0,\infty), \mathbb{R})$ such that*

$$\int_{t_0}^{\infty} \left(\theta(s) \sum_{i=1}^{k} q_i(s)\, P_n^{\gamma}(\delta_i(s)) - \varpi(s)\right) \mathrm{d}s = \infty \tag{33}$$

and

$$\int_{t_0}^{\infty} \left(P_1 v(s) \int_{t}^{\infty} \left(\frac{1}{r(\varrho)} \int_{\varrho}^{\infty} \sum_{i=1}^{k} q_i(s) \left(\frac{\tau^{-1}(\sigma(s))}{s}\right)^{\alpha} \mathrm{d}s\right)^{1/\alpha} \mathrm{d}\varrho - \pi(s)\right) \mathrm{d}s = \infty, \tag{34}$$

where

$$\varpi(t) := \frac{(n-2)!^{\alpha}}{(\alpha+1)^{\alpha+1}} \frac{r\left(\tau^{-1}(\sigma(t))\right)(\theta'(t))^{\alpha+1}}{\left(\mu_1 \theta(t)\left(\tau^{-1}(\sigma(t))\right)'\left(\tau^{-1}(\sigma(t))\right)^{n-2}\right)^{\alpha}}$$

and

$$\pi(t) := \frac{(v'(s))^2}{4v(s)},$$

then (1) is oscillatory.

Example 1. *Consider the equation*

$$\left(x(t) + 16x\left(\frac{1}{2}t\right)\right)^{(4)} + \frac{q_0}{t^4} x\left(\frac{1}{3}t\right) = 0, \quad t \geq 1, \tag{35}$$

where $q_0 > 0$. *We note that* $r(t) = 1$, $p(t) = 16$, $\tau(t) = t/2$, $\sigma(t) = t/3$ *and* $q(t) = q_0/t^4$.

Thus, we have

$$P_1(t) = \frac{1}{32},\ P_2(t) = \frac{7}{128}.$$

Now, we obtain

$$\int_{t_0}^{\infty}\left(\theta(s)\sum_{i=1}^{k} q_i(s)\,P_n^{\gamma}(\delta_i(s)) - \varpi(s)\right)\mathrm{d}s = \infty$$

and

$$\begin{aligned}&\int_{t_0}^{\infty}\left(P_1 v(s)\int_t^{\infty}\left(\frac{1}{r(\varrho)}\int_{\varrho}^{\infty}\sum_{i=1}^{k} q_i(s)\left(\frac{\tau^{-1}(\sigma(s))}{s}\right)^{\alpha}\mathrm{d}s\right)^{1/\alpha}\mathrm{d}\varrho - \pi(t)\right)\mathrm{d}s\\ &= \int_{t_0}^{\infty}\left(\frac{7q_0}{1152} - \frac{1}{4}\right)\mathrm{d}s,\\ &= \infty,\quad \textit{if } q_0 > 41.14.\end{aligned}$$

Thus, by using Corollary 2, Equation (35) is oscillatory if $q_0 > 41.14$.

4. Conclusions

The aim of this article was to provide a study of asymptotic nature for a class of even-order neutral delay differential equations. We used a generalized Riccati substitution and the integral averaging technique to ensure that every solution of the studied equation is oscillatory. The results presented here complement some of the known results reported in the literature.

A further extension of this article is to use our results to study a class of systems of higher order neutral differential equations as well as of fractional order. For all these there is already some research in progress.

Author Contributions: O.M. and O.B.: Writing–original draft, and writing–review & editing. I.D.: Formal analysis, writing–review & editing, funding and supervision. All authors have read and agreed to the published version of the manuscript.

Funding: This work is supported by the Science Foundation Ireland (SFI), by funding Ioannis Dassios, under Investigator Programme Grant No. SFI/15 /IA/3074.

Acknowledgments: The authors thank the referees for their careful reading and valuable comments.

Conflicts of Interest: The authors declare no conflict of interest.

References

1. Fite, W.B. Concerning the zeros of the solutions of certain differential equations. *Trans. Am. Math. Soc.* **1918**, *19*, 341–352. [CrossRef]
2. Agarwal, R.; Grace, S.; O'Regan, D. *Oscillation Theory for Difference and Functional Differential Equations*; Kluwer Acad. Publ.: Dordrecht, The Netherlands, 2000.
3. Hale, J.K. *Theory of Functional Differential Equations*; Springer: New York, NY, USA, 1977.
4. Bazighifan, O.; Elabbasy, E.M.; Moaaz, O. Oscillation of higher-order differential equations with distributed delay. *J. Inequal. Appl.* **2019**, *55*, 1–9. [CrossRef]
5. Elabbasy, E.M.; Cesarano, C.; Bazighifan, O.; Moaaz, O. Asymptotic and oscillatory behavior of solutions of a class of higher order differential equation. *Symmetry* **2019**, *11*, 1434. [CrossRef]
6. Kiguradze, I.T.; Chanturiya, T.A. *Asymptotic Properties of Solutions of Nonautonomous Ordinary Differential Equations*; Kluwer Acad. Publ.: Dordrecht, The Netherlands, 1993.
7. Kitamura, Y.; Kusano, T. Oscillation of first-order nonlinear differential equations with deviating arguments. *Proc. Am. Math. Soc.* **1980**, *78*, 64–68. [CrossRef]

8. Philos, C.G. A new criterion for the oscillatory and asymptotic behavior of delay differential equations. *Bull. Acad. Pol. Sci. Sér. Sci. Math.* **1981**, *39*, 61–64.
9. Philos, C.G. On the existence of non-oscillatory solutions tending to zero at ∞ for differential equations with positive delays. *Arch. Math.* **1981**, *36*, 168–178. [CrossRef]
10. Ladas, G.; Lakshmikantham, V.; Papadakis, L.S. *Oscillations of Higher-Order Retarded Differential Equations Generated By the Retarded Arguments, Delay and Functional Differential Equations and their Applications*; Academic Press: New York, NY, USA, 1972; pp. 219–231.
11. Koplatadze, R.G.; Chanturija, T.A. Oscillating and monotone solutions of first-order differential equations with deviating argument. *Differ. Uravn.* **1982**, *18*, 1463–1465. (In Russian)
12. Agarwal, R.P.; Bohner, M.; Li, T.; Zhang, C. A new approach in the study of oscillatory behavior of even-order neutral delay diferential equations. *Appl. Math. Comput.* **2013**, *225*, 787–794.
13. Baculikova, B.; Dzurina, J. Oscillation theorems for second-order nonlinear neutral differential equations. *Comput. Math. Appl.* **2011**, *62*, 4472–4478. [CrossRef]
14. Baculikova, B.; Dzurina, J.; Li, T. Oscillation results for even-order quasi linear neutral functional differential equations. *Electron. J. Difer. Equ.* **2011**, *2011*, 1–9.
15. Baculikova, B.; Dzurina, J. Oscillation theorems for higher order neutral diferential equations. *Appl. Math. Comput.* **2012**, *219*, 3769–3778.
16. Bazighifan, O.; Cesarano, C. Some New Oscillation Criteria for Second-Order Neutral Differential Equations with Delayed Arguments. *Mathematics* **2019**, *7*, 619. [CrossRef]
17. Chatzarakis, G.E.; Elabbasy, E.M.; Bazighifan, O. An oscillation criterion in 4th-order neutral differential equations with a continuously distributed delay. *Adv. Differ. Equ.* **2019**, *336*, 1–9.
18. Liu, M.; Dassios, I.; Milano, F. On the Stability Analysis of Systems of Neutral Delay Differential Equations. *Circuits Syst. Signal Process.* **2019**, 38, 1639–1653. [CrossRef]
19. Elabbasy, E.M.; Hassan, T.S.; Moaaz, O. Oscillation behavior of second-order nonlinear neutral differential equations with deviating arguments. *Opusc. Math.* **2012**, *32*, 719–730. [CrossRef]
20. Li, T.; Han, Z.; Zhao, P.; Sun, S. Oscillation of even-order neutral delay differential equations. *Adv. Differ. Equ.* **2010**, *2010*, 184180 . [CrossRef]
21. Moaaz, O. New criteria for oscillation of nonlinear neutral differential equations. *Adv. Differ. Equ.* **2019**, *2019*, 484. [CrossRef]
22. Moaaz, O.; Elabbasy, E.M.; Muhib, A. Oscillation criteria for even-order neutral differential equations with distributed deviating arguments. *Adv. Differ. Equ.* **2019**, *297*, 1–10. [CrossRef]
23. Moaaz, O.; Awrejcewicz, J.; Bazighifan, O. A New Approach in the Study of Oscillation Criteria of Even-Order Neutral Differential Equations. *Mathematics* **2020**, *2020*, 179. [CrossRef]
24. Moaaz, O.; El-Nabulsi, R.; Bazighifan, O. Oscillatory behavior of fourth-order differential equations with neutral delay. *Symmetry* **2020**, *12*, 371. [CrossRef]
25. Moaaz, O.; Elabbasy, E.M.; Shaaban, E. Oscillation criteria for a class of third order damped differential equations. *Arab. J. Math. Sci.* **2018**, *24*, 16–30. [CrossRef]
26. Parhi, N.; Tripathy, A. On oscillatory fourth order linear neutral differential equations-I. *Math. Slovaca* **2004**, *54*, 389–410.
27. Moaaz, O.; Elabbasy, E.M.; Bazighifan, O. On the asymptotic behavior of fourth-order functional differential equations. *Adv. Differ. Equ.* **2017**, *2017*, 261. [CrossRef]
28. Xing, G.; Li, T.; Zhang, C. Oscillation of higher-order quasi linear neutral differential equations. *Adv. Differ. Equ.* **2011**, *2011*, 45. [CrossRef]
29. Zafer, A. Oscillation criteria for even order neutral differential equations. *Appl. Math. Lett.* **1998**, *11*, 21–25. [CrossRef]
30. Zhang, Q.; Yan, J. Oscillation behavior of even order neutral differential equations with variable coefficients. *Appl. Math. Lett.* **2006**, *19*, 1202–1206. [CrossRef]
31. Braverman, E.; Karpuz, B. On oscillation of differential and difference equations with non-monotone delays. *Appl. Math. Comput.* **2011**, *218*, 3880–3887. [CrossRef]
32. Pao, B.M.; Liu, C.; Yin, G. *Topics in Stochastic Analysis and Nonparametric Estimation*; Science Business Media: New York, NY, USA, 2008.
33. Kolmanovskii, V.B.; Nosov, V.R. *Stability and Periodic Modes of Control Systems with Aftereffect*; Nauka: Moscow, Russia, 1981.

34. Gopalsamy, K.; Zhang, B. On a neutral delay-logistic equation. *Dyn. Stab. Syst.* **1987**, *2*, 183. [CrossRef]
35. Bellen, N.G.A.; Ruehli, A. Methods for linear systems of circuit delay differential equations of neutral type. *IEEE Trans. Circuits Syst. I Fundam. Theory Appl.* **1999**, *1*, 212. [CrossRef]

Article

Alternating Asymmetric Iterative Algorithm Based on Domain Decomposition for 3D Poisson Problem

Qiuyan Xu and Zhiyong Liu *

School of Mathematics and Statistics, Ningxia University, Yinchuan 750021, Ningxia, China; qiuyanxu@nxu.edu.cn
* Correspondence: zhiyongliu1983@163.com

Received: 2 January 2020; Accepted: 15 February 2020; Published: 19 February 2020

Abstract: Poisson equation is a widely used partial differential equation. It is very important to study its numerical solution. Based on the strategy of domain decomposition, the alternating asymmetric iterative algorithm for 3D Poisson equation is provided. The solution domain is divided into several sub-domains, and eight asymmetric iterative schemes with the relaxation factor for 3D Poisson equation are constructed. When the numbers of iteration are odd or even, the computational process of the presented iterative algorithm are proposed respectively. In the calculation of the inner interfaces, the group explicit method is used, which makes the algorithm to be performed fast and in parallel, and avoids the difficulty of solving large-scale linear equations. Furthermore, the convergence of the algorithm is analyzed theoretically. Finally, by comparing with the numerical experimental results of Jacobi and Gauss Seidel iterative algorithms, it is shown that the alternating asymmetric iterative algorithm based on domain decomposition has shorter computation time, fewer iteration numbers and good parallelism.

Keywords: poisson equation; domain decomposition; asymmetric iterative schemes; group explicit; parallel computation

---

1. Introduction

Poisson equation is an elliptic partial differential equation, which frequently appears in many fields such as fluid dynamics, heat transfer, electromagnetics, acoustics, electrostatics mechanical engineering and so on. Many researches on studding the numerical techniques to approximate the solution of Poisson equation have been made in the past few decades. The application of finite difference methods for solving Poisson equation will normally lead to a large, block, and sparse system of equations. Direct methods and iterative methods [1] are normally considered as common approaches for solving such system of equations. Several high precision multigrid and compact difference methods are given in [2–6]. Romao et al. [7,8] provides the Galerkin and least-squares finite element methods in the solution of 3D Poisson equation. In [9,10], the Haar wavelet methods are given. Speyer et al. [11] provide a preconditioned bi-conjugate gradient stabilized method which is efficient, albeit nonmonotonic and convergent.

With the continuous improvement of computer hardware, people are more and more focused on solving large-scale scientific and engineering problems quickly and efficiently on parallel computers. Therefore, people wish to find some direct methods and iterative methods, which have the characteristic of much better solving elliptic equations and easier parallel implementation. In recent years, parallel algorithms are also constantly emerging. Several new parallel methods of direct solution are proposed. P. Valero-Lara and A. Pinelli et al. [12] provide the implementation of a fast solver based on a block cyclic reduction algorithm for the linear systems of a three dimensional separable elliptic problem. And they also study on the parallel characteristics of an algorithm for the direct solution of linear systems with a block-tridiagonal coefficient matrix (BLKTRI problem) [13]. C. P. Stone et al. [14] analyze the performance of a block tridiagonal benchmark. Many authors have given the implementation of scalar tridiagonal solver on GPUs [15–17]. Y. Zhang [16] also illustrates several methods to solve tridiagonal systems on GPUs. Because of the direct method to solve large-scale sparse and block diagonal equation systems, when the coefficient matrix is close to singularity, the calculation will often stop or make mistakes. So people also find iterative methods which can be solved by constructing some efficient iterative schemes to approximate the problem itself, so that the iteration can reach a certain accuracy. In [18–21], a class of efficient parallel finite difference iterative algorithms for Poisson equation were also proposed.

In addition, the domain decomposition method [22] is also a powerful tool for parallel implementation, which studies parallelization from the model level of physical problems. This kind of method can decompose scale problem into small-scale problem and solve serial problem into parallel problem. The explicit-implicit domain decomposition method is proposed by Kuznetsov [23]. Because the numerical boundary conditions on the internal boundary are often not the same as those of the original mathematical model or the corresponding physical problems, different methods to obtain the internal boundary information form different explicit-implicit domain decomposition (EIDD) methods. This leads to the idea of parallel implementation for iterative method based on domain decomposition. In [24], the authors have proposed a kind of finite difference parallel iterative algorithm for two-dimensional Poisson problem, and verified its efficiency and accuracy.

This paper extends to the study of the domain decomposition method for three-dimensional Poisson problem. Several finite difference asymmetric iterative schemes are constructed, and each asymmetric iterative schemes are used to solve the sub-domains alternatively and in parallel; in the processing of inner interfaces, group explicit (GE) method [25,26] is used. The calculation on the whole solution domain is explicit but using the implicit iterative schemes, which greatly avoids the difficulty of solving linear equations and improves the calculation speed and accuracy. When the number of iteration is odd or even, the iterative process of the presented algorithm is given respectively, and a kind of efficient iterative algorithm is established based on domain decomposition for solving three-dimensional Poisson equation.

This paper is outlined as follows. In Section 2, we present several asymmetric iterative schemes. Section 3 gives the alternating asymmetric iterative algorithm. And the convergence and the optimal relaxation factor are obtained in Section 4. In Section 5, we perform the numerical experiments to examine the presented algorithm. Finally we give the conclusion of this paper in Section 6.

2. Asymmetric Iterative Schemes

Consider the three-dimensional Poisson problem,

$$\frac{\partial^2 u}{\partial x^2} + \frac{\partial^2 u}{\partial y^2} + \frac{\partial^2 u}{\partial z^2} = f(x,y,z), (x,y,z) \in \Omega, \tag{1}$$

with the boundary condition,

$$u(x,y,z) = g(x,y,z), \ (x,y,z) \in \partial\Omega. \tag{2}$$

where $\Omega = [0,L] \times [0,M] \times [0,K]$, and $\partial\Omega$ is the boundary of the domain Ω. We divide the solution domain Ω into uniform grid, the space step $h_x = L/l$ in x direction, $h_y = M/m$ in y direction and $h_z = K/s$ in z direction. For implicity, the space steps are assumed equal that $h_x = h_y = h_z = h$. Denote $x_i = ih, i = 0,1,...,l$; $y_j = jh, j = 0,1,...,m$; $z_k = kh, k = 0,1,...,s$; $u_{i,j,k}^{(n)}$ as numerical solution on the nth iteration level at the grid node (x_i, y_j, z_k). We can give the classical difference discretization in Equation (3) for the 3D Poisson Equation (1),

$$\frac{u_{i+1,j,k} - 2u_{i,j,k} + u_{i-1,j,k}}{h^2} + \frac{u_{i,j+1,k} - 2u_{i,j,k} + u_{i,j-1,k}}{h^2} + \frac{u_{i,j,k+1} - 2u_{i,j,k} + u_{i,j,k-1}}{h^2} = f_{i,j,k}, \tag{3}$$

namely,

$$u_{i,j,k} - \frac{1}{6}(u_{i+1,j,k} + u_{i-1,j,k} + u_{i,j+1,k} + u_{i,j-1,k} + u_{i,j,k+1} + u_{i,j,k-1} - h^2 f_{i,j,k}) = 0. \tag{4}$$

Then we construct eight asymmetric iterative schemes by the difference operator L with the relaxation factor ω as follows,

$$\begin{aligned} L_1 u_{i,j,k}^{(n+1)} = u_{i,j,k}^{(n+1)} - \frac{1}{6}\Big[&\omega(u_{i+1,j,k}^{(n+1)} + u_{i,j+1,k}^{(n+1)} + u_{i,j,k+1}^{(n+1)}) + u_{i-1,j,k}^{(n)} + u_{i,j-1,k}^{(n)} + u_{i,j,k-1}^{(n)} \\ &+(1-\omega)(u_{i+1,j,k}^{(n)} + u_{i,j+1,k}^{(n)} + u_{i,j,k+1}^{(n)}) - h^2 f_{i,j,k}\Big], \end{aligned} \tag{5}$$

$$\begin{aligned} L_2 u_{i,j,k}^{(n+1)} = u_{i,j,k}^{(n+1)} - \frac{1}{6}\Big[&\omega(u_{i-1,j,k}^{(n+1)} + u_{i,j+1,k}^{(n+1)} + u_{i,j,k+1}^{(n+1)}) + u_{i+1,j,k}^{(n)} + u_{i,j-1,k}^{(n)} + u_{i,j,k-1}^{(n)} \\ &+(1-\omega)(u_{i-1,j,k}^{(n)} + u_{i,j+1,k}^{(n)} + u_{i,j,k+1}^{(n)}) - h^2 f_{i,j,k}\Big], \end{aligned} \tag{6}$$

$$\begin{aligned} L_3 u_{i,j,k}^{(n+1)} = u_{i,j,k}^{(n+1)} - \frac{1}{6}\Big[&\omega(u_{i-1,j,k}^{(n+1)} + u_{i,j-1,k}^{(n+1)} + u_{i,j,k+1}^{(n+1)}) + u_{i+1,j,k}^{(n)} + u_{i,j+1,k}^{(n)} + u_{i,j,k-1}^{(n)} \\ &+(1-\omega)(u_{i-1,j,k}^{(n)} + u_{i,j-1,k}^{(n)} + u_{i,j,k+1}^{(n)}) - h^2 f_{i,j,k}\Big], \end{aligned} \tag{7}$$

$$\begin{aligned} L_4 u_{i,j,k}^{(n+1)} = u_{i,j,k}^{(n+1)} - \frac{1}{6}\Big[&\omega(u_{i+1,j,k}^{(n+1)} + u_{i,j-1,k}^{(n+1)} + u_{i,j,k+1}^{(n+1)}) + u_{i-1,j,k}^{(n)} + u_{i,j+1,k}^{(n)} + u_{i,j,k-1}^{(n)} \\ &+(1-\omega)(u_{i+1,j,k}^{(n)} + u_{i,j-1,k}^{(n)} + u_{i,j,k+1}^{(n)}) - h^2 f_{i,j,k}\Big], \end{aligned} \tag{8}$$

$$\begin{aligned} L_5 u_{i,j,k}^{(n+1)} = u_{i,j,k}^{(n+1)} - \frac{1}{6}\Big[&\omega(u_{i+1,j,k}^{(n+1)} + u_{i,j+1,k}^{(n+1)} + u_{i,j,k-1}^{(n+1)}) + u_{i-1,j,k}^{(n)} + u_{i,j-1,k}^{(n)} + u_{i,j,k+1}^{(n)} \\ &+(1-\omega)(u_{i+1,j,k}^{(n)} + u_{i,j+1,k}^{(n)} + u_{i,j,k-1}^{(n)}) - h^2 f_{i,j,k}\Big], \end{aligned} \tag{9}$$

$$\begin{aligned} L_6 u_{i,j,k}^{(n+1)} = u_{i,j,k}^{(n+1)} - \frac{1}{6}\Big[&\omega(u_{i-1,j,k}^{(n+1)} + u_{i,j+1,k}^{(n+1)} + u_{i,j,k-1}^{(n+1)}) + u_{i+1,j,k}^{(n)} + u_{i,j-1,k}^{(n)} + u_{i,j,k+1}^{(n)} \\ &+(1-\omega)(u_{i-1,j,k}^{(n)} + u_{i,j+1,k}^{(n)} + u_{i,j,k-1}^{(n)}) - h^2 f_{i,j,k}\Big], \end{aligned} \tag{10}$$

$$\begin{aligned} L_7 u_{i,j,k}^{(n+1)} = u_{i,j,k}^{(n+1)} - \frac{1}{6}\Big[&\omega(u_{i-1,j,k}^{(n+1)} + u_{i,j-1,k}^{(n+1)} + u_{i,j,k-1}^{(n+1)}) + u_{i+1,j,k}^{(n)} + u_{i,j+1,k}^{(n)} + u_{i,j,k+1}^{(n)} \\ &+(1-\omega)(u_{i-1,j,k}^{(n)} + u_{i,j-1,k}^{(n)} + u_{i,j,k-1}^{(n)}) - h^2 f_{i,j,k}\Big], \end{aligned} \tag{11}$$

$$L_8 u_{i,j,k}^{(n+1)} = u_{i,j,k}^{(n+1)} - \frac{1}{6}\Big[\omega(u_{i+1,j,k}^{(n+1)} + u_{i,j-1,k}^{(n+1)} + u_{i,j,k-1}^{(n+1)}) + u_{i-1,j,k}^{(n)} + u_{i,j+1,k}^{(n)} + u_{i,j,k+1}^{(n)} + (1-\omega)(u_{i+1,j,k}^{(n)} + u_{i,j-1,k}^{(n)} + u_{i,j,k-1}^{(n)}) - h^2 f_{i,j,k}\Big], \tag{12}$$

Figure 1 represents the distribution of unknown solution at the $(n+1)$th iteration level for the eight asymmetric iterative schemes (5)–(12).

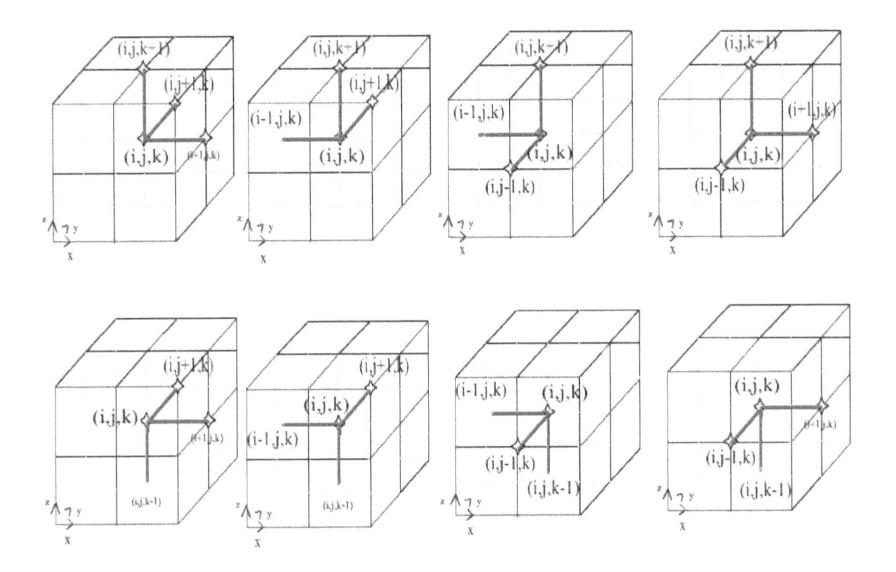

Figure 1. The asymmetric iterative schemes (5)–(12) for the 3D Poisson equation with the relaxation factor ω.

3. Alternating Asymmetric Iterative Algorithm Based on Domain Decomposition

3.1. The Domain Decomposition

We can divide the 3D solution domain Ω into multi-subdomains. For simplicity, we use six grid planes $x = p, x = p+1, y = q, y = q+1, z = r, z = r+1$ to discrete the solution domain Ω into eight sub-domains, and note $\Omega_i, i = 1,2,...,8$ as subsets of grid points, while p, q, r are positive integers with $p \in [1,l], q \in [1,m], r \in [1,s]$. Denote π_i is the interfaces of the sub-domain Ω_i. The sorting order of sub-domains is as follows: the subspaces above $z = r+1$ are sorted anticlockwise starting from the upper right sub-domain of the inner layer, and the sub-domains under $z = r$ are sorted anticlockwise starting from the lower right subspace (as shown in Figure 2). The specific description is as follows:

$$
\begin{aligned}
\Omega_1: &\ \{(x,y,z)|x = l-1, l-2, ..., p+1; y = m-1, m-2, ..., q+1; z = s-1, s-2, ..., r+1\}, \\
\Omega_2: &\ \{(x,y,z)|x = 1,2,...,p; y = m-1, m-2, ..., q+1; z = s-1, s-2, ..., r+1\}, \\
\Omega_3: &\ \{(x,y,z)|x = 1,2,...,p; y = 1,2,...,q; z = s-1, s-2, ..., r+1\}, \\
\Omega_4: &\ \{(x,y,z)|x = l-1, l-2, ..., p+1; y = 1,2,...,q; z = s-1, s-2, ..., r+1\}, \\
\Omega_5: &\ \{(x,y,z)|x = l-1, l-2, ..., p+1; y = m-1, m-2, ..., q+1; z = 1,2,...,r\}, \\
\Omega_6: &\ \{(x,y,z)|x = 1,2,...,p; y = m-1, m-2, ..., q+1; z = 1,2,...,r\}, \\
\Omega_7: &\ \{(x,y,z)|x = 1,2,...,p; y = 1,2,...,q; z = 1,2,...,r\}, \\
\Omega_8: &\ \{(x,y,z)|x = l-1, l-2, ..., p+1; y = 1,2,...,q; z = 1,2,...,r\}.
\end{aligned}
$$

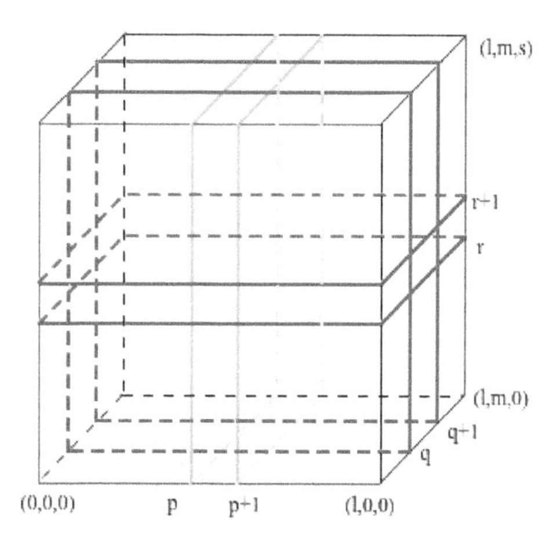

Figure 2. The solution domain is divided into eight sub-domains.

3.2. Algorithm Implementation

In this subsection, we provide a new alternating asymmetric iterative (AAI) algorithm based on domain decomposition for 3D Poisson problem (1) and (2). We give different computational processes in each sub-domains at the odd iteration layers and even iteration layers respectively, and use the asymmetric iterative schemes alternatively. The Group Explicit (GE) method is used to solve the inner interfaces, which makes the algorithm to be computed fast and in parallel, and avoids the difficulty of solving large-scale linear equations.

3.2.1. Implementation of Odd Level Iteration

When the iteration number are odd, namely, $n = 2a + 1, a = 0, 1, ...,$ we solve the grid nodes from the boundaries to the inner interfaces step by step, that is, using the asymmetric iterative schemes (5)–(12) to solve the grid points in $\Omega_i, i = 1, 2, ..., 8$ respectively:

$$\begin{cases} L_1 u_{i,j,k}^{(2a+1)} = 0, & (i,j,k) \in \Omega_1, \\ L_2 u_{i,j,k}^{(2a+1)} = 0, & (i,j,k) \in \Omega_2, \\ L_3 u_{i,j,k}^{(2a+1)} = 0, & (i,j,k) \in \Omega_3, \\ L_4 u_{i,j,k}^{(2a+1)} = 0, & (i,j,k) \in \Omega_4, \\ L_5 u_{i,j,k}^{(2a+1)} = 0, & (i,j,k) \in \Omega_5, \\ L_6 u_{i,j,k}^{(2a+1)} = 0, & (i,j,k) \in \Omega_6, \\ L_7 u_{i,j,k}^{(2a+1)} = 0, & (i,j,k) \in \Omega_7, \\ L_8 u_{i,j,k}^{(2a+1)} = 0, & (i,j,k) \in \Omega_8. \end{cases} \tag{13}$$

Obviously, the numerical solution can be obtained independently in parallel when the iteration numbers are odd, which saves a lot of computational time compared with the full-implicit iteration case. In addition, although the asymmetric iterative schemes are implicit, the computational process can be transformed into explicit, which can obviously improve the calculation speed and avoid solving large and complex linear equations.

3.2.2. Implementation of Even Level Iteration

When the iteration number is even, namely, $n = 2a + 2, a = 0, 1, ...,$ we calculate the numerical solution from the inner interfaces to the boundaries step by step. Where the computational process of the interfaces $\pi = \bigcup \pi_i, i = 1, 2, ..., 8$ includes three parts:

- *Interfaces I* (namely, the grid nodes at the center of the domain Ω) (shown in Figure 3): $(p,q,r+1), (p+1,q,r+1), (p+1,q+1,r+1), (p,q+1,r+1), (p,q,r), (p+1,q,r), (p+1,q+1,r), (p,q+1,r)$.
- *Interfaces II*: the interface lines except Interfaces I (shown in Figure 3).
- *Interfaces III*: the interfaces except Interfaces I and II, namely,

  $\pi \setminus Interfaces\ I \cup Interfaces\ II.$

Therefore, it can be seen that the interfaces π = Interfaces I $\cup$ Interfaces II $\cup$ Interfaces III. When the interfaces π are solved, the inner grid nodes in the domain Ω can be solved in order like the odd case of iteration numbers in Section 3.2.1. We give the computational procedures in detail as follows.

(1) The solution to *Interfaces I*

We use the asymmetric iterative schemes (5)–(12) to solve the *Interfaces I*, then the following linear equations can be obtained:

$$M_1 \begin{bmatrix} u^{(2a+2)}_{p+1,q+1,r+1} \\ u^{(2a+2)}_{p,q+1,r+1} \\ u^{(2a+2)}_{p,q,r+1} \\ u^{(2a+2)}_{p+1,q,r+1} \\ u^{(2a+2)}_{p+1,q+1,r} \\ u^{(2a+2)}_{p,q+1,r} \\ u^{(2a+2)}_{p,q,r} \\ u^{(2a+2)}_{p+1,q,r} \end{bmatrix} = N_1, \tag{14}$$

where matrices M_1 and N_1 are represented as bellow,

$$M_1 = \begin{bmatrix} 6 & -\omega & & -\omega & -\omega & & & \\ -\omega & 6 & -\omega & & & -\omega & & \\ & -\omega & 6 & -\omega & & & -\omega & \\ -\omega & & -\omega & 6 & & & & -\omega \\ -\omega & & & & 6 & -\omega & & -\omega \\ & -\omega & & & -\omega & 6 & -\omega & \\ & & -\omega & & & -\omega & 6 & -\omega \\ & & & -\omega & -\omega & & -\omega & 6 \end{bmatrix}, \quad N_1 = \begin{bmatrix} e_1 \\ e_2 \\ e_3 \\ e_4 \\ e_5 \\ e_6 \\ e_7 \\ e_8 \end{bmatrix},$$

$$\begin{aligned}
e_1 &= u^{(2a+1)}_{p+2,q+1,r+1} + u^{(2a+1)}_{p+1,q+2,r+1} + u^{(2a+1)}_{p+1,q+1,r+2} + (1-\omega)(u^{(2a+1)}_{p,q+1,r+1} + u^{(2a+1)}_{p+1,q,r+1} \\
&\quad + u^{(2a+1)}_{p+1,q+1,r}) - h^2 f_{p+1,q+1,r+1}, \\
e_2 &= u^{(2a+1)}_{p-1,q+1,r+1} + u^{(2a+1)}_{p,q+2,r+1} + u^{(2a+1)}_{p,q+1,r+2} + (1-\omega)(u^{(2a+1)}_{p+1,q+1,r+1} + u^{(2a+1)}_{p,q,r+1} + u^{(2a+1)}_{p,q+1,r}) \\
&\quad - h^2 f_{p,q+1,r+1}, \\
e_3 &= u^{(2a+1)}_{p-1,q,r+1} + u^{(2a+1)}_{p,q-1,r+1} + u^{(2a+1)}_{p,q,r+2} + (1-\omega)(u^{(2a+1)}_{p+1,q,r+1} + u^{(2a+1)}_{p,q+1,r+1} + u^{(2a+1)}_{p,q,r}) \\
&\quad - h^2 f_{p,q,r+1}, \\
e_4 &= u^{(2a+1)}_{p+2,q,r+1} + u^{(2a+1)}_{p+1,q-1,r+1} + u^{(2a+1)}_{p+1,q,r+2} + (1-\omega)(u^{(2a+1)}_{p,q,r+1} + u^{(2a+1)}_{p+1,q+1,r+1} + u^{(2a+1)}_{p+1,q,r}) \\
&\quad - h^2 f_{p+1,q,r+1}, \\
e_5 &= u^{(2a+1)}_{p+2,q+1,r} + u^{(2a+1)}_{p+1,q+2,r} + u^{(2a+1)}_{p+1,q+1,r-1} + (1-\omega)(u^{(2a+1)}_{p,q+1,r} + u^{(2a+1)}_{p+1,q,r} + u^{(2a+1)}_{p+1,q+1,r+1}) \\
&\quad - h^2 f_{p+1,q+1,r}, \\
e_6 &= u^{(2a+1)}_{p-1,q+1,r} + u^{(2a+1)}_{p,q+2,r} + u^{(2a+1)}_{p,q+1,r-1} + (1-\omega)(u^{(2a+1)}_{p+1,q+1,r} + u^{(2a+1)}_{p,q,r} + u^{(2a+1)}_{p,q+1,r+1}) \\
&\quad - h^2 f_{p,q+1,r}, \\
e_7 &= u^{(2a+1)}_{p-1,q,r} + u^{(2a+1)}_{p,q-1,r} + u^{(2a+1)}_{p,q,r-1} + (1-\omega)(u^{(2a+1)}_{p+1,q,r} + u^{(2a+1)}_{p,q+1,r} + u^{(2a+1)}_{p,q,r+1}) \\
&\quad - h^2 f_{p,q,r}, \\
e_8 &= u^{(2a+1)}_{p+2,q,r} + u^{(2a+1)}_{p+1,q-1,r} + u^{(2a+1)}_{p+1,q,r-1} + (1-\omega)(u^{(2a+1)}_{p,q,r} + u^{(2a+1)}_{p+1,q+1,r} + u^{(2a+1)}_{p+1,q,r+1}) \\
&\quad - h^2 f_{p+1,q,r}.
\end{aligned}$$

Then we just solve the above eight-order sparse linear Equation (14) to obtain the numerical solution of the *interface I*.

(2) The solution to *Interfaces II*

The computational procedure of the *Interfaces I* is depending on the use of GE method based on eight points per group. Similarly, we use the GE method based on four points per group to solve the *Interfaces II* between the inner boundaries of eight subspaces $\Omega_i, i = 1, 2, ..., 8$. Take one group of the *Interfaces II* for example to illustrate the order of the solution process. Figure 3 gives the direction of the iteration computation.

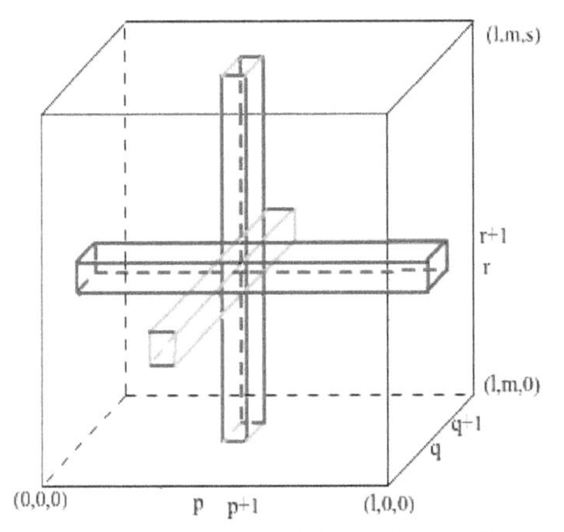

Figure 3. The computation of the interfaces I, II, III.

Using the asymmetric iterative schemes (6), (7), (10), (11) to solve the grid nodes $(i,q,r), (i,q,r+1), (i,q+1,r+1), (i,q+1,r) i = p+2, p+3, ..., l-1$ (shown in Figure 3), then we can provide the following fourth-order linear equations:

$$\begin{bmatrix} 6 & -\omega & & -\omega \\ -\omega & 6 & -\omega & \\ & -\omega & 6 & -\omega \\ -\omega & & -\omega & 6 \end{bmatrix} \begin{bmatrix} u_{i,q,r}^{(2a+2)} \\ u_{i,q,r+1}^{(2a+2)} \\ u_{i,q+1,r+1}^{(2a+2)} \\ u_{i,q+1,r}^{(2a+2)} \end{bmatrix} = \begin{bmatrix} d_1 \\ d_2 \\ d_3 \\ d_4 \end{bmatrix}, \tag{15}$$

where

$$
\begin{aligned}
d_1 = \quad & \omega u_{i-1,q,r}^{(2a+2)} + u_{i+1,q,r}^{(2a+1)} + u_{i,q-1,r}^{(2a+1)} + u_{i,q,r-1}^{(2a+1)} + (1-\omega)(u_{i-1,q,r}^{(2a+1)} + u_{i,q+1,r}^{(2a+1)} + u_{i,q,r+1}^{(2a+1)}), \\
d_2 = \quad & \omega u_{i-1,q,r+1}^{(2a+2)} + u_{i+1,q,r+1}^{(2a+1)} + u_{i,q-1,r+1}^{(2a+1)} + u_{i,q,r+2}^{(2a+1)} + (1-\omega)(u_{i-1,q,r+1}^{(2a+1)} + u_{i,q+1,r+1}^{(2a+1)} \\
& + u_{i,q,r}^{(2a+1)}), \\
d_3 = \quad & \omega u_{i-1,q+1,r+1}^{(2a+2)} + u_{i+1,q+1,r+1}^{(2a+1)} + u_{i,q+2,r+1}^{(2a+1)} + u_{i,q+1,r+2}^{(2a+1)} + (1-\omega)(u_{i-1,q+1,r+1}^{(2a+1)} \\
& + u_{i,q,r+1}^{(2a+1)} + u_{i,q+1,r}^{(2a+1)}), \\
d_4 = \quad & \omega u_{i-1,q+1,r}^{(2a+2)} + u_{i+1,q+1,r}^{(2a+1)} + u_{i,q+2,r}^{(2a+1)} + u_{i,q+1,r-1}^{(2a+1)} + (1-\omega)(u_{i-1,q+1,r}^{(2a+1)} + u_{i,q,r}^{(2a+1)} \\
& + u_{i,q+1,r+1}^{(2a+1)}).
\end{aligned}
$$

Then the numerical solution of such a set of inner boundary points can be calculated quickly only by solving the fourth order sparse linear Equation (15). In the same way, the points on the other five groups of inner boundary lines are also calculated by Group Explicit method, and we will not represent them one by one here.

(3) The solution to *Interfaces III*

It can be seen from the calculation process of *Interfaces I* and *II* we solve the *Interfaces III* just depending on the group explicit method based on two points a group. The specific calculation process is the same as above (1) and (2), and we do not repeat it.

Finally, taking the above results as the interface conditions, we use the asymmetric iterative schemes different from the schemes at the odd levels to solve the inner points on $\Omega_i, i = 1, 2, ..., 8$.

$$
\begin{cases}
L_7 u_{i,j,k}^{(2a+2)} = 0, & (i,j,k) \in \Omega_1 \backslash \pi_1, \\
L_8 u_{i,j,k}^{(2a+2)} = 0, & (i,j,k) \in \Omega_2 \backslash \pi_2, \\
L_5 u_{i,j,k}^{(2a+2)} = 0, & (i,j,k) \in \Omega_3 \backslash \pi_3, \\
L_6 u_{i,j,k}^{(2a+2)} = 0, & (i,j,k) \in \Omega_4 \backslash \pi_4, \\
L_3 u_{i,j,k}^{(2a+2)} = 0, & (i,j,k) \in \Omega_5 \backslash \pi_5, \\
L_4 u_{i,j,k}^{(2a+2)} = 0, & (i,j,k) \in \Omega_6 \backslash \pi_6, \\
L_1 u_{i,j,k}^{(2a+2)} = 0, & (i,j,k) \in \Omega_7 \backslash \pi_7, \\
L_2 u_{i,j,k}^{(2a+2)} = 0, & (i,j,k) \in \Omega_8 \backslash \pi_8.
\end{cases}
\tag{16}
$$

Through the above specific implementation process of the domain decomposition iteration algorithm, we can see that the calculation of numerical solution can transform implicit iteration to explicit calculation no matter on the odd or even iteration layer. Combining with the domain decomposition method, the alternating asymmetric iterative (AAI) algorithm is well performed in parallel.

4. The Algorithm Convergence

In the last section, we propose a new AAI algorithm based domain decomposition for solving the three-dimensional Poisson problem (1)–(2), which can be written in the following matrix form,

$$
u^{(n+1)} = T_\omega u^{(n)} + b, \tag{17}
$$

while T_ω is the iterative matrix of AAI algorithm and b is the right-term. Then we can give the following theorem:

Theorem 1. *The sufficient and necessary conditions for the convergence of AAI algorithm are as follows:*

$$\rho(T_\omega) < 1, \tag{18}$$

where $\rho(T_\omega)$ is the corresponding spectral radius of the iterative matrix T_ω.

Consider the eigenvalue problem of Equation (17):

$$T_\omega x = \lambda x, \tag{19}$$

Due to the asymmetry of the schemes (5) and (12) in the calculation direction, we take one of the iteration scheme (5) as an example,

$$\lambda u_{i,j,k} - \frac{1}{6}[(\lambda\omega + 1 - \omega)u_{i,j,k} + (\lambda\omega + 1 - \omega)u_{i,j-1,k} + (\lambda\omega + 1 - \omega)u_{i,j,k-1} + u_{i+1,j,k} + u_{i,j+1,k} + u_{i,j,k+1}] = 0. \tag{20}$$

Firstly, we give the relationship between the eigenvalues μ of Jacobi iterative matrix B and the eigenvalues λ of the AAI iterative matrix T_ω. Let $V_{i,j,k}$ be the eigenvectors of the Jacobi iterative matrix, then

$$u_{i,j,k} = [\pm(\lambda\omega + 1 - \omega)^{\frac{1}{2}}]^{i+j+k} V_{i,j,k}. \tag{21}$$

Taking Equation (21) into Equation (20), we can obtain,

$$\mu V_{i,j,k} - \frac{1}{6}[V_{i-1,j,k} + V_{i,j-1,k} + V_{i,j,k-1} + V_{i+1,j,k} + V_{i,j+1,k} + V_{i,j,k+1}] = 0. \tag{22}$$

where

$$\mu = \pm\frac{\lambda}{(\lambda\omega + 1 - \omega)^{\frac{1}{2}}}. \tag{23}$$

If λ is the eigenvalue of the matrix T_ω, then

$$\mu^2(\lambda\omega + 1 - \omega) = \lambda^2. \tag{24}$$

Equation (24) determines that μ is eigenvalue of the matrix B, which is Jacobi iteration matrix of Poisson equation. On the contrary, if μ is eigenvalue of the matrix B, it can be determined only if there is a relationship between the eigenvalues λ of Jacobi iteration matrix and the eigenvalues μ of the given iteration matrix in the Equation (24).

In particular, it is shown that the iterative schemes (5)–(12) are Gauss-Seidel iterative schemes in fact when $\omega = 1$. Then the presented AAI algorithm has obvious convergence since $\lambda = \mu^2 < 1$.

Second, we discuss the changes of $\rho(T_\omega)$ about ω.

From Equation (24), we can see that the eigenvalue λ depends on the relaxation factor ω and the eigenvalue μ of Jacobi iteration matrix. Suppose $0 \le \mu \le 1, 0 < \omega < 2$, the two eigenvalues are obtained by Equation (24):

$$\lambda_1(\omega, \mu) = \frac{\mu^2\omega}{2} + \mu\sqrt{(\frac{\mu\omega}{2})^2 - (\omega - 1)}, \tag{25}$$

$$\lambda_2(\omega,\mu) = \frac{\mu^2\omega}{2} - \mu\sqrt{(\frac{\mu\omega}{2})^2 - (\omega-1)}, \tag{26}$$

Define

$$M(\omega,\mu) = \max\{|\lambda_1(\omega,\mu)|, |\lambda_2(\omega,\mu)|\}, \tag{27}$$

by the discriminant equaling to zero, namely,

$$\Delta = \mu^4\omega^2 - 4\mu^2(\omega-1) = 0. \tag{28}$$

Then the root of the Equation (24) is

$$\omega_\mu = \frac{2(1-\sqrt{1-\mu^2})}{\mu^2}, 0 < \omega_\mu < 2. \tag{29}$$

When $0 < \omega < \omega_\mu, \Delta > 0$, we can get

$$\lambda_1(\omega,\mu) > \lambda_2(\omega,\mu) > 0. \tag{30}$$

When $\omega_\mu < \omega < 2$, the eigenvalue $\lambda_1(\omega,\mu)$ and $\lambda_2(\omega,\mu)$ are conjugate complex, therefore

$$|\lambda_1(\omega,\mu)| = |\lambda_2(\omega,\mu)| = \mu^2(\omega-1). \tag{31}$$

Due to Equations (30) and (31), we can give

$$M(\omega,\mu) = \begin{cases} \lambda_1(\omega,\mu), & 0 < \omega < \omega_\mu, \\ \mu^2(\omega-1), & \omega_\mu < \omega < 2. \end{cases} \tag{32}$$

It is obviously seen that

$$M(\omega,\mu) < 1. \tag{33}$$

In fact, if $\omega_\mu < \omega < 2$, Equation (33) is ture clearly; Otherwise $0 < \omega < \omega_\mu$, and

$$\begin{aligned} M(\omega,\mu) &= \lambda_1(\omega,\mu) < \tfrac{\mu^2\omega}{2} + \mu\sqrt{(\tfrac{\mu\omega}{2})^2 - \mu\omega + 1}, (0 < \omega < \omega_\mu) \\ &= \mu < 1. \end{aligned} \tag{34}$$

Therefore, $\rho(T_\omega) < 1$, Equation (18) is proved and the presented AAI algorithm is convergent.

Obviously, the spectrum radius $\rho(T_\omega)$ of the presented iterative matrix depends on the relaxation factor ω, so choosing approximate ω is important to the number of iterations and the convergence rate.

Since the optimal relaxation factor ω_{opt} is obtained for 2D Poisson problem in [25], we can also provide the same computation for 3D case. When

$$\omega = \omega_{opt} = \frac{2}{1+\sqrt{1-\rho(B)^2+\varepsilon}}, \quad (\varepsilon > 0), \tag{35}$$

$\rho(T_{\omega opt})$ obtains the minimum

$$\rho(T_{\omega opt}) = (1-\sqrt{1-\rho(B)^2})^2 + \varepsilon\rho(B)^2, \quad (\varepsilon > 0), \tag{36}$$

where $\rho(B)$ is the spectrum radius of Jacobi iterative matrix, and ε is a positive, sufficiently small number. The optimal relaxation factor ω_{opt} can be theoretically evaluated by Equation (36).

5. Numerical Experiments

In order to confirm the effectiveness of the AAI algorithm, the following experiments are carried out. The initial iterative values $u_{i,j,k}^{(0)} = 0$ $(i = 1, 2, \cdots, l-1;\ j = 1, 2, \cdots, m-1;\ k = 1, 2, ..., s-1)$ is given.
(1) Consider the 3D Laplace equation

$$\frac{\partial^2 u}{\partial x^2} + \frac{\partial^2 u}{\partial y^2} + \frac{\partial^2 u}{\partial z^2} = 0, (x, y, z) \in [0, 1]^3, \tag{37}$$

with the boundary condition,

$$\begin{aligned} u(0, y, z) &= sin(y + z); \\ u(1, y, z) &= exp(\sqrt{2})sin(y + z); \\ u(x, 0, z) &= exp(\sqrt{2x})sin(z); \\ u(x, 1, z) &= exp(\sqrt{2x})sin(1 + z); \\ u(x, y, 0) &= exp(\sqrt{2x})sin(y); \\ u(x, y, 1) &= exp(\sqrt{2x})sin(y + 1). \end{aligned} \tag{38}$$

The exact solution of the 3D Poisson problem (37)–(38) is $u(x, y, z) = exp(\sqrt{2x})sin(y + z)$. Let $u(x_i, y_j, z_k)$ be the exact solution and $u_{i,j,k}^{(n)}$ the nth iterative solution, the errors are calculated in L_∞-norm as:

$$\|E^{(n)}\|_{\infty,h} = \max_{i,j,k}(e_h^{(n)}(i, j, k)) = \max_{i,j,k} |u(x_i, y_j, z_k) - u_{i,j,k}^{(n)}|. \tag{39}$$

Moreover, the rate of convergence in space is calculated by

$$Rate\ of\ convergence \approx \frac{log(\|E\|_{\infty,h_1} / \|E\|_{\infty,h_2})}{log(h_1/h_2)}.$$

where h_1, h_2 are the space steps.

Table 1 gives the errors $\|E\|_\infty$ of the presented alternating asymmetric iteration algorithm based on domain decomposition for the 3D Laplace problem (37)–(38) with different values of ω when $l = m = s = 31$, $h = 1/30, n = 150$, we can obviously see that the errors is relatively smaller when the relaxation factor ω is about 1.9. we further see that the errors get the minimum when ω is about 1.82 shown in Figure 4a, which is match with the result of Equation (35). Figure 4b performs the errors with $z = 0.5$ when $\omega = 1.82$, which illustrate the effectiveness of the AAI algorithm.

From Tables 2 and 3, we can see the iteration numbers of the AAI algorithm is the least during the Jacobi, Gauss-Seidel iterative methods under some error controls when $h = 1/30, 1/50$. In addition, the AAI algorithm obtains shorter times than the Jacobi and the Gauss-Seidel methods when the number of the grid nodes is in increasing. Table 4 gives the convergence rates and errors of the AAI algorithm. In computation of the rates of convergence in space, the spatial steps are taken as $h = 1/(16 + 8d)$, $d = 0, 1, \cdots, 4$. We can see the rates is of order 2 in space and the errors can up to 10^{-5}.

Figure 5 provides the errors, relative errors and numerical solutions at $z = 1/3, 2/3$ when $l = m = s = 31, h = 1/30, n = 150, \omega = 1.82$, which shows the AAI algorithm is effect and accurate.

Table 1. The errors $\|E\|_\infty$ of alternating asymmetric iterative (AAI) algorithm based on domain decomposition with the different values of ω when $l = m = s = 31,\ h = 1/30, n = 150$.

ω	$\| E \|_\infty$	ω	$\| E \|_\infty$
1.0	4.4434×10^{-1}	1.6	3.9316×10^{-2}
1.1	3.6971×10^{-1}	1.7	1.0478×10^{-2}
1.2	2.9383×10^{-1}	1.8	4.8059×10^{-4}
1.3	2.1896×10^{-1}	1.9	2.0334×10^{-4}
1.4	1.4838×10^{-1}	2.0	errors
1.5	8.6993×10^{-2}	–	–

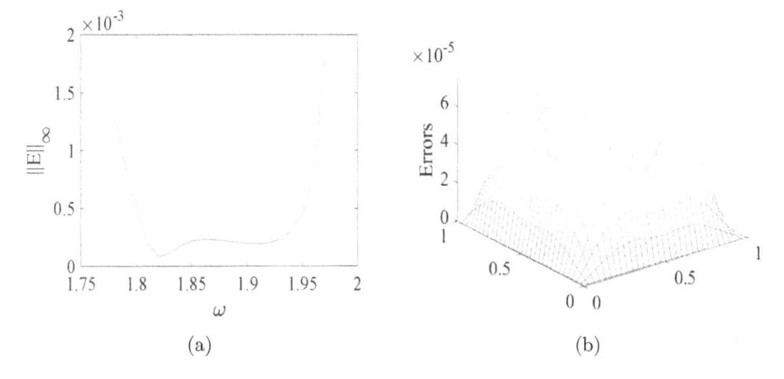

Figure 4. The $\|E\|_\infty$ with the different ω and the errors at $z = 0.5$ when $l = m = s = 31, h = 1/30, n = 150$. (**a**) $\|E\|_\infty$; (**b**) the errors at $z = 0.5$ when $\omega = 1.82$.

Table 2. The iteration numbers and time(s) of Jacobi, Gauss-Seidel and the AAI algorithm under the different error controls when $l = m = s = 31,\ h = 1/30$.

$\|E\|_\infty$	10^{-3}		10^{-4}		10^{-5}	
	Numbers	**Time(s)**	**Numbers**	**Time(s)**	**Numbers**	**Time(s)**
Jacobi	987	3.3906	1401	4.4219	1774	5.0000
Gauss-Seidel	491	2.4219	698	3.1406	885	3.5469
AAI ($\omega = 1.82$)	93	6.8906	123	9.6406	145	10.1093

Table 3. The iteration numbers and time(s) of Jacobi, Gauss-Seidel and the AAI algorithm under the different error controls when $l = m = s = 51,\ h = 1/50$.

$\|E\|_\infty$	10^{-3}		10^{-4}		10^{-5}	
	Numbers	**Time(s)**	**Numbers**	**Time(s)**	**Numbers**	**Time(s)**
Jacobi	2745	21.5156	3905	34.5000	5018	37.9219
Gauss-Seidel	1368	17.2344	1948	20.5938	2505	35.4688
AAI ($\omega = 1.94$)	115	9.4375	209	18.3437	283	22.1250

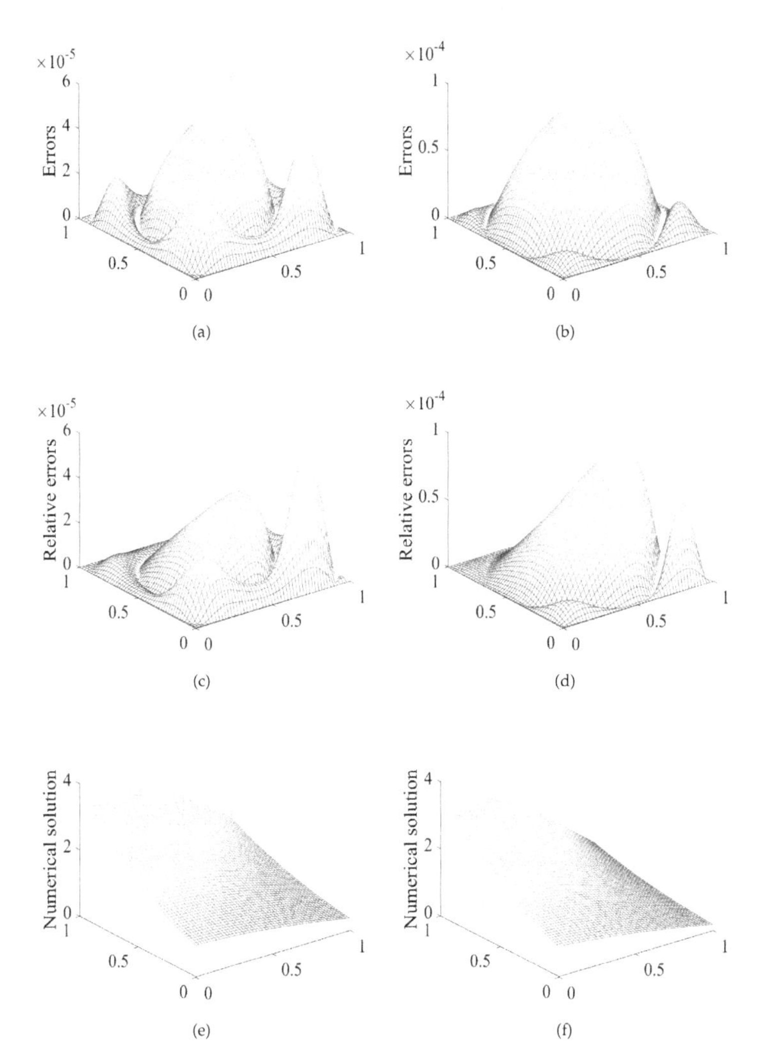

Figure 5. The errors, relative errors and numerical solutions of the AAI algorithm at $z = 1/3, 2/3$ when $l = m = s = 51, h = 1/50, n = 150, \omega = 1.94$. (**a**) The errors at $z = 1/3$; (**b**) The errors at $z = 2/3$; (**c**) The relative errors at $z = 1/3$; (**d**) The relative errors at $z = 2/3$; (**e**) The numerical solution at $z = 1/3$; (**f**) The numerical solution at $z = 2/3$.

Table 4. The convergence rates and errors $\|E\|_\infty$ of the presented iterative algorithm when $\omega = 1.95, n = 3000$.

Numbers	$16 \times 16 \times 16$	$24 \times 24 \times 24$	$32 \times 32 \times 32$	$40 \times 40 \times 40$	$48 \times 48 \times 48$
Rates	–	1.9909	1.9906	1.9956	1.9979
Errors	1.4277×10^{-4}	6.3687×10^{-5}	3.5920×10^{-5}	2.3011×10^{-5}	1.5986×10^{-5}

(2) Consider the 3D Poisson equation

$$\frac{\partial^2 u}{\partial x^2} + \frac{\partial^2 u}{\partial y^2} + \frac{\partial^2 u}{\partial z^2} = -3sin(x)sin(y)sin(z), (x, y, z) \in [0,1]^3, \tag{40}$$

with the boundary condition,

$$\begin{aligned} &u(0, y, z) = 0; \\ &u(1, y, z) = sin(1)sin(y)sin(z); \\ &u(x, 0, z) = 0; \\ &u(x, 1, z) = sin(x)sin(1)sin(z); \\ &u(x, y, 0) = 0; \\ &u(x, y, 1) = sin(x)sin(y)sin(1). \end{aligned} \tag{41}$$

The exact solution of the 3D Poisson problem (40)–(41) is $u(x, y, z) = sin(x)sin(y)sin(z)$.

Table 5 gives the errors $\|E\|_\infty$ of AAI algorithm for the problem 2 with the different values of ω when $l = m = s = 31, h = 1/30, n = 150$, and Figure 6 shows the errors get nearly the minimum 2.2319×10^{-4} while $\omega = 1.76$. which show the effect of ω to the AAI algorithm. Tables 6–8 give the iteration numbers and times under some error controls, which also show obviously the presented algorithm has smaller iteration numbers than the Jacobi and Gauss-Seidel methods. The computational times are shorter with the grid points increasing.

Figure 7 shows the errors, relative errors and numerical solutions of the AAI iterative algorithm based on domain decomposition for the problem 2 at $z = 1/3, 2/3$ when $l = m = s = 51, h = 1/50$, $n = 150, \omega = 1.96$. All of the numerical experiments examine the effectiveness and accuracy of the presented AAI algorithm.

Table 5. The errors $\|E\|_\infty$ of AAI algorithm based on domain decomposition with the different values of ω when $l = m = s = 31,\ h = 1/30, n = 150$.

ω	$\| E \|_\infty$	ω	$\| E \|_\infty$
1.0	4.2402×10^{-2}	1.6	3.6712×10^{-3}
1.1	3.4981×10^{-2}	1.7	9.4888×10^{-4}
1.2	2.7756×10^{-2}	1.8	3.9125×10^{-4}
1.3	2.0657×10^{-2}	1.9	5.8138×10^{-4}
1.4	1.3986×10^{-2}	2.0	errors
1.5	8.1573×10^{-3}	–	–

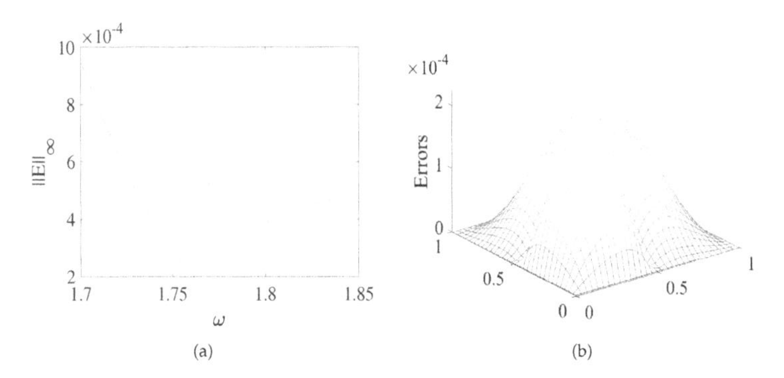

Figure 6. The $\|E\|_\infty$ with the different ω and the errors at $z = 0.5$ when $l = m = s = 31, h = 1/30, n = 150$. (**a**) The errors $\|E\|_\infty$ with the different ω; (**b**) The errors at $z = 0.5$ when $\omega = 1.76$.

Table 6. The iteration numbers and time(s) of Jacobi, Gauss-Seidel and the AAI algorithm under the different error controls when $l = m = s = 31,\ h = 1/30$.

$\|E\|_\infty$	10^{-3}		10^{-4}	
	Numbers	**Time(s)**	**Numbers**	**Time(s)**
Jacobi	557	2.6719	976	3.0781
Gauss-Seidel	288	0.8906	498	1.4688
AAI ($\omega = 1.96$)	29	5.6719	135	13.9531

Table 7. The iteration numbers and time(s) of Jacobi, Gauss-Seidel and the AAI algorithm under the different error controls when $l = m = s = 51,\ h = 1/50$.

$\|E\|_\infty$	10^{-3}		10^{-4}	
	Numbers	**Time(s)**	**Numbers**	**Time(s)**
Jacobi	1548	15.7031	2712	24.1875
Gauss-Seidel	790	8.3594	1372	15.2500
AAI ($\omega = 1.96$)	51	14.5469	181	30.2344

Table 8. The iteration numbers and time(s) of Jacobi, Gauss-Seidel and the AAI algorithm under the different error controls when $l = m = s = 71,\ h = 1/70$.

$\|E\|_\infty$	10^{-3}		10^{-4}	
	Numbers	**Time(s)**	**Numbers**	**Time(s)**
Jacobi	3034	98.5468	5317	176.6562
Gauss-Seidel	1538	53.5156	2681	92.9531
AAI ($\omega = 1.96$)	91	31.7187	201	54.2968

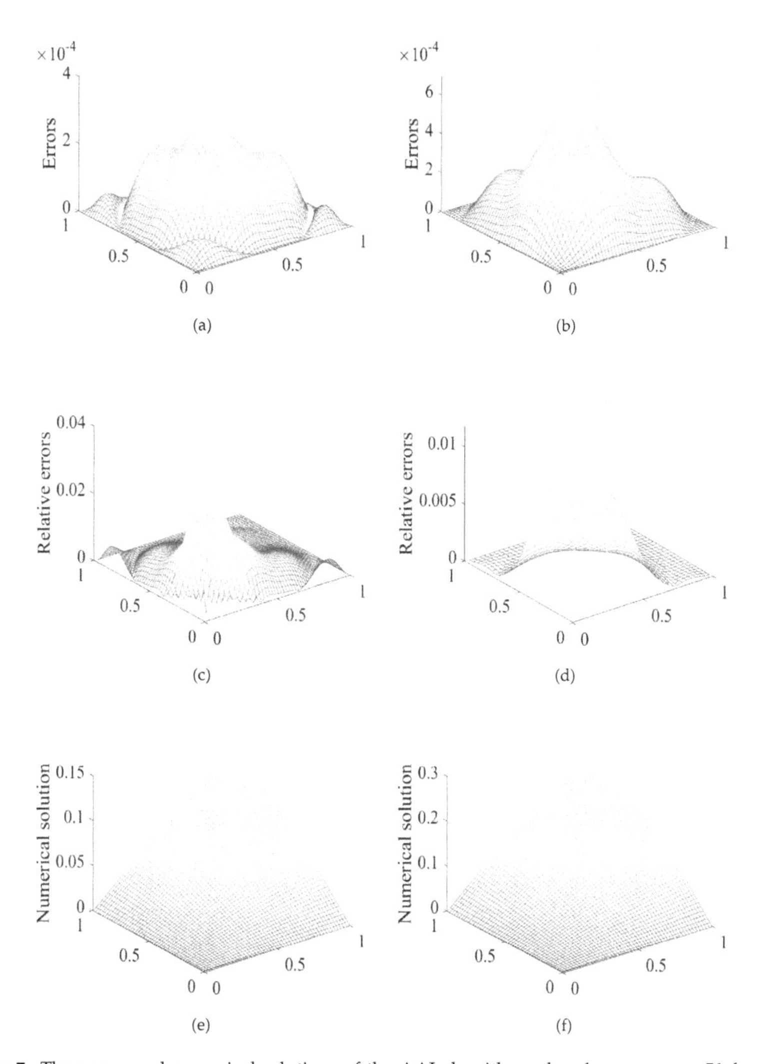

Figure 7. The errors and numerical solutions of the AAI algorithm when $l = m = s = 51, h = 1/50$, $n = 150, \omega = 1.96$. (**a**) The errors at $z = 1/3$; (**b**) The errors at $z = 2/3$; (**c**) The relative errors at $z = 1/3$; (**d**) The relative errors at $z = 2/3$; (**e**) The numerical solution at $z = 1/3$; (**f**) The numerical solution at $z = 2/3$.

Since the presented AAI algorithm based on domain decomposition is constructed by the asymmetrical iterative schemes and GE method, which has interior parallelism and is easy to be implemented. During the process of the implementation of the AAI algorithm, there's no need to solve the large-scale sparse block tridiagonal matrices. When the iteration numbers are odd or even, we just to solve the 3D problems by the constructed iterative schemes, which are computed independently. Once the interfaces are solved by GE method, the other grid points can also be solved by the constructed iterative schemes directly and in parallel. Therefore, the key of parallel implementation lies in information transfer and time cost of the inner boundary. In fact, the whole computation is explicit but convergent, which save the most of the consuming time.

So In this paper, we use the Matlab software to implement the presented AAI algorithm. We extend this idea to solve the other time-dependent high-dimensional problems, and compare the times, speedup, caches and so on. The detailed parallel implementation and performance analysis are provided in [27].

6. Conclusions

In this paper, we provide a new alternating asymmetric iterative (AAI) algorithm for 3D Poisson problem based on domain decomposition. We use several asymmetrical iterative schemes to solve the sub-domains respectively. Meanwhile the asymmetrical iterative schemes are alternatively used on odd and even iteration levels to improve the accuracy. Moreover, we give the convergence of the algorithm and the optimal relaxation factor. Finally, several numerical experiments are taken to examine the effectiveness and accuracy of the presented algorithm.

The study will be extended to other high-dimensional diffusion problems and wave problems and so on, and also can be used to solve on more multi-subdomains, and the corresponding new algorithms will be designed. we will report these soon.

Author Contributions: Conceptualization, and Methodology and Writing–original draft preparation, Q.X.; Formal analysis and Writing–review, Z.L. All authors have read and agreed to the published version of the manuscript.

Funding: The research of the first author was partially supported by the Natural Science Foundations of China (No. 61662059), the Major Innovation Projects for Building First-calss Universities in China's Western Region (No. ZKZD2017009), the Natural Science Foundations of Ningxia Province (No. NZ2018AAC03026), and the Fourth Batch of the Ningxia Youth Talents Supporting Program (No.TJGC2019012). The research of the second author was partially supported by the Natural Science Foundations of China (No. 11501313), the Natural Science Foundations of Ningxia Province (No. 2019AAC02001), the Project funded by the China Postdoctoral Science Foundation (No. 2017M621343), and the Third Batch of the Ningxia Youth Talents Supporting Program (No. TJGC2018037).

Acknowledgments: The authors thank the Reviewers and the Editors for their valuable comments and suggestions on an earlier version of this article.

Conflicts of Interest: The authors declare no conflicts of interest.

References

1. Saad, Y. *Iterative Methods for Sparse Linear Systems*, 2nd ed.; SIAM: Philadelphia, PA, USA, 2003.
2. Ge, Y.; Cao, F.; Zhang, J. A transformation-free HOC scheme and multigrid method for solving the 3D Poisson equation on nonuniform grids. *J. Comput. Phys.* **2013**, *234*, 199–216.
3. Abide, S.; Zeghmati, B. Multigrid defect correction and fourth-order compact scheme for Poisson equation. *Comput. Math. Appl.* **2017**, *73*, 1433–1444.
4. Fen, H.; Zhang, B.L.; Liu, Y. Mathematics Stencil of the finite difference method for Poisson equation and its application. *China Sci.* **2005**, *35*, 901–909. (In Chinese)
5. Spotz, W.F.; Carey, G.F. A high-order compact formulation for the 3D Poisson equation. *Numer. Methods Part. Diff. Equ.* **1996**, *12*, 235–243.
6. Gupta, M.M.; Kouatchou, J. Symbolic derivation of finite difference approximations for the three dimensional Poisson equation. *Numer. Methods Part. Diff. Equ.* **1998**, *14*, 593–606.
7. Romao, E.C.; Campos, M.D.; Moura, L.F.M. Application of the galerkin and least-squares finite element methods in the solution of 3D Poisson and Helmholtz equations. *Comput. Math. Appl.* **2011**, *62*, 4288–4299.

8. Nintcheu Fata, S. Semi-analytic treatment of the three-dimensional Poisson equation via a Galerkin BIE method. *J. Comput. Appl. Math.* **2011**, *236*, 1216–1225.
9. Shi, Z.; Cao, Y.Y.; Chen, Q.J. Solving 2D and 3D Poisson equations and biharmonic equations by the Haar wavelet method. *Appl. Math. Model.* **2012**, *36*, 5143–5161.
10. Shi, Z.; Cao, Y.Y. A spectral collocation method based on Haar wavelets for Poisson equations and biharmonic equations. *Appl. Math. Model.* **2011**, *54*, 2858–2868.
11. Speyer, G.; Vasileska, D.; Goodnick, S.M. Efficient Poisson equation solvers for large scale 3D simulations. In Proceedings of the 2001 International Conference on Modeling and Simulation of Microsystems-MSM, Hilton Head Island, SC, USA, 19–21 March 2001; pp. 23–26.
12. Pedro, V.-L.; Alfredo, P.; Manuel, P.-M. Fast finite difference Poisson solvers on heterogeneous architectures. *Comput. Phys. Commun.* **2014**, *185*, 1265–1272.
13. Pedro, V.-L.; Alfredo, P.; Julien, F.; Manuel, P.-M. Block tridiagonal solvers on heterogeneous architectures. In Proceedings of the 2012 IEEE 10th International Symposium on Parallel and Distributed Processing with Applications, Leganes, Spain, 10–13 July 2012; pp. 609–617.
14. Stone, C.P.; Duque, E.P.N.; Zhang, Y.; Car, D.; Owens, J.D.; Davis, R.L. 20th AIAA Computational Fluid Dynamics Conference. *AIAA-306* **2011**, *3221*, 307.
15. Yang, W.D.; Li, K.L.; Li, K.Q. A parallel solving method for block-tridiagonal equations on CPUCGPU heterogeneous computing systems. *J. Supercomput.* **2017**, *73*, 1760–1781.
16. Zhang, Y.; Cohen, J.; Owens, J.D. *Proceedings of the 15th ACM SIGPLAN Symposium on Principles and Practice of Parallel Programming*; ACM: New York, NY, USA, 2010; p. 127.
17. Davidson, A.; Zhang, Y.; Owens, J.D. *IEEE International Parallel and Distributed Processing Symposium*; IEEE: Piscataway, NJ, USA, 2011; p. 956.
18. Zhang, B.L.; Yuan, G.X.; Liu, X.P. *Parallel Finite Difference Methods for Partial Differential Equations*; Science Press: Beijing, China, 1994; pp. 7–67.
19. Mohanty, R.K. The samrt-BLAGE algorithm for singularly perturbed 2D elliptic partial differential equations. *Appl. Math. Comput.* **2007**, *190*, 321–331.
20. Tavakoli, R.; Davami, P. A new parallel Gauss-Seidel method based on alternating group explicit method and domain decomposition method. *Appl. Math. Comput.* **2007**, *188*, 713–719.
21. Abdullah, A.R.; Ali, N.M. The comparative study of parallel alternating-type iterative methods. *Appl. Math. Comput.* **1996**, *74*, 331–344.
22. Keyes, D.E.; Gropp, W.D. A comparison of domain decomposition on techniques for elliptic partial differential equations and their parallel implementation. *SIAM J. Sci. Stat. Comput.* **1987**, *8*, s166–s202.
23. Kuznetsov, Y. New algorithm for approximate realization of implicit difference scheme. *Soviet J. Numer. Anal. Math. Model.* **1988**, *3*, 99–114.
24. Xu, Q.Y.; Wang, W.Q. Wenqiang, W. A new parallel iterative algorithm for solving 2D Poisson equation. *Numer. Methods Part. Differ. Eqs.* **2011**, *27*, 829–853.
25. Ng, K.F.; Mohd Ali, N.H. Performance analysis of explicit group parallel algorithms for distributed memory multicomputer. *Parallel Comput.* **2008**, *34*, 427–440.
26. Evans, D. Alternating group explicit method for the diffusion equations. *Appl. Math. Model.* **1985**, *9*, 201–206.
27. Xu, Q.Y.; Liu, Z.Y. On the parallel implementation of several iterative algorithms for the 3D Poisson and Diffusion problems. **2020**, in preparation.

Article

Weighted Fractional Iyengar Type Inequalities in the Caputo Direction

George A. Anastassiou

Department of Mathematical Sciences, University of Memphis, Memphis, TN 38152, USA; ganastss@memphis.edu

Received: 8 October 2019; Accepted: 14 November 2019; Published: 16 November 2019

Abstract: Here we present weighted fractional Iyengar type inequalities with respect to L_p norms, with $1 \leq p \leq \infty$. Our employed fractional calculus is of Caputo type defined with respect to another function. Our results provide quantitative estimates for the approximation of the Lebesgue–Stieljes integral of a function, based on its values over a finite set of points including at the endpoints of its interval of definition. Our method relies on the right and left generalized fractional Taylor's formulae. The iterated generalized fractional derivatives case is also studied. We give applications at the end.

Keywords: Iyengar inequality; right and left generalized fractional derivatives; iterated generalized fractional derivatives; generalized fractional Taylor's formulae

MSC: 26A33; 26D10; 26D15

---

1. Introduction

We are motivated by the following famous Iyengar inequality (1938), [1].

Theorem 1. *Let f be a differentiable function on $[a,b]$ and $|f'(x)| \leq M$. Then*

$$\left| \int_a^b f(x)\,dx - \frac{1}{2}(b-a)(f(a)+f(b)) \right| \leq \frac{M(b-a)^2}{4} - \frac{(f(b)-f(a))^2}{4M}. \quad (1)$$

We need

Definition 1 ([2]). *Let $\alpha > 0$, $\lceil \alpha \rceil = n$, $\lceil \cdot \rceil$ the ceiling of the number. Here $g \in AC([a,b])$ (absolutely continuous functions) and strictly increasing. We assume that $\left(f \circ g^{-1}\right)^{(n)} \circ g \in L_\infty([a,b])$. We define the left generalized g-fractional derivative of f of order α as follows:*

$$\left(D_{a+;g}^{\alpha} f\right)(x) := \frac{1}{\Gamma(n-\alpha)} \int_a^x (g(x)-g(t))^{n-\alpha-1} g'(t) \left(f \circ g^{-1}\right)^{(n)}(g(t))\,dt, \quad (2)$$

$x \geq a$.

If $\alpha \notin \mathbb{N}$, by [3], pp. 360–361, we have that $D_{a+;g}^{\alpha} f \in C([a,b])$.

We see that

$$\left(I_{a+;g}^{n-\alpha}\left(\left(f \circ g^{-1}\right)^{(n)} \circ g\right)\right)(x) = \left(D_{a+;g}^{\alpha} f\right)(x), \; x \geq a. \quad (3)$$

We set

$$D_{a+;g}^{n} f(x) := \left(\left(f \circ g^{-1}\right)^{(n)} \circ g\right)(x), \quad (4)$$

$$D_{a+;g}^{0} f(x) = f(x), \; \forall\, x \in [a,b]. \quad (5)$$

When $g = id$, then

$$D_{a+;g}^{\alpha} f = D_{a+;id}^{\alpha} f = D_{*a}^{\alpha} f, \tag{6}$$

the usual left Caputo fractional derivative.

We mention the following g-left fractional generalized Taylor's formula:

Theorem 2 ([2]). *Let g be a strictly increasing function and $g \in AC([a,b])$. We assume that $(f \circ g^{-1}) \in AC^n([g(a), g(b)])$, i.e., $(f \circ g^{-1})^{(n-1)} \in AC([g(a), g(b)])$, where $\mathbb{N} \ni n = \lceil \alpha \rceil$, $\alpha > 0$. Also we assume that $(f \circ g^{-1})^{(n)} \circ g \in L_\infty([a,b])$. Then*

$$f(x) = f(a) + \sum_{k=1}^{n-1} \frac{(f \circ g^{-1})^{(k)}(g(a))}{k!} (g(x) - g(a))^k +$$

$$\frac{1}{\Gamma(\alpha)} \int_a^x (g(x) - g(t))^{\alpha-1} g'(t) \left(D_{a+;g}^{\alpha} f \right)(t)\, dt, \ \forall x \in [a,b]. \tag{7}$$

Calling $R_n(a,x)$ the remainder of (7), we find that

$$R_n(a,x) = \frac{1}{\Gamma(\alpha)} \int_{g(a)}^{g(x)} (g(x) - z)^{\alpha-1} \left(\left(D_{a+;g}^{\alpha} f \right) \circ g^{-1} \right)(z)\, dz, \ \forall x \in [a,b]. \tag{8}$$

We need

Definition 2 ([2]). *Here $g \in AC([a,b])$ and is strictly increasing. We assume that $(f \circ g^{-1})^{(n)} \circ g \in L_\infty([a,b])$, where $N \ni n = \lceil \alpha \rceil$, $\alpha > 0$. We define the right generalized g-fractional derivative of f of order α as follows:*

$$\left(D_{b-;g}^{\alpha} f \right)(x) := \frac{(-1)^n}{\Gamma(n-\alpha)} \int_x^b (g(t) - g(x))^{n-\alpha-1} g'(t) \left(f \circ g^{-1} \right)^{(n)} (g(t))\, dt, \tag{9}$$

all $x \in [a,b]$.

If $\alpha \notin \mathbb{N}$, by [3], p. 378, we find that $\left(D_{b-;g}^{\alpha} f \right) \in C([a,b])$.

We see that

$$I_{b-;g}^{n-\alpha} \left((-1)^n \left(f \circ g^{-1} \right)^{(n)} \circ g \right)(x) = \left(D_{b-;g}^{\alpha} f \right)(x), \ a \le x \le b. \tag{10}$$

We set

$$D_{b-;g}^{n} f(x) = (-1)^n \left(\left(f \circ g^{-1} \right)^{(n)} \circ g \right)(x), \tag{11}$$

$$D_{b-;g}^{0} f(x) = f(x), \ \forall x \in [a,b].$$

When $g = id$, then

$$D_{b-;g}^{\alpha} f(x) = D_{b-;id}^{\alpha} f(x) = D_{b-}^{\alpha} f, \tag{12}$$

the usual right Caputo fractional derivative.

We mention the g-right generalized fractional Taylor's formula:

Theorem 3 ([2]). *Let g be a strictly increasing function and $g \in AC([a,b])$. We assume that $(f \circ g^{-1}) \in AC^n([g(a), g(b)])$, where $\mathbb{N} \ni n = \lceil \alpha \rceil$, $\alpha > 0$. Also we assume that $(f \circ g^{-1})^{(n)} \circ g \in L_\infty([a,b])$. Then*

$$f(x) = f(b) + \sum_{k=1}^{n-1} \frac{(f \circ g^{-1})^{(k)}(g(b))}{k!} (g(x) - g(b))^k +$$

$$\frac{1}{\Gamma(\alpha)} \int_x^b (g(t) - g(x))^{\alpha-1} g'(t) \left(D_{b-;g}^{\alpha} f \right)(t) \, dt, \text{ all } a \le x \le b. \tag{13}$$

Calling $R_n(b,x)$ the remainder in (13), we find that

$$R_n(b,x) = \frac{1}{\Gamma(\alpha)} \int_{g(x)}^{g(b)} (z - g(x))^{\alpha-1} \left(\left(D_{b-;g}^{\alpha} f \right) \circ g^{-1} \right)(z) \, dz, \ \forall x \in [a,b]. \tag{14}$$

Denote by

$$D_{b-;g}^{n\alpha} := D_{b-;g}^{\alpha} D_{b-;g}^{\alpha} ... D_{b-;g}^{\alpha} \ (n\text{-times}), n \in \mathbb{N}. \tag{15}$$

We mention the following g-right generalized modified Taylor's formula:

Theorem 4 ([2]). *Suppose that $F_k := D_{b-;g}^{k\alpha} f$, for $k = 0, 1, ..., n+1$, fulfill: $F_k \circ g^{-1} \in AC([c,d])$, where $c = g(a)$, $d = g(b)$, and $(F_k \circ g^{-1})' \circ g \in L_\infty([a,b])$, where $0 < \alpha \le 1$. Then*

$$f(x) = \sum_{i=0}^{n} \frac{(g(b) - g(x))^{i\alpha}}{\Gamma(i\alpha + 1)} \left(D_{b-;g}^{i\alpha} f \right)(b) +$$

$$\frac{1}{\Gamma((n+1)\alpha)} \int_x^b (g(t) - g(x))^{(n+1)\alpha-1} g'(t) \left(D_{b-;g}^{(n+1)\alpha} f \right)(t) \, dt = \tag{16}$$

$$\sum_{i=0}^{n} \frac{(g(b) - g(x))^{i\alpha}}{\Gamma(i\alpha + 1)} \left(D_{b-;g}^{i\alpha} f \right)(b) + \frac{\left(D_{b-;g}^{(n+1)\alpha} f \right)(\psi_x)}{\Gamma((n+1)\alpha + 1)} (g(b) - g(x))^{(n+1)\alpha}, \tag{17}$$

where $\psi_x \in [x,b]$, any $x \in [a,b]$.

Denote by

$$D_{a+;g}^{n\alpha} := D_{a+;g}^{\alpha} D_{a+;g}^{\alpha} ... D_{a+;g}^{\alpha} \ (n\text{-times}), n \in \mathbb{N}. \tag{18}$$

We mention the following g-left generalized modified Taylor's formula:

Theorem 5 ([2]). *Suppose that $F_k := D_{a+;g}^{k\alpha} f$, for $k = 0, 1, ..., n+1$, fulfill: $F_k \circ g^{-1} \in AC([c,d])$, where $c = g(a)$, $d = g(b)$, and $(F_k \circ g^{-1})' \circ g \in L_\infty([a,b])$, where $0 < \alpha \le 1$. Then*

$$f(x) = \sum_{i=0}^{n} \frac{(g(x) - g(a))^{i\alpha}}{\Gamma(i\alpha + 1)} \left(D_{a+;g}^{i\alpha} f \right)(a) + \tag{19}$$

$$\frac{1}{\Gamma((n+1)\alpha)} \int_a^x (g(x) - g(t))^{(n+1)\alpha-1} g'(t) \left(D_{a+;g}^{(n+1)\alpha} f \right)(t) \, dt =$$

$$\sum_{i=0}^{n} \frac{(g(x) - g(a))^{i\alpha}}{\Gamma(i\alpha + 1)} \left(D_{a+;g}^{i\alpha} f \right)(a) + \frac{\left(D_{a+;g}^{(n+1)\alpha} f \right)(\psi_x)}{\Gamma((n+1)\alpha + 1)} (g(x) - g(a))^{(n+1)\alpha}, \tag{20}$$

where $\psi_x \in [a,x]$, any $x \in [a,b]$.

Next we present generalized fractional Iyengar type inequalities.

2. Main Results

We present the following Caputo type generalized g-fractional Iyengar type inequality:

Theorem 6. *Let g be a strictly increasing function and $g \in AC([a,b])$. We assume that $(f \circ g^{-1}) \in AC^n([g(a), g(b)])$, where $\mathbb{N} \ni n = \lceil \alpha \rceil$, $\alpha > 0$. We also assume that $(f \circ g^{-1})^{(n)} \circ g \in L_\infty([a,b])$ (clearly here it is $f \in C([a,b])$). Then*

(i)

$$\left| \int_a^b f(x)\,dg(x) - \sum_{k=0}^{n-1} \frac{1}{(k+1)!} \left[\left(f \circ g^{-1}\right)^{(k)} (g(a)) (g(t) - g(a))^{k+1} + (-1)^k \left(f \circ g^{-1}\right)^{(k)} (g(b)) (g(b) - g(t))^{k+1} \right] \right| \leq \frac{\max\left\{ \left\| D^{\alpha}_{a+;g} f \right\|_{L_\infty([a,b])}, \left\| D^{\alpha}_{b-;g} f \right\|_{L_\infty([a,b])} \right\}}{\Gamma(\alpha+2)} \left[(g(t) - g(a))^{\alpha+1} + (g(b) - g(t))^{\alpha+1} \right], \tag{21}$$

$\forall\, t \in [a,b]$,

(ii) at $g(t) = \frac{g(a)+g(b)}{2}$, the right hand side of (21) is minimized, and we have:

$$\left| \int_a^b f(x)\,dg(x) - \sum_{k=0}^{n-1} \frac{1}{(k+1)!} \frac{(g(b) - g(a))^{k+1}}{2^{k+1}} \left[\left(f \circ g^{-1}\right)^{(k)} (g(a)) + (-1)^k \left(f \circ g^{-1}\right)^{(k)} (g(b)) \right] \right| \leq \frac{\max\left\{ \left\| D^{\alpha}_{a+;g} f \right\|_{L_\infty([a,b])}, \left\| D^{\alpha}_{b-;g} f \right\|_{L_\infty([a,b])} \right\}}{\Gamma(\alpha+2)} \frac{(g(b) - g(a))^{\alpha+1}}{2^{\alpha}}, \tag{22}$$

(iii) if $(f \circ g^{-1})^{(k)} (g(a)) = (f \circ g^{-1})^{(k)} (g(b)) = 0$, for $k = 0, 1, ..., n-1$, we obtain

$$\left| \int_a^b f(x)\,dg(x) \right| \leq \max\left\{ \left\| D^{\alpha}_{a+;g} f \right\|_{L_\infty([a,b])}, \left\| D^{\alpha}_{b-;g} f \right\|_{L_\infty([a,b])} \right\} \frac{(g(b) - g(a))^{\alpha+1}}{\Gamma(\alpha+2)\, 2^{\alpha}}, \tag{23}$$

which is a sharp inequality,

(iv) more generally, for $j = 0, 1, 2, ..., N \in \mathbb{N}$, it holds

$$\left| \int_a^b f(x)\,dg(x) - \sum_{k=0}^{n-1} \frac{1}{(k+1)!} \left(\frac{g(b) - g(a)}{N} \right)^{k+1} \left[j^{k+1} \left(f \circ g^{-1}\right)^{(k)} (g(a)) + (-1)^k (N-j)^{k+1} \left(f \circ g^{-1}\right)^{(k)} (g(b)) \right] \right| \leq \frac{\max\left\{ \left\| D^{\alpha}_{a+;g} f \right\|_{L_\infty([a,b])}, \left\| D^{\alpha}_{b-;g} f \right\|_{L_\infty([a,b])} \right\}}{\Gamma(\alpha+2)} \left(\frac{g(b) - g(a)}{N} \right)^{\alpha+1} \left[j^{\alpha+1} + (N-j)^{\alpha+1} \right], \tag{24}$$

(v) if $\left(f \circ g^{-1}\right)^{(k)}(g(a)) = \left(f \circ g^{-1}\right)^{(k)}(g(b)) = 0$, *for* $k = 1, ..., n-1$, *from (24) we obtain*

$$\left| \int_a^b f(x)\, dg(x) - \left(\frac{g(b) - g(a)}{N}\right)[jf(a) + (N-j) f(b)] \right| \leq$$

$$\frac{\max\left\{ \left\| D_{a+;g}^{\alpha} f \right\|_{L_\infty([a,b])}, \left\| D_{b-;g}^{\alpha} f \right\|_{L_\infty([a,b])} \right\}}{\Gamma(\alpha+2)}$$

$$\left(\frac{g(b) - g(a)}{N}\right)^{\alpha+1} \left[j^{\alpha+1} + (N-j)^{\alpha+1} \right], \tag{25}$$

$j = 0, 1, 2, ..., N$,

(vi) when $N = 2$, $j = 1$, *(25) turns to*

$$\left| \int_a^b f(x)\, dg(x) - \left(\frac{g(b) - g(a)}{2}\right)(f(a) + f(b)) \right| \leq$$

$$\frac{\max\left\{ \left\| D_{a+;g}^{\alpha} f \right\|_{L_\infty([a,b])}, \left\| D_{b-;g}^{\alpha} f \right\|_{L_\infty([a,b])} \right\}}{\Gamma(\alpha+2)} \frac{(g(b) - g(a))^{\alpha+1}}{2^{\alpha}}. \tag{26}$$

(vii) when $0 < \alpha \leq 1$, *inequality (26) is again valid without any boundary conditions.*

Proof. We have by (7) that

$$f(x) - \sum_{k=0}^{n-1} \frac{\left(f \circ g^{-1}\right)^{(k)}(g(a))}{k!} (g(x) - g(a))^k =$$

$$\frac{1}{\Gamma(\alpha)} \int_a^x (g(x) - g(t))^{\alpha-1} g'(t) \left(D_{a+;g}^{\alpha} f\right)(t)\, dt, \tag{27}$$

$\forall\, x \in [a, b]$.

Also by (13) we obtain

$$f(x) - \sum_{k=0}^{n-1} \frac{\left(f \circ g^{-1}\right)^{(k)}(g(b))}{k!} (g(x) - g(b))^k =$$

$$\frac{1}{\Gamma(\alpha)} \int_x^b (g(t) - g(x))^{\alpha-1} g'(t) \left(D_{b-;g}^{\alpha} f\right)(t)\, dt, \tag{28}$$

$\forall\, x \in [a, b]$.

By (27) we derive (by [4], p. 107)

$$\left| f(x) - \sum_{k=0}^{n-1} \frac{\left(f \circ g^{-1}\right)^{(k)}(g(a))}{k!} (g(x) - g(a))^k \right| \leq$$

$$\frac{\left\| D_{a+;g}^{\alpha} f \right\|_{L_\infty([a,b])}}{\Gamma(\alpha+1)} (g(x) - g(a))^{\alpha}, \tag{29}$$

and by (28) we obtain

$$\left| f(x) - \sum_{k=0}^{n-1} \frac{\left(f \circ g^{-1}\right)^{(k)}(g(b))}{k!} (g(x) - g(b))^k \right| \leq$$

$$\frac{\left\| D^{\alpha}_{b-;g} f \right\|_{L_{\infty}([a,b])}}{\Gamma(\alpha+1)} (g(b) - g(x))^{\alpha}, \tag{30}$$

$\forall\, x \in [a,b]$.

Call

$$\varphi_1 := \frac{\left\| D^{\alpha}_{a+;g} f \right\|_{L_{\infty}([a,b])}}{\Gamma(\alpha+1)}, \tag{31}$$

and

$$\varphi_2 := \frac{\left\| D^{\alpha}_{b-;g} f \right\|_{L_{\infty}([a,b])}}{\Gamma(\alpha+1)}. \tag{32}$$

Set

$$\varphi := \max\{\varphi_1, \varphi_2\}. \tag{33}$$

That is

$$\left| f(x) - \sum_{k=0}^{n-1} \frac{\left(f \circ g^{-1}\right)^{(k)}(g(a))}{k!} (g(x) - g(a))^k \right| \leq \varphi (g(x) - g(a))^{\alpha},$$

and

$$\left| f(x) - \sum_{k=0}^{n-1} \frac{\left(f \circ g^{-1}\right)^{(k)}(g(b))}{k!} (g(x) - g(b))^k \right| \leq \varphi (g(b) - g(x))^{\alpha}, \tag{34}$$

$\forall\, x \in [a,b]$.

Equivalently, we have

$$\sum_{k=0}^{n-1} \frac{\left(f \circ g^{-1}\right)^{(k)}(g(a))}{k!} (g(x) - g(a))^k - \varphi (g(x) - g(a))^{\alpha} \leq \tag{35}$$

$$f(x) \leq \sum_{k=0}^{n-1} \frac{\left(f \circ g^{-1}\right)^{(k)}(g(a))}{k!} (g(x) - g(a))^k + \varphi (g(x) - g(a))^{\alpha},$$

and

$$\sum_{k=0}^{n-1} \frac{\left(f \circ g^{-1}\right)^{(k)}(g(b))}{k!} (g(x) - g(b))^k - \varphi (g(b) - g(x))^{\alpha} \leq \tag{36}$$

$$f(x) \leq \sum_{k=0}^{n-1} \frac{\left(f \circ g^{-1}\right)^{(k)}(g(b))}{k!} (g(x) - g(b))^k + \varphi (g(b) - g(x))^{\alpha},$$

$\forall\, x \in [a,b]$.

Let any $t \in [a,b]$, then by integration against g over $[a,t]$ and $[t,b]$, respectively, we obtain

$$\sum_{k=0}^{n-1} \frac{\left(f \circ g^{-1}\right)^{(k)}(g(a))}{(k+1)!} (g(t) - g(a))^{k+1} - \frac{\varphi}{(\alpha+1)} (g(t) - g(a))^{\alpha+1}$$

$$\leq \int_a^t f(x)\, dg(x) \leq$$

$$\sum_{k=0}^{n-1} \frac{\left(f \circ g^{-1}\right)^{(k)}(g(a))}{(k+1)!} (g(t) - g(a))^{k+1} + \frac{\varphi}{(\alpha+1)} (g(t) - g(a))^{\alpha+1}, \tag{37}$$

and

$$-\sum_{k=0}^{n-1}\frac{\left(f\circ g^{-1}\right)^{(k)}(g(b))}{(k+1)!}(g(t)-g(b))^{k+1}-\frac{\varphi}{(\alpha+1)}(g(b)-g(t))^{\alpha+1}$$
$$\leq\int_t^b f(x)\,dg(x)\leq$$
$$-\sum_{k=0}^{n-1}\frac{\left(f\circ g^{-1}\right)^{(k)}(g(b))}{(k+1)!}(g(t)-g(b))^{k+1}+\frac{\varphi}{(\alpha+1)}(g(b)-g(t))^{\alpha+1}. \tag{38}$$

Adding (37) and (38), we obtain

$$\left\{\sum_{k=0}^{n-1}\frac{1}{(k+1)!}\left[\left(f\circ g^{-1}\right)^{(k)}(g(a))(g(t)-g(a))^{k+1}-\right.\right.$$
$$\left.\left.\left(f\circ g^{-1}\right)^{(k)}(g(b))(g(t)-g(b))^{k+1}\right]\right\}-$$
$$\frac{\varphi}{(\alpha+1)}\left[(g(t)-g(a))^{\alpha+1}+(g(b)-g(t))^{\alpha+1}\right]$$
$$\leq\int_a^b f(x)\,dg(x)\leq$$
$$\left\{\sum_{k=0}^{n-1}\frac{1}{(k+1)!}\left[\left(f\circ g^{-1}\right)^{(k)}(g(a))(g(t)-g(a))^{k+1}-\right.\right.$$
$$\left.\left.\left(f\circ g^{-1}\right)^{(k)}(g(b))(g(t)-g(b))^{k+1}\right]\right\}+$$
$$\frac{\varphi}{(\alpha+1)}\left[(g(t)-g(a))^{\alpha+1}+(g(b)-g(t))^{\alpha+1}\right], \tag{39}$$

$\forall\, t\in[a,b]$.

Consequently we derive:

$$\left|\int_a^b f(x)\,dg(x)-\sum_{k=0}^{n-1}\frac{1}{(k+1)!}\left[\left(f\circ g^{-1}\right)^{(k)}(g(a))(g(t)-g(a))^{k+1}\right.\right. \tag{40}$$
$$\left.\left.+(-1)^k\left(f\circ g^{-1}\right)^{(k)}(g(b))(g(b)-g(t))^{k+1}\right]\right|\leq$$
$$\frac{\varphi}{(\alpha+1)}\left[(g(t)-g(a))^{\alpha+1}+(g(b)-g(t))^{\alpha+1}\right],$$

$\forall\, t\in[a,b]$.

Let us consider

$$\theta(z):=(z-g(a))^{\alpha+1}+(g(b)-z)^{\alpha+1},\ \forall\, z\in[g(a),g(b)].$$

That is

$$\theta(g(t))=(g(t)-g(a))^{\alpha+1}+(g(b)-g(t))^{\alpha+1},\ \forall\, t\in[a,b].$$

We have that

$$\theta'(z)=(\alpha+1)\left[(z-g(a))^{\alpha}-(g(b)-z)^{\alpha}\right]=0,$$

giving $(z-g(a))^{\alpha}=(g(b)-z)^{\alpha}$ and $z-g(a)=g(b)-z$, that is $z=\frac{g(a)+g(b)}{2}$ the only critical number of θ. We have that $\theta(g(a))=\theta(g(b))=(g(b)-g(a))^{\alpha+1}$, and $\theta\left(\frac{g(a)+g(b)}{2}\right)=\frac{(g(b)-g(a))^{\alpha+1}}{2^{\alpha}}$, which is the minimum of θ over $[g(a),g(b)]$.

Consequently the right hand side of (40) is minimized when $g(t)=\frac{g(a)+g(b)}{2}$, with value $\frac{\varphi}{(\alpha+1)}\frac{(g(b)-g(a))^{\alpha+1}}{2^{\alpha}}$.

Assuming $\left(f\circ g^{-1}\right)^{(k)}(g(a))=\left(f\circ g^{-1}\right)^{(k)}(g(b))=0$, for $k=0,1,...,n-1$, then we obtain that

$$\left|\int_a^b f(x)\,dg(x)\right|\leq\frac{\varphi}{(\alpha+1)}\frac{(g(b)-g(a))^{\alpha+1}}{2^{\alpha}}, \tag{41}$$

which is a sharp inequality.

When $g(t)=\frac{g(a)+g(b)}{2}$, then (40) becomes

$$\left|\int_a^b f(x)\,dg(x)-\sum_{k=0}^{n-1}\frac{1}{(k+1)!}\frac{(g(b)-g(a))^{k+1}}{2^{k+1}}\right.$$

$$\left.\left[\left(f\circ g^{-1}\right)^{(k)}(g(a))+(-1)^k\left(f\circ g^{-1}\right)^{(k)}(g(b))\right]\right|\leq$$

$$\frac{\varphi}{(\alpha+1)}\frac{(g(b)-g(a))^{\alpha+1}}{2^{\alpha}}. \tag{42}$$

Next let $N\in\mathbb{N}$, $j=0,1,2,...,N$ and $g(t_j)=g(a)+j\left(\frac{g(b)-g(a)}{N}\right)$, that is $g(t_0)=g(a)$, $g(t_1)=g(a)+\frac{(g(b)-g(a))}{N},...,g(t_N)=g(b)$.

Hence it holds

$$g(t_j)-g(a)=j\left(\frac{g(b)-g(a)}{N}\right),\ \ g(b)-g(t_j)=(N-j)\left(\frac{g(b)-g(a)}{N}\right), \tag{43}$$

$j=0,1,2,...,N$.

We notice

$$(g(t_j)-g(a))^{\alpha+1}+(g(b)-g(t_j))^{\alpha+1}=$$

$$\left(\frac{g(b)-g(a)}{N}\right)^{\alpha+1}\left[j^{\alpha+1}+(N-j)^{\alpha+1}\right], \tag{44}$$

$j=0,1,2,...,N$,

and (for $k=0,1,...,n-1$)

$$\left[\left(f\circ g^{-1}\right)^{(k)}(g(a))\,(g(t_j)-g(a))^{k+1}+\right.$$

$$\left.(-1)^k\left(f\circ g^{-1}\right)^{(k)}(g(b))\,(g(b)-g(t_j))^{k+1}\right]=$$

$$\left(\frac{g(b)-g(a)}{N}\right)^{k+1}\left[\left(f\circ g^{-1}\right)^{(k)}(g(a))\,j^{k+1}+\right.$$

$$\left.(-1)^k\left(f\circ g^{-1}\right)^{(k)}(g(b))\,(N-j)^{k+1}\right], \tag{45}$$

$j=0,1,2,...,N$.

By (40) we have

$$\left| \int_a^b f(x)\,dg(x) - \sum_{k=0}^{n-1} \frac{1}{(k+1)!} \left(\frac{g(b)-g(a)}{N} \right)^{k+1} \right.$$

$$\left. \left[\left(f \circ g^{-1}\right)^{(k)} (g(a))\, j^{k+1} + (-1)^k \left(f \circ g^{-1}\right)^{(k)} (g(b))\,(N-j)^{k+1} \right] \right| \leq$$

$$\left(\frac{\varphi}{\alpha+1} \right) \left(\frac{g(b)-g(a)}{N} \right)^{\alpha+1} \left[j^{\alpha+1} + (N-j)^{\alpha+1} \right], \tag{46}$$

$j = 0, 1, 2, ..., N$.

If $\left(f \circ g^{-1}\right)^{(k)} (g(a)) = \left(f \circ g^{-1}\right)^{(k)} (g(b)) = 0$, $k = 1, ..., n-1$, then (46) becomes

$$\left| \int_a^b f(x)\,dg(x) - \left(\frac{g(b)-g(a)}{N} \right) [jf(a) + (N-j) f(b)] \right| \leq$$

$$\left(\frac{\varphi}{\alpha+1} \right) \left(\frac{g(b)-g(a)}{N} \right)^{\alpha+1} \left[j^{\alpha+1} + (N-j)^{\alpha+1} \right], \tag{47}$$

$j = 0, 1, 2, ..., N$.

When $N = 2$ and $j = 1$, then (47) becomes

$$\left| \int_a^b f(x)\,dg(x) - \left(\frac{g(b)-g(a)}{2} \right) (f(a) + f(b)) \right| \leq$$

$$\left(\frac{\varphi}{\alpha+1} \right) 2 \frac{(g(b)-g(a))^{\alpha+1}}{2^{\alpha+1}} = \left(\frac{\varphi}{\alpha+1} \right) \frac{(g(b)-g(a))^{\alpha+1}}{2^{\alpha}}. \tag{48}$$

Let $0 < \alpha \leq 1$, then $n = \lceil \alpha \rceil = 1$.

In that case, without any boundary conditions, we derive from (48) again that

$$\left| \int_a^b f(x)\,dg(x) - \left(\frac{g(b)-g(a)}{2} \right) (f(a) + f(b)) \right| \leq$$

$$\left(\frac{\varphi}{\alpha+1} \right) \frac{(g(b)-g(a))^{\alpha+1}}{2^{\alpha}}. \tag{49}$$

We have proved theorem in all possible cases. □

Next we give modified g-fractional Iyengar type inequalities:

Theorem 7. *Let g be a strictly increasing function and $g \in AC([a,b])$, and $f \in C([a,b])$. Let $0 < \alpha \leq 1$, and $F_k := D^{k\alpha}_{a+;g} f$, for $k = 0, 1, ..., n+1$; $n \in \mathbb{N}$. We assume that $F_k \circ g^{-1} \in AC([g(a), g(b)])$ and $\left(F_k \circ g^{-1}\right)' \circ g \in L_\infty([a,b])$. Also let $\overline{F_k} := D^{k\alpha}_{b-;g} f$, for $k = 0, 1, ..., n+1$, they fulfill $\overline{F_k} \circ g^{-1} \in AC([g(a), g(b)])$ and $\left(\overline{F_k} \circ g^{-1}\right)' \circ g \in L_\infty([a,b])$. Then*

(i)

$$\left| \int_a^b f(x)\,dg(x) - \left\{ \sum_{i=0}^{n} \frac{1}{\Gamma(i\alpha+2)} \left[\left(D^{i\alpha}_{a+;g} f \right)(a)\,(g(t) - g(a))^{i\alpha+1} \right. \right. \right.$$

$$\left. \left. \left. + \left(D^{i\alpha}_{b-;g} f \right)(b)\,(g(b) - g(t))^{i\alpha+1} \right] \right\} \right| \leq$$

$$\frac{\max \left\{ \left\| D^{(n+1)\alpha}_{a+;g} f \right\|_{\infty,[a,b]}, \left\| D^{(n+1)\alpha}_{b-;g} f \right\|_{\infty,[a,b]} \right\}}{\Gamma((n+1)\alpha+2)}$$

$$\left[(g(t)-g(a))^{(n+1)\alpha+1}+(g(b)-g(t))^{(n+1)\alpha+1}\right], \tag{50}$$

$\forall\, t \in [a,b]$,

(ii) at $g(t)=\frac{g(a)+g(b)}{2}$*, the right hand side of (50) is minimized, and we have:*

$$\left|\int_a^b f(x)\,dg(x)-\left\{\sum_{i=0}^{n}\frac{1}{\Gamma(i\alpha+2)}\frac{(g(b)-g(a))^{i\alpha+1}}{2^{i\alpha+1}}\right.\right.$$

$$\left.\left.\left[\left(D_{a+;g}^{i\alpha}f\right)(a)+\left(D_{b-;g}^{i\alpha}f\right)(b)\right]\right\}\right|\leq$$

$$\frac{\max\left\{\left\|D_{a+;g}^{(n+1)\alpha}f\right\|_{\infty,[a,b]},\left\|D_{b-;g}^{(n+1)\alpha}f\right\|_{\infty,[a,b]}\right\}}{\Gamma((n+1)\alpha+2)}\frac{(g(b)-g(a))^{(n+1)\alpha+1}}{2^{(n+1)\alpha}}, \tag{51}$$

(iii) assuming $\left(D_{a+;g}^{i\alpha}f\right)(a)=\left(D_{b-;g}^{i\alpha}f\right)(b)=0$*, for* $i=0,1,...,n$*, we obtain*

$$\left|\int_a^b f(x)\,dg(x)\right|\leq$$

$$\frac{\max\left\{\left\|D_{a+;g}^{(n+1)\alpha}f\right\|_{\infty,[a,b]},\left\|D_{b-;g}^{(n+1)\alpha}f\right\|_{\infty,[a,b]}\right\}}{\Gamma((n+1)\alpha+2)}\frac{(g(b)-g(a))^{(n+1)\alpha+1}}{2^{(n+1)\alpha}}, \tag{52}$$

which is a sharp inequality,

(iv) more generally, for $j=0,1,2,...,N\in\mathbb{N}$*, it holds*

$$\left|\int_a^b f(x)\,dg(x)-\left\{\sum_{i=0}^{n}\frac{1}{\Gamma(i\alpha+2)}\left(\frac{g(b)-g(a)}{N}\right)^{i\alpha+1}\right.\right.$$

$$\left.\left.\left[\left(D_{a+;g}^{i\alpha}f\right)(a)\,j^{i\alpha+1}+\left(D_{b-;g}^{i\alpha}f\right)(b)\,(N-j)^{i\alpha+1}\right]\right\}\right|\leq$$

$$\frac{\max\left\{\left\|D_{a+;g}^{(n+1)\alpha}f\right\|_{\infty,[a,b]},\left\|D_{b-;g}^{(n+1)\alpha}f\right\|_{\infty,[a,b]}\right\}}{\Gamma((n+1)\alpha+2)}$$

$$\left(\frac{g(b)-g(a)}{N}\right)^{(n+1)\alpha+1}\left[j^{(n+1)\alpha+1}+(N-j)^{(n+1)\alpha+1}\right], \tag{53}$$

(v) if $\left(D_{a+;g}^{i\alpha}f\right)(a)=\left(D_{b-;g}^{i\alpha}f\right)(b)=0$*, for* $i=1,...,n$*, from (53) we obtain:*

$$\left|\int_a^b f(x)\,dg(x)-\left(\frac{g(b)-g(a)}{N}\right)[jf(a)+(N-j)f(b)]\right|\leq$$

$$\frac{\max\left\{\left\|D_{a+;g}^{(n+1)\alpha}f\right\|_{\infty,[a,b]},\left\|D_{b-;g}^{(n+1)\alpha}f\right\|_{\infty,[a,b]}\right\}}{\Gamma((n+1)\alpha+2)}$$

$$\left(\frac{g(b)-g(a)}{N}\right)^{(n+1)\alpha+1}\left[j^{(n+1)\alpha+1}+(N-j)^{(n+1)\alpha+1}\right], \tag{54}$$

for $j=0,1,2,...,N$*,*

(vi) when $N=2$*,* $j=1$*, (54) becomes*

$$\left|\int_a^b f(x)\,dg(x)-\left(\frac{g(b)-g(a)}{2}\right)(f(a)+f(b))\right|\leq$$

$$\frac{\max\left\{\left\|D_{a+;g}^{(n+1)\alpha}f\right\|_{\infty,[a,b]},\left\|D_{b-;g}^{(n+1)\alpha}f\right\|_{\infty,[a,b]}\right\}}{\Gamma\left((n+1)\alpha+2\right)}\frac{\left(g\left(b\right)-g\left(a\right)\right)^{(n+1)\alpha+1}}{2^{(n+1)\alpha}}. \tag{55}$$

Proof. We have by (19) that

$$f\left(x\right)=\sum_{i=0}^{n}\frac{\left(g\left(x\right)-g\left(a\right)\right)^{i\alpha}}{\Gamma\left(i\alpha+1\right)}\left(D_{a+;g}^{i\alpha}f\right)\left(a\right)+$$

$$\frac{1}{\Gamma\left((n+1)\alpha\right)}\int_{a}^{x}\left(g\left(x\right)-g\left(t\right)\right)^{(n+1)\alpha-1}g'\left(t\right)\left(D_{a+;g}^{(n+1)\alpha}f\right)\left(t\right)dt, \tag{56}$$

$\forall\, x\in\left[a,b\right].$

Also by (16) we find

$$f\left(x\right)=\sum_{i=0}^{n}\frac{\left(g\left(b\right)-g\left(x\right)\right)^{i\alpha}}{\Gamma\left(i\alpha+1\right)}\left(D_{b-;g}^{i\alpha}f\right)\left(b\right)+$$

$$\frac{1}{\Gamma\left((n+1)\alpha\right)}\int_{x}^{b}\left(g\left(t\right)-g\left(x\right)\right)^{(n+1)\alpha-1}g'\left(t\right)\left(D_{b-;g}^{(n+1)\alpha}f\right)\left(t\right)dt, \tag{57}$$

$\forall\, x\in\left[a,b\right].$

Clearly here it is $D_{a+;g}^{(n+1)\alpha}f,\ D_{b-;g}^{(n+1)\alpha}f\in C\left(\left[a,b\right]\right).$

By (56) we derive (by [4], p. 107)

$$\left|f\left(x\right)-\sum_{i=0}^{n}\frac{\left(g\left(x\right)-g\left(a\right)\right)^{i\alpha}}{\Gamma\left(i\alpha+1\right)}\left(D_{a+;g}^{i\alpha}f\right)\left(a\right)\right|\leq$$

$$\left\|D_{a+;g}^{(n+1)\alpha}f\right\|_{\infty,[a,b]}\frac{\left(g\left(x\right)-g\left(a\right)\right)^{(n+1)\alpha}}{\Gamma\left((n+1)\alpha+1\right)}, \tag{58}$$

and by (57) we obtain

$$\left|f\left(x\right)-\sum_{i=0}^{n}\frac{\left(g\left(b\right)-g\left(x\right)\right)^{i\alpha}}{\Gamma\left(i\alpha+1\right)}\left(D_{b-;g}^{i\alpha}f\right)\left(b\right)\right|\leq$$

$$\left\|D_{b-;g}^{(n+1)\alpha}f\right\|_{\infty,[a,b]}\frac{\left(g\left(b\right)-g\left(x\right)\right)^{(n+1)\alpha}}{\Gamma\left((n+1)\alpha+1\right)}, \tag{59}$$

$\forall\, x\in\left[a,b\right].$

Call

$$\gamma_1:=\frac{\left\|D_{a+;g}^{(n+1)\alpha}f\right\|_{\infty,[a,b]}}{\Gamma\left((n+1)\alpha+1\right)}, \tag{60}$$

and

$$\gamma_2:=\frac{\left\|D_{b-;g}^{(n+1)\alpha}f\right\|_{\infty,[a,b]}}{\Gamma\left((n+1)\alpha+1\right)}. \tag{61}$$

Set

$$\gamma:=\max\left\{\gamma_1,\gamma_2\right\}. \tag{62}$$

That is

$$\left|f\left(x\right)-\sum_{i=0}^{n}\frac{\left(g\left(x\right)-g\left(a\right)\right)^{i\alpha}}{\Gamma\left(i\alpha+1\right)}\left(D_{a+;g}^{i\alpha}f\right)\left(a\right)\right|\leq\gamma\left(g\left(x\right)-g\left(a\right)\right)^{(n+1)\alpha}, \tag{63}$$

and

$$\left|f(x)-\sum_{i=0}^{n}\frac{(g(b)-g(x))^{i\alpha}}{\Gamma(i\alpha+1)}\left(D_{b-;g}^{i\alpha}f\right)(b)\right|\leq\gamma(g(b)-g(x))^{(n+1)\alpha},\tag{64}$$

$\forall\, x\in[a,b]$.

Equivalently, we have

$$\sum_{i=0}^{n}\frac{(g(x)-g(a))^{i\alpha}}{\Gamma(i\alpha+1)}\left(D_{a+;g}^{i\alpha}f\right)(a)-\gamma(g(x)-g(a))^{(n+1)\alpha}\leq f(x)\leq$$

$$\sum_{i=0}^{n}\frac{(g(x)-g(a))^{i\alpha}}{\Gamma(i\alpha+1)}\left(D_{a+;g}^{i\alpha}f\right)(a)+\gamma(g(x)-g(a))^{(n+1)\alpha},\tag{65}$$

and

$$\sum_{i=0}^{n}\frac{(g(b)-g(x))^{i\alpha}}{\Gamma(i\alpha+1)}\left(D_{b-;g}^{i\alpha}f\right)(b)-\gamma(g(b)-g(x))^{(n+1)\alpha}\leq f(x)\leq$$

$$\sum_{i=0}^{n}\frac{(g(b)-g(x))^{i\alpha}}{\Gamma(i\alpha+1)}\left(D_{b-;g}^{i\alpha}f\right)(b)+\gamma(g(b)-g(x))^{(n+1)\alpha},\tag{66}$$

$\forall\, x\in[a,b]$.

Let any $t\in[a,b]$, then by integration against g over $[a,t]$ and $[t,b]$, respectively, we obtain

$$\sum_{i=0}^{n}\left(D_{a+;g}^{i\alpha}f\right)(a)\frac{(g(t)-g(a))^{i\alpha+1}}{\Gamma(i\alpha+2)}-\frac{\gamma}{((n+1)\alpha+1)}(g(t)-g(a))^{(n+1)\alpha+1}$$

$$\leq\int_{a}^{t}f(x)\,dg(x)\leq$$

$$\sum_{i=0}^{n}\left(D_{a+;g}^{i\alpha}f\right)(a)\frac{(g(t)-g(a))^{i\alpha+1}}{\Gamma(i\alpha+2)}+\frac{\gamma}{((n+1)\alpha+1)}(g(t)-g(a))^{(n+1)\alpha+1},\tag{67}$$

and

$$\sum_{i=0}^{n}\frac{(g(b)-g(t))^{i\alpha+1}}{\Gamma(i\alpha+2)}\left(D_{b-;g}^{i\alpha}f\right)(b)-\frac{\gamma}{((n+1)\alpha+1)}(g(b)-g(t))^{(n+1)\alpha+1}$$

$$\leq\int_{t}^{b}f(x)\,dg(x)\leq$$

$$\sum_{i=0}^{n}\frac{(g(b)-g(t))^{i\alpha+1}}{\Gamma(i\alpha+2)}\left(D_{b-;g}^{i\alpha}f\right)(b)+\frac{\gamma}{((n+1)\alpha+1)}(g(b)-g(t))^{(n+1)\alpha+1}.\tag{68}$$

Adding (67) and (68), we obtain

$$\left\{\sum_{i=0}^{n}\frac{1}{\Gamma(i\alpha+2)}\left[\left(D_{a+;g}^{i\alpha}f\right)(a)(g(t)-g(a))^{i\alpha+1}+\left(D_{b-;g}^{i\alpha}f\right)(b)(g(b)-g(t))^{i\alpha+1}\right]\right\}$$

$$-\frac{\gamma}{((n+1)\alpha+1)}\left[(g(t)-g(a))^{(n+1)\alpha+1}+(g(b)-g(t))^{(n+1)\alpha+1}\right]$$

$$\leq\int_{a}^{b}f(x)\,dg(x)\leq$$

$$\left\{\sum_{i=0}^{n}\frac{1}{\Gamma(i\alpha+2)}\left[\left(D_{a+;g}^{i\alpha}f\right)(a)(g(t)-g(a))^{i\alpha+1}+\left(D_{b-;g}^{i\alpha}f\right)(b)(g(b)-g(t))^{i\alpha+1}\right]\right\}$$

$$+\frac{\gamma}{((n+1)\alpha+1)}\left[(g(t)-g(a))^{(n+1)\alpha+1}+(g(b)-g(t))^{(n+1)\alpha+1}\right],\tag{69}$$

$\forall\, t \in [a,b]$.

Consequently, we derive:

$$\left| \int_a^b f(x)\, dg(x) - \left\{ \sum_{i=0}^{n} \frac{1}{\Gamma(i\alpha+2)} \left[\left(D_{a+;g}^{i\alpha} f \right)(a) \left(g(t) - g(a) \right)^{i\alpha+1} \right.\right.\right.$$

$$\left.\left.\left. + \left(D_{b-;g}^{i\alpha} f \right)(b) \left(g(b) - g(t) \right)^{i\alpha+1} \right] \right\} \right| \leq$$

$$\frac{\gamma}{((n+1)\alpha+1)} \left[\left(g(t) - g(a) \right)^{(n+1)\alpha+1} + \left(g(b) - g(t) \right)^{(n+1)\alpha+1} \right], \tag{70}$$

$\forall\, t \in [a,b]$.

Let us consider

$$\phi(z) := (z - g(a))^{(n+1)\alpha+1} + (g(b) - z)^{(n+1)\alpha+1},$$

$\forall\, z \in [g(a), g(b)]$.

That is

$$\phi(g(t)) = (g(t) - g(a))^{(n+1)\alpha+1} + (g(b) - g(t))^{(n+1)\alpha+1},$$

$\forall\, t \in [a,b]$.

We have that

$$\phi'(z) = ((n+1)\alpha+1) \left[(z - g(a))^{(n+1)\alpha} - (g(b) - z)^{(n+1)\alpha} \right] = 0,$$

giving $(z - g(a))^{(n+1)\alpha} = (g(b) - z)^{(n+1)\alpha}$ and $z - g(a) = g(b) - z$, that is $z = \frac{g(a)+g(b)}{2}$ the only critical number of ϕ. We have that

$$\phi(g(a)) = \phi(g(b)) = (g(b) - g(a))^{(n+1)\alpha+1},$$

and

$$\phi\left(\frac{g(a)+g(b)}{2} \right) = \frac{(g(b) - g(a))^{(n+1)\alpha+1}}{2^{(n+1)\alpha}},$$

which is the minimum of ϕ over $[g(a), g(b)]$.

Consequently, the right hand side of (70) is minimized when $g(t) = \frac{g(a)+g(b)}{2}$, for some $t \in [a,b]$, with value $\frac{\gamma}{((n+1)\alpha+1)} \frac{(g(b)-g(a))^{(n+1)\alpha+1}}{2^{(n+1)\alpha}}$.

Assuming $\left(D_{a+;g}^{i\alpha} f \right)(a) = \left(D_{b-;g}^{i\alpha} f \right)(b) = 0$, $i = 0, 1, \ldots, n$, then we obtain that

$$\left| \int_a^b f(x)\, dg(x) \right| \leq \frac{\gamma}{((n+1)\alpha+1)} \frac{(g(b) - g(a))^{(n+1)\alpha+1}}{2^{(n+1)\alpha}}, \tag{71}$$

which is a sharp inequality.

When $g(t) = \frac{g(a)+g(b)}{2}$, then (70) becomes

$$\left| \int_a^b f(x)\, dg(x) - \left\{ \sum_{i=0}^{n} \frac{1}{\Gamma(i\alpha+2)} \frac{(g(b) - g(a))^{i\alpha+1}}{2^{i\alpha+1}} \right.\right.$$

$$\left.\left. \left[\left(D_{a+;g}^{i\alpha} f \right)(a) + \left(D_{b-;g}^{i\alpha} \right)(b) \right] \right\} \right| \leq$$

$$\frac{\gamma}{((n+1)\alpha+1)} \frac{(g(b) - g(a))^{(n+1)\alpha+1}}{2^{(n+1)\alpha}}. \tag{72}$$

Next let $N \in \mathbb{N}$, $j = 0, 1, 2, ..., N$ and $g(t_j) = g(a) + j\left(\frac{g(b)-g(a)}{N}\right)$, that is $g(t_0) = g(a)$, $g(t_1) = g(a) + \frac{(g(b)-g(a))}{N}, ..., g(t_N) = g(b)$.

Hence it holds

$$g(t_j) - g(a) = j\left(\frac{g(b)-g(a)}{N}\right),\ g(b) - g(t_j) = (N-j)\left(\frac{g(b)-g(a)}{N}\right), \tag{73}$$

$j = 0, 1, 2, ..., N$.

We notice

$$(g(t_j) - g(a))^{(n+1)\alpha+1} + (g(b) - g(t_j))^{(n+1)\alpha+1} =$$

$$\left(\frac{g(b)-g(a)}{N}\right)^{(n+1)\alpha+1}\left[j^{(n+1)\alpha+1} + (N-j)^{(n+1)\alpha+1}\right], \tag{74}$$

$j = 0, 1, 2, ..., N$,

and (for $i = 0, 1, ..., n$)

$$\left[\left(D^{i\alpha}_{a+;g}f\right)(a)\,(g(t_j) - g(a))^{i\alpha+1} + \left(D^{i\alpha}_{b-;g}f\right)(b)\,(g(b) - g(t_j))^{i\alpha+1}\right] =$$

$$\left(\frac{g(b)-g(a)}{N}\right)^{i\alpha+1}\left[\left(D^{i\alpha}_{a+;g}f\right)(a)\,j^{i\alpha+1} + \left(D^{i\alpha}_{b-;g}\right)f(b)\,(N-j)^{i\alpha+1}\right], \tag{75}$$

for $j = 0, 1, 2, ..., N$.

By (70) we have

$$\left|\int_a^b f(x)\,dg(x) - \left\{\sum_{i=0}^{n}\frac{1}{\Gamma(i\alpha+2)}\left(\frac{g(b)-g(a)}{N}\right)^{i\alpha+1}\right.\right.$$

$$\left.\left.\left[\left(D^{i\alpha}_{a+;g}f\right)(a)\,j^{i\alpha+1} + \left(D^{i\alpha}_{b-;g}f\right)(b)\,(N-j)^{i\alpha+1}\right]\right\}\right| \leq$$

$$\frac{\gamma}{((n+1)\alpha+1)}\left(\frac{g(b)-g(a)}{N}\right)^{(n+1)\alpha+1}\left[j^{(n+1)\alpha+1} + (N-j)^{(n+1)\alpha+1}\right], \tag{76}$$

$j = 0, 1, 2, ..., N$.

If $\left(D^{i\alpha}_{a+;g}f\right)(a) = \left(D^{i\alpha}_{b-;g}f\right)(b) = 0$, $i = 1, ..., n$, then (76) becomes

$$\left|\int_a^b f(x)\,dg(x) - \left(\frac{g(b)-g(a)}{N}\right)[jf(a) + (N-j)f(b)]\right| \leq$$

$$\frac{\gamma}{((n+1)\alpha+1)}\left(\frac{g(b)-g(a)}{N}\right)^{(n+1)\alpha+1}\left[j^{(n+1)\alpha+1} + (N-j)^{(n+1)\alpha+1}\right], \tag{77}$$

$j = 0, 1, 2, ..., N$.

When $N = 2$ and $j = 1$, then (77) becomes

$$\left|\int_a^b f(x)\,dg(x) - \left(\frac{g(b)-g(a)}{2}\right)(f(a) + f(b))\right| \leq$$

$$\frac{\gamma}{((n+1)\alpha+1)}\frac{2(g(b)-g(a))^{(n+1)\alpha+1}}{2^{(n+1)\alpha+1}} =$$

$$\frac{\gamma}{((n+1)\alpha+1)}\frac{(g(b)-g(a))^{(n+1)\alpha+1}}{2^{(n+1)\alpha}}. \tag{78}$$

We have proved theorem in all possible cases. □

We give L_1 variants of last theorems:

Theorem 8. *All as in Theorem 6 with $\alpha \geq 1$. If $\alpha = n \in \mathbb{N}$, we assume that $\left(f \circ g^{-1}\right)^{(n)} \circ g \in C([a,b])$. Then*
(i)

$$\left| \int_a^b f(x)\, dg(x) - \sum_{k=0}^{n-1} \frac{1}{(k+1)!} \left[\left(f \circ g^{-1}\right)^{(k)} (g(a)) (g(t) - g(a))^{k+1} \right.\right.$$
$$\left.\left. + (-1)^k \left(f \circ g^{-1}\right)^{(k)} (g(b)) (g(b) - g(t))^{k+1} \right] \right| \leq$$
$$\frac{\max\left\{ \left\| D_{a+;g}^{\alpha} f \right\|_{L_1([a,b],g)}, \left\| D_{b-;g}^{\alpha} f \right\|_{L_1([a,b],g)} \right\}}{\Gamma(\alpha+1)}$$
$$\left[(g(t) - g(a))^{\alpha} + (g(b) - g(t))^{\alpha} \right], \tag{79}$$

$\forall\, t \in [a,b]$,
(ii) at $g(t) = \frac{g(a)+g(b)}{2}$, the right hand side of (79) is minimized, and we find:

$$\left| \int_a^b f(x)\, dg(x) - \sum_{k=0}^{n-1} \frac{1}{(k+1)!} \frac{(g(b) - g(a))^{k+1}}{2^{k+1}} \right.$$
$$\left. \left[\left(f \circ g^{-1}\right)^{(k)} (g(a)) + (-1)^k \left(f \circ g^{-1}\right)^{(k)} (g(b)) \right] \right| \leq$$
$$\frac{\max\left\{ \left\| D_{a+;g}^{\alpha} f \right\|_{L_1([a,b],g)}, \left\| D_{b-;g}^{\alpha} f \right\|_{L_1([a,b],g)} \right\}}{\Gamma(\alpha+1)} \frac{(g(b) - g(a))^{\alpha}}{2^{\alpha-1}}, \tag{80}$$

(iii) if $\left(f \circ g^{-1}\right)^{(k)} (g(a)) = \left(f \circ g^{-1}\right)^{(k)} (g(b)) = 0$, for $k = 0, 1, ..., n-1$, we obtain

$$\left| \int_a^b f(x)\, dg(x) \right| \leq$$
$$\frac{\max\left\{ \left\| D_{a+;g}^{\alpha} f \right\|_{L_1([a,b],g)}, \left\| D_{b-;g}^{\alpha} f \right\|_{L_1([a,b],g)} \right\}}{\Gamma(\alpha+1)} \frac{(g(b) - g(a))^{\alpha}}{2^{\alpha-1}}, \tag{81}$$

which is a sharp inequality,
(iv) more generally, for $j = 0, 1, 2, ..., N \in \mathbb{N}$, it holds that

$$\left| \int_a^b f(x)\, dg(x) - \sum_{k=0}^{n-1} \frac{1}{(k+1)!} \left(\frac{g(b) - g(a)}{N} \right)^{k+1} \right.$$
$$\left. \left[j^{k+1} \left(f \circ g^{-1}\right)^{(k)} (g(a)) + (-1)^k (N-j)^{k+1} \left(f \circ g^{-1}\right)^{(k)} (g(b)) \right] \right| \leq$$
$$\frac{\max\left\{ \left\| D_{a+;g}^{\alpha} f \right\|_{L_1([a,b],g)}, \left\| D_{b-;g}^{\alpha} f \right\|_{L_1([a,b],g)} \right\}}{\Gamma(\alpha+1)}$$
$$\left(\frac{g(b) - g(a)}{N} \right)^{\alpha} \left[j^{\alpha} + (N-j)^{\alpha} \right], \tag{82}$$

(v) if $\left(f \circ g^{-1}\right)^{(k)}(g(a)) = \left(f \circ g^{-1}\right)^{(k)}(g(b)) = 0$, for $k = 1, ..., n-1$, from (82) we obtain

$$\left|\int_a^b f(x)\,dg(x) - \left(\frac{g(b)-g(a)}{N}\right)[jf(a) + (N-j)f(b)]\right| \leq$$

$$\frac{\max\left\{\left\|D_{a+;g}^{\alpha} f\right\|_{L_1([a,b],g)}, \left\|D_{b-;g}^{\alpha} f\right\|_{L_1([a,b],g)}\right\}}{\Gamma(\alpha+1)}$$

$$\left(\frac{g(b)-g(a)}{N}\right)^{\alpha}\left[j^{\alpha} + (N-j)^{\alpha}\right], \tag{83}$$

$j = 0, 1, 2, ..., N$,

(vi) when $N = 2$, $j = 1$, (83) turns to

$$\left|\int_a^b f(x)\,dg(x) - \left(\frac{g(b)-g(a)}{2}\right)(f(a) + f(b))\right| \leq$$

$$\frac{\max\left\{\left\|D_{a+;g}^{\alpha} f\right\|_{L_1([a,b],g)}, \left\|D_{b-;g}^{\alpha} f\right\|_{L_1([a,b],g)}\right\}}{\Gamma(\alpha+1)} \frac{(g(b)-g(a))^{\alpha}}{2^{\alpha-1}}. \tag{84}$$

Proof. From (27) we have

$$\left|f(x) - \sum_{k=0}^{n-1} \frac{\left(f \circ g^{-1}\right)^{(k)}(g(a))}{k!}(g(x)-g(a))^k\right| \leq$$

$$\frac{1}{\Gamma(\alpha)}\int_a^x (g(x)-g(t))^{\alpha-1} g'(t)\left|\left(D_{a+;g}^{\alpha} f\right)(t)\right| dt \leq$$

$$\frac{(g(x)-g(a))^{\alpha-1}}{\Gamma(\alpha)}\int_a^x g'(t)\left|\left(D_{a+;g}^{\alpha} f\right)(t)\right| dt \leq \tag{85}$$

$$\frac{(g(x)-g(a))^{\alpha-1}}{\Gamma(\alpha)}\int_a^b g'(t)\left|\left(D_{a+;g}^{\alpha} f\right)(t)\right| dt =$$

$$\frac{(g(x)-g(a))^{\alpha-1}}{\Gamma(\alpha)}\int_a^b \left|\left(D_{a+;g}^{\alpha} f\right)(t)\right| dg(t) =$$

$$\frac{\left\|D_{a+;g}^{\alpha} f\right\|_{L_1([a,b],g)}}{\Gamma(\alpha)}(g(x)-g(a))^{\alpha-1},$$

$\forall\, x \in [a,b]$.

Similarly, from (28) we obtain

$$\left|f(x) - \sum_{k=0}^{n-1} \frac{\left(f \circ g^{-1}\right)^{(k)}(g(b))}{k!}(g(x)-g(b))^k\right| \leq$$

$$\frac{1}{\Gamma(\alpha)}\int_x^b (g(t)-g(x))^{\alpha-1} g'(t)\left|\left(D_{b-;g}^{\alpha} f\right)(t)\right| dt \leq$$

$$\frac{(g(b)-g(x))^{\alpha-1}}{\Gamma(\alpha)}\int_x^b \left|\left(D_{b-;g}^{\alpha} f\right)(t)\right| dg(t) \leq \tag{86}$$

$$\frac{\left\|D_{b-;g}^{\alpha}f\right\|_{L_1([a,b],g)}}{\Gamma(\alpha)}(g(b)-g(x))^{\alpha-1},$$

$\forall\, x \in [a,b]$.

Call

$$\delta := \max\left\{\left\|D_{a+;g}^{\alpha}f\right\|_{L_1([a,b],g)}, \left\|D_{b-;g}^{\alpha}f\right\|_{L_1([a,b],g)}\right\}. \tag{87}$$

We have proved that

$$\left|f(x)-\sum_{k=0}^{n-1}\frac{\left(f\circ g^{-1}\right)^{(k)}(g(a))}{k!}(g(x)-g(a))^{k}\right| \leq$$

$$\frac{\delta}{\Gamma(\alpha)}(g(x)-g(a))^{\alpha-1}, \tag{88}$$

and

$$\left|f(x)-\sum_{k=0}^{n-1}\frac{\left(f\circ g^{-1}\right)^{(k)}(g(b))}{k!}(g(x)-g(b))^{k}\right| \leq$$

$$\frac{\delta}{\Gamma(\alpha)}(g(b)-g(x))^{\alpha-1}, \tag{89}$$

$\forall\, x \in [a,b]$.

The rest of the proof is as in Theorem 6. □

It follows

Theorem 9. *All as in Theorem 7, with* $\frac{1}{n+1} \leq \alpha \leq 1$. *Call*

$$\rho := \max\left\{\left\|D_{a+;g}^{(n+1)\alpha}f\right\|_{L_1([a,b],g)}, \left\|D_{b-;g}^{(n+1)\alpha}f\right\|_{L_1([a,b],g)}\right\}. \tag{90}$$

Then

(i)

$$\left|\int_a^b f(x)\,dg(x) - \left\{\sum_{i=0}^{n}\frac{1}{\Gamma(i\alpha+2)}\left[\left(D_{a+;g}^{i\alpha}f\right)(a)(g(t)-g(a))^{i\alpha+1}\right.\right.\right.$$

$$\left.\left.\left.+\left(D_{b-;g}^{i\alpha}f\right)(b)(g(b)-g(t))^{i\alpha+1}\right]\right\}\right| \leq$$

$$\frac{\rho}{\Gamma((n+1)\alpha+1)}\left[(g(t)-g(a))^{(n+1)\alpha}+(g(b)-g(t))^{(n+1)\alpha}\right], \tag{91}$$

$\forall\, t \in [a,b]$,

(ii) at $g(t) = \frac{g(a)+g(b)}{2}$, *the right hand side of (91) is minimized, and we find:*

$$\left|\int_a^b f(x)\,dg(x) - \left\{\sum_{i=0}^{n}\frac{1}{\Gamma(i\alpha+2)}\frac{(g(b)-g(a))^{i\alpha+1}}{2^{i\alpha+1}}\right.\right.$$

$$\left.\left.\left[\left(D_{a+;g}^{i\alpha}f\right)(a)+\left(D_{b-;g}^{i\alpha}f\right)(b)\right]\right\}\right| \leq$$

$$\frac{\rho}{\Gamma((n+1)\alpha+1)}\frac{(g(b)-g(a))^{(n+1)\alpha}}{2^{(n+1)\alpha-1}}, \tag{92}$$

(iii) assuming $\left(D_{a+;g}^{i\alpha}f\right)(a)=\left(D_{b-;g}^{i\alpha}f\right)(b)=0$, $i=0,1,...,n$, *we obtain*

$$\left|\int_a^b f(x)\,dg(x)\right|\leq$$

$$\frac{\rho}{\Gamma((n+1)\alpha+1)}\frac{(g(b)-g(a))^{(n+1)\alpha}}{2^{(n+1)\alpha-1}}, \tag{93}$$

which is a sharp inequality,

(iv) more generally, for $j=0,1,2,...,N\in\mathbb{N}$, *it holds that*

$$\left|\int_a^b f(x)\,dg(x)-\left\{\sum_{i=0}^{n}\frac{1}{\Gamma(i\alpha+2)}\left(\frac{g(b)-g(a)}{N}\right)^{i\alpha+1}\right.\right.$$

$$\left.\left.\left[\left(D_{a+;g}^{i\alpha}f\right)(a)\,j^{i\alpha+1}+\left(D_{b-;g}^{i\alpha}f\right)(b)\,(N-j)^{i\alpha+1}\right]\right\}\right|\leq$$

$$\frac{\rho}{\Gamma((n+1)\alpha+1)}\left(\frac{g(b)-g(a)}{N}\right)^{(n+1)\alpha}\left[j^{(n+1)\alpha}+(N-j)^{(n+1)\alpha}\right], \tag{94}$$

(v) if $\left(D_{a+;g}^{i\alpha}f\right)(a)=\left(D_{b-;g}^{i\alpha}f\right)(b)=0$, $i=1,...,n$, *from (94) we find:*

$$\left|\int_a^b f(x)\,dg(x)-\left(\frac{g(b)-g(a)}{N}\right)[jf(a)+(N-j)f(b)]\right|\leq$$

$$\frac{\rho}{\Gamma((n+1)\alpha+1)}\left(\frac{g(b)-g(a)}{N}\right)^{(n+1)\alpha}\left[j^{(n+1)\alpha}+(N-j)^{(n+1)\alpha}\right], \tag{95}$$

for $j=0,1,2,...,N$,

(vi) when $N=2$ *and* $j=1$, *(95) becomes*

$$\left|\int_a^b f(x)\,dg(x)-\left(\frac{g(b)-g(a)}{2}\right)(f(a)+f(b))\right|\leq$$

$$\frac{\rho}{\Gamma((n+1)\alpha+1)}\frac{(g(b)-g(a))^{(n+1)\alpha}}{2^{(n+1)\alpha-1}}. \tag{96}$$

Proof. By (56) we obtain

$$\left|f(x)-\sum_{i=0}^{n}\frac{(g(x)-g(a))^{i\alpha}}{\Gamma(i\alpha+1)}\left(D_{a+;g}^{i\alpha}f\right)(a)\right|\leq$$

$$\frac{1}{\Gamma((n+1)\alpha)}\int_a^x (g(x)-g(t))^{(n+1)\alpha-1}g'(t)\left|\left(D_{a+;g}^{(n+1)\alpha}f\right)(t)\right|dt\leq$$

$$\frac{(g(x)-g(a))^{(n+1)\alpha-1}}{\Gamma((n+1)\alpha)}\int_a^x g'(t)\left|\left(D_{a+;g}^{(n+1)\alpha}f\right)(t)\right|dt\leq \tag{97}$$

$$\frac{(g(x)-g(a))^{(n+1)\alpha-1}}{\Gamma((n+1)\alpha)}\int_a^b g'(t)\left|\left(D_{a+;g}^{(n+1)\alpha}f\right)(t)\right|dt=$$

$$\frac{(g(x)-g(a))^{(n+1)\alpha-1}}{\Gamma((n+1)\alpha)}\int_a^b \left|\left(D_{a+;g}^{(n+1)\alpha}f\right)(t)\right|dg(t)=$$

$$\frac{\left\| D_{a+;g}^{(n+1)\alpha} f \right\|_{L_1([a,b],g)}}{\Gamma((n+1)\alpha)} (g(x) - g(a))^{(n+1)\alpha - 1},$$

$\forall\, x \in [a,b]$.

Similarly, from (57) we derive

$$\begin{aligned}
&\left| f(x) - \sum_{i=0}^{n} \frac{(g(b) - g(x))^{i\alpha}}{\Gamma(i\alpha + 1)} \left(D_{b-;g}^{i\alpha} f \right)(b) \right| \leq \\
&\frac{1}{\Gamma((n+1)\alpha)} \int_x^b (g(t) - g(x))^{(n+1)\alpha - 1} g'(t) \left| \left(D_{b-;g}^{(n+1)\alpha} f \right)(t) \right| dt \leq \\
&\frac{(g(b) - g(x))^{(n+1)\alpha - 1}}{\Gamma((n+1)\alpha)} \int_x^b \left| \left(D_{b-;g}^{(n+1)\alpha} f \right)(t) \right| dg(t) \leq \\
&\frac{\left\| D_{b-;g}^{(n+1)\alpha} f \right\|_{L_1([a,b],g)}}{\Gamma((n+1)\alpha)} (g(b) - g(x))^{(n+1)\alpha - 1},
\end{aligned} \tag{98}$$

$\forall\, x \in [a,b]$.

We have proved that

$$\left| f(x) - \sum_{i=0}^{n} \frac{(g(x) - g(a))^{i\alpha}}{\Gamma(i\alpha + 1)} \left(D_{a+;g}^{i\alpha} f \right)(a) \right| \leq \frac{\rho}{\Gamma((n+1)\alpha)} (g(x) - g(a))^{(n+1)\alpha - 1}, \tag{99}$$

and

$$\left| f(x) - \sum_{i=0}^{n} \frac{(g(b) - g(x))^{i\alpha}}{\Gamma(i\alpha + 1)} \left(D_{b-;g}^{i\alpha} f \right)(b) \right| \leq \frac{\rho}{\Gamma((n+1)\alpha)} (g(b) - g(x))^{(n+1)\alpha - 1}, \tag{100}$$

$\forall\, x \in [a,b]$.

The rest of the proof is as in Theorem 7. □

Next follow L_p variants of Theorems 6 and 7.

Theorem 10. *All as in Theorem 6 with $\alpha \geq 1$, and $p, q > 1 : \frac{1}{p} + \frac{1}{q} = 1$. If $\alpha = n \in \mathbb{N}$, we assume that $\left(f \circ g^{-1}\right)^{(n)} \circ g \in C([a,b])$. Set*

$$\mu := \max \left\{ \left\| D_{a+;g}^{\alpha} f \right\|_{L_q([a,b],g)}, \left\| D_{b-;g}^{\alpha} f \right\|_{L_q([a,b],g)} \right\}. \tag{101}$$

Then

(i)

$$\begin{aligned}
&\left| \int_a^b f(x)\, dg(x) - \sum_{k=0}^{n-1} \frac{1}{(k+1)!} \left[\left(f \circ g^{-1}\right)^{(k)} (g(a)) (g(t) - g(a))^{k+1} \right.\right. \\
&\left.\left. + (-1)^k \left(f \circ g^{-1}\right)^{(k)} (g(b)) (g(b) - g(t))^{k+1} \right] \right| \leq \\
&\frac{\mu}{\Gamma(\alpha) \left(\alpha + \frac{1}{p}\right) (p(\alpha - 1) + 1)^{\frac{1}{p}}}
\end{aligned}$$

$$\left[(g(t) - g(a))^{\alpha+\frac{1}{p}} + (g(b) - g(t))^{\alpha+\frac{1}{p}} \right], \tag{102}$$

$\forall t \in [a, b]$,

(ii) at $g(t) = \frac{g(a)+g(b)}{2}$, *the right hand side of (102) is minimized, and we have:*

$$\left| \int_a^b f(x)\, dg(x) - \sum_{k=0}^{n-1} \frac{1}{(k+1)!} \frac{(g(b) - g(a))^{k+1}}{2^{k+1}} \right.$$

$$\left. \left[\left(f \circ g^{-1}\right)^{(k)} (g(a)) + (-1)^k \left(f \circ g^{-1}\right)^{(k)} (g(b)) \right] \right| \leq$$

$$\frac{\mu}{\Gamma(\alpha)\left(\alpha + \frac{1}{p}\right)(p(\alpha-1)+1)^{\frac{1}{p}}} \frac{(g(b) - g(a))^{\alpha+\frac{1}{p}}}{2^{\alpha-\frac{1}{q}}}, \tag{103}$$

(iii) if $\left(f \circ g^{-1}\right)^{(k)} (g(a)) = \left(f \circ g^{-1}\right)^{(k)} (g(b)) = 0$, *for* $k = 0, 1, ..., n-1$, *we obtain*

$$\left| \int_a^b f(x)\, dg(x) \right| \leq$$

$$\frac{\mu}{\Gamma(\alpha)\left(\alpha + \frac{1}{p}\right)(p(\alpha-1)+1)^{\frac{1}{p}}} \frac{(g(b) - g(a))^{\alpha+\frac{1}{p}}}{2^{\alpha-\frac{1}{q}}}, \tag{104}$$

which is a sharp inequality,

(iv) more generally, for $j = 0, 1, 2, ..., N \in \mathbb{N}$, *it holds*

$$\left| \int_a^b f(x)\, dg(x) - \sum_{k=0}^{n-1} \frac{1}{(k+1)!} \left(\frac{g(b) - g(a)}{N} \right)^{k+1} \right.$$

$$\left. \left[j^{k+1} \left(f \circ g^{-1}\right)^{(k)} (g(a)) + (-1)^k (N-j)^{k+1} \left(f \circ g^{-1}\right)^{(k)} (g(b)) \right] \right| \leq$$

$$\frac{\mu}{\Gamma(\alpha)\left(\alpha + \frac{1}{p}\right)(p(\alpha-1)+1)^{\frac{1}{p}}} \left(\frac{g(b) - g(a)}{N} \right)^{\alpha+\frac{1}{p}} \left[j^{\alpha+\frac{1}{p}} + (N-j)^{\alpha+\frac{1}{p}} \right], \tag{105}$$

(v) if $\left(f \circ g^{-1}\right)^{(k)} (g(a)) = \left(f \circ g^{-1}\right)^{(k)} (g(b)) = 0$, *for* $k = 1, ..., n-1$, *from (105) we obtain*

$$\left| \int_a^b f(x)\, dg(x) - \left(\frac{g(b) - g(a)}{N} \right) [jf(a) + (N-j) f(b)] \right| \leq$$

$$\frac{\mu}{\Gamma(\alpha)\left(\alpha + \frac{1}{p}\right)(p(\alpha-1)+1)^{\frac{1}{p}}} \left(\frac{g(b) - g(a)}{N} \right)^{\alpha+\frac{1}{p}} \left[j^{\alpha+\frac{1}{p}} + (N-j)^{\alpha+\frac{1}{p}} \right], \tag{106}$$

$j = 0, 1, 2, ..., N$,

(vi) when $N = 2$, $j = 1$, *(106) turns to*

$$\left| \int_a^b f(x)\, dg(x) - \left(\frac{g(b) - g(a)}{2} \right) (f(a) + f(b)) \right| \leq$$

$$\frac{\mu}{\Gamma(\alpha)\left(\alpha + \frac{1}{p}\right)(p(\alpha-1)+1)^{\frac{1}{p}}} \frac{(g(b) - g(a))^{\alpha+\frac{1}{p}}}{2^{\alpha-\frac{1}{q}}}. \tag{107}$$

Proof. From (27) we find

$$\left| f(x) - \sum_{k=0}^{n-1} \frac{(f \circ g^{-1})^{(k)}(g(a))}{k!} (g(x) - g(a))^k \right| \leq$$

$$\frac{1}{\Gamma(\alpha)} \int_a^x (g(x) - g(t))^{\alpha-1} g'(t) \left| \left(D_{a+;g}^{\alpha} f \right)(t) \right| dt =$$

(by [5], p. 439)

$$\frac{1}{\Gamma(\alpha)} \int_a^x (g(x) - g(t))^{\alpha-1} \left| \left(D_{a+;g}^{\alpha} f \right)(t) \right| dg(t) \leq \tag{108}$$

(by [6])

$$\frac{1}{\Gamma(\alpha)} \left(\int_a^x (g(x) - g(t))^{p(\alpha-1)} dg(t) \right)^{\frac{1}{p}} \left(\int_a^x \left| \left(D_{a+;g}^{\alpha} f \right)(t) \right|^q dg(t) \right)^{\frac{1}{q}} \leq$$

$$\frac{1}{\Gamma(\alpha)} \frac{(g(x) - g(a))^{\alpha - \frac{1}{q}}}{(p(\alpha-1)+1)^{\frac{1}{p}}} \left\| D_{a+;g}^{\alpha} f \right\|_{L_q([a,b],g)}.$$

That is

$$\left| f(x) - \sum_{k=0}^{n-1} \frac{(f \circ g^{-1})^{(k)}(g(a))}{k!} (g(x) - g(a))^k \right| \leq$$

$$\frac{\left\| D_{a+;g}^{\alpha} f \right\|_{L_q([a,b],g)}}{\Gamma(\alpha)(p(\alpha-1)+1)^{\frac{1}{p}}} (g(x) - g(a))^{\alpha - \frac{1}{q}}, \tag{109}$$

$\forall\, x \in [a,b]$.

Similarly, from (28) we obtain

$$\left| f(x) - \sum_{k=0}^{n-1} \frac{(f \circ g^{-1})^{(k)}(g(b))}{k!} (g(x) - g(b))^k \right| \leq$$

$$\frac{1}{\Gamma(\alpha)} \int_x^b (g(t) - g(x))^{\alpha-1} g'(t) \left| \left(D_{b-;g}^{\alpha} f \right)(t) \right| dt =$$

(by [5], p. 439)

$$\frac{1}{\Gamma(\alpha)} \int_x^b (g(t) - g(x))^{\alpha-1} \left| \left(D_{b-;g}^{\alpha} f \right)(t) \right| dg(t) \leq$$

(by [6])

$$\frac{1}{\Gamma(\alpha)} \left(\int_x^b (g(t) - g(x))^{p(\alpha-1)} dg(t) \right)^{\frac{1}{p}} \left(\int_x^b \left| \left(D_{b-;g}^{\alpha} f \right)(t) \right|^q dg(t) \right)^{\frac{1}{q}} \leq \tag{110}$$

$$\frac{1}{\Gamma(\alpha)} \frac{(g(b) - g(x))^{\alpha - \frac{1}{q}}}{(p(\alpha-1)+1)^{\frac{1}{p}}} \left\| D_{b-;g}^{\alpha} f \right\|_{L_q([a,b],g)}.$$

That is

$$\left| f(x) - \sum_{k=0}^{n-1} \frac{(f \circ g^{-1})^{(k)}(g(b))}{k!} (g(x) - g(b))^k \right| \leq$$

$$\frac{\left\| D_{b-;g}^{\alpha} f \right\|_{L_q([a,b],g)}}{\Gamma(\alpha)(p(\alpha-1)+1)^{\frac{1}{p}}} (g(b) - g(x))^{\alpha - \frac{1}{q}}, \tag{111}$$

$\forall\, x \in [a,b]$.

We have proved that

$$\left| f(x) - \sum_{k=0}^{n-1} \frac{\left(f \circ g^{-1}\right)^{(k)}(g(a))}{k!} (g(x) - g(a))^k \right| \leq$$

$$\frac{\mu}{\Gamma(\alpha)(p(\alpha-1)+1)^{\frac{1}{p}}} (g(x) - g(a))^{\alpha - \frac{1}{q}}, \tag{112}$$

and

$$\left| f(x) - \sum_{k=0}^{n-1} \frac{\left(f \circ g^{-1}\right)^{(k)}(g(b))}{k!} (g(x) - g(b))^k \right| \leq$$

$$\frac{\mu}{\Gamma(\alpha)(p(\alpha-1)+1)^{\frac{1}{p}}} (g(b) - g(x))^{\alpha - \frac{1}{q}}, \tag{113}$$

$\forall\, x \in [a,b]$.

The rest of the proof is as in Theorem 6. □

We continue with

Theorem 11. *All as in Theorem 7, with $\frac{1}{n+1} \leq \alpha \leq 1$, and $p,q > 1 : \frac{1}{p} + \frac{1}{q} = 1$. Set*

$$\theta := \max\left\{ \left\| D_{a+;g}^{(n+1)\alpha} f \right\|_{L_q([a,b],g)}, \left\| D_{b-;g}^{(n+1)\alpha} f \right\|_{L_q([a,b],g)} \right\}. \tag{114}$$

Then

(i)

$$\left| \int_a^b f(x)\, dg(x) - \left\{ \sum_{i=0}^{n} \frac{1}{\Gamma(i\alpha+2)} \left[\left(D_{a+;g}^{i\alpha} f\right)(a)(g(t) - g(a))^{i\alpha+1} \right.\right.\right.$$

$$\left.\left.\left. + \left(D_{b-;g}^{i\alpha} f\right)(b)(g(b) - g(t))^{i\alpha+1} \right] \right\} \right| \leq$$

$$\frac{\theta}{\Gamma((n+1)\alpha)\left((n+1)\alpha + \frac{1}{p}\right)(p((n+1)\alpha - 1) + 1)^{\frac{1}{p}}}$$

$$\left[(g(t) - g(a))^{(n+1)\alpha + \frac{1}{p}} + (g(b) - g(t))^{(n+1)\alpha + \frac{1}{p}} \right], \tag{115}$$

$\forall\, t \in [a,b]$,

(ii) at $g(t) = \frac{g(a)+g(b)}{2}$, the right hand side of (115) is minimized, and we have:

$$\left| \int_a^b f(x)\, dg(x) - \left\{ \sum_{i=0}^{n} \frac{1}{\Gamma(i\alpha+2)} \frac{(g(b) - g(a))^{i\alpha+1}}{2^{i\alpha+1}} \right.\right.$$

$$\left.\left. \left[\left(D_{a+;g}^{i\alpha} f\right)(a) + \left(D_{b-;g}^{i\alpha} f\right)(b) \right] \right\} \right| \leq$$

$$\frac{\theta}{\Gamma((n+1)\alpha)\left((n+1)\alpha + \frac{1}{p}\right)(p((n+1)\alpha - 1) + 1)^{\frac{1}{p}}} \frac{(g(b) - g(a))^{(n+1)\alpha + \frac{1}{p}}}{2^{(n+1)\alpha - \frac{1}{q}}}, \tag{116}$$

(iii) assuming $\left(D_{a+;g}^{i\alpha}f\right)(a)=\left(D_{b-;g}^{i\alpha}f\right)(b)=0$, $i=0,1,...,n$, *we obtain*

$$\left|\int_a^b f(x)\,dg(x)\right|\leq$$

$$\frac{\theta}{\Gamma((n+1)\alpha)\left((n+1)\alpha+\frac{1}{p}\right)(p((n+1)\alpha-1)+1)^{\frac{1}{p}}}\frac{(g(b)-g(a))^{(n+1)\alpha+\frac{1}{p}}}{2^{(n+1)\alpha-\frac{1}{q}}},\tag{117}$$

which is a sharp inequality,

(iv) more generally, for $j=0,1,2,...,N\in\mathbb{N}$, *it holds that*

$$\left|\int_a^b f(x)\,dg(x)-\left\{\sum_{i=0}^{n}\frac{1}{\Gamma(i\alpha+2)}\left(\frac{g(b)-g(a)}{N}\right)^{i\alpha+1}\right.\right.$$

$$\left.\left.\left[\left(D_{a+;g}^{i\alpha}f\right)(a)\,j^{i\alpha+1}+\left(D_{b-;g}^{i\alpha}f\right)(b)\,(N-j)^{i\alpha+1}\right]\right\}\right|\leq$$

$$\frac{\theta}{\Gamma((n+1)\alpha)\left((n+1)\alpha+\frac{1}{p}\right)(p((n+1)\alpha-1)+1)^{\frac{1}{p}}}$$

$$\left(\frac{g(b)-g(a)}{N}\right)^{(n+1)\alpha+\frac{1}{p}}\left[j^{(n+1)\alpha+\frac{1}{p}}+(N-j)^{(n+1)\alpha+\frac{1}{p}}\right],\tag{118}$$

(v) if $\left(D_{a+;g}^{i\alpha}f\right)(a)=\left(D_{b-;g}^{i\alpha}f\right)(b)=0$, $i=1,...,n$, *from (118) we obtain:*

$$\left|\int_a^b f(x)\,dg(x)-\left(\frac{g(b)-g(a)}{N}\right)[jf(a)+(N-j)f(b)]\right|\leq$$

$$\frac{\theta}{\Gamma((n+1)\alpha)\left((n+1)\alpha+\frac{1}{p}\right)(p((n+1)\alpha-1)+1)^{\frac{1}{p}}}$$

$$\left(\frac{g(b)-g(a)}{N}\right)^{(n+1)\alpha+\frac{1}{p}}\left[j^{(n+1)\alpha+\frac{1}{p}}+(N-j)^{(n+1)\alpha+\frac{1}{p}}\right],\tag{119}$$

$j=0,1,2,...,N$,

(vi) when $N=2$, $j=1$, *(119) turns to*

$$\left|\int_a^b f(x)\,dg(x)-\left(\frac{g(b)-g(a)}{2}\right)(f(a)+f(b))\right|\leq$$

$$\frac{\theta}{\Gamma((n+1)\alpha)\left((n+1)\alpha+\frac{1}{p}\right)(p((n+1)\alpha-1)+1)^{\frac{1}{p}}}\frac{(g(b)-g(a))^{(n+1)\alpha+\frac{1}{p}}}{2^{(n+1)\alpha-\frac{1}{q}}}.\tag{120}$$

Proof. By (56) we find

$$\left|f(x)-\sum_{i=0}^{n}\frac{(g(x)-g(a))^{i\alpha}}{\Gamma(i\alpha+1)}\left(D_{a+;g}^{i\alpha}f\right)(a)\right|\leq\tag{121}$$

$$\frac{1}{\Gamma((n+1)\alpha)}\int_a^x (g(x)-g(t))^{(n+1)\alpha-1}g'(t)\left|\left(D_{a+;g}^{(n+1)\alpha}f\right)(t)\right|dt=$$

(by [5])

$$\frac{1}{\Gamma((n+1)\alpha)}\int_a^x (g(x)-g(t))^{(n+1)\alpha-1}\left|\left(D_{a+;g}^{(n+1)\alpha}f\right)(t)\right|dg(t)\leq$$

(by [6])

$$\frac{1}{\Gamma((n+1)\alpha)}\left(\int_a^x (g(x)-g(t))^{p((n+1)\alpha-1)}\,dg(t)\right)^{\frac{1}{p}}$$

$$\left(\int_a^x \left|\left(D_{a+;g}^{(n+1)\alpha} f\right)(t)\right|^q dg(t)\right)^{\frac{1}{q}} \leq$$

$$\frac{1}{\Gamma((n+1)\alpha)}\frac{(g(x)-g(a))^{\frac{p((n+1)\alpha-1)+1}{p}}}{(p((n+1)\alpha-1)+1)^{\frac{1}{p}}}\left\|D_{a+;g}^{(n+1)\alpha} f\right\|_{L_q([a,b],g)}.$$

That is

$$\left|f(x)-\sum_{i=0}^{n}\frac{(g(x)-g(a))^{i\alpha}}{\Gamma(i\alpha+1)}\left(D_{a+;g}^{i\alpha}f\right)(a)\right| \leq$$

$$\frac{\left\|D_{a+;g}^{(n+1)\alpha} f\right\|_{L_q([a,b],g)}}{\Gamma((n+1)\alpha)(p((n+1)\alpha-1)+1)^{\frac{1}{p}}}(g(x)-g(a))^{(n+1)\alpha-\frac{1}{q}}, \tag{122}$$

$\forall\, x \in [a,b]$.

Similarly, from (57) we derive

$$\left|f(x)-\sum_{i=0}^{n}\frac{(g(b)-g(x))^{i\alpha}}{\Gamma(i\alpha+1)}\left(D_{b-;g}^{i\alpha}f\right)(b)\right| \leq$$

$$\frac{1}{\Gamma((n+1)\alpha)}\int_x^b (g(t)-g(x))^{(n+1)\alpha-1} g'(t)\left|\left(D_{b-;g}^{(n+1)\alpha} f\right)(t)\right| dt =$$

(by [5])

$$\frac{1}{\Gamma((n+1)\alpha)}\int_x^b (g(t)-g(x))^{(n+1)\alpha-1}\left|\left(D_{b-;g}^{(n+1)\alpha} f\right)(t)\right| dg(t) \leq$$

(by [6])

$$\frac{1}{\Gamma((n+1)\alpha)}\left(\int_x^b (g(t)-g(x))^{p((n+1)\alpha-1)}\,dg(t)\right)^{\frac{1}{p}}$$

$$\left(\int_x^b \left|\left(D_{b-;g}^{(n+1)\alpha} f\right)(t)\right|^q dg(t)\right)^{\frac{1}{q}} \leq \tag{123}$$

$$\frac{1}{\Gamma((n+1)\alpha)}\frac{(g(b)-g(x))^{\frac{p((n+1)\alpha-1)+1}{p}}}{(p((n+1)\alpha-1)+1)^{\frac{1}{p}}}\left\|D_{b-;g}^{(n+1)\alpha} f\right\|_{L_q([a,b],g)}.$$

That is

$$\left|f(x)-\sum_{i=0}^{n}\frac{(g(b)-g(x))^{i\alpha}}{\Gamma(i\alpha+1)}\left(D_{b-;g}^{i\alpha}f\right)(b)\right| \leq$$

$$\frac{\left\|D_{b-;g}^{(n+1)\alpha} f\right\|_{L_q([a,b],g)}}{\Gamma((n+1)\alpha)(p((n+1)\alpha-1)+1)^{\frac{1}{p}}}(g(b)-g(x))^{(n+1)\alpha-\frac{1}{q}}, \tag{124}$$

$\forall\, x \in [a,b]$.

We have proved that

$$\left|f(x)-\sum_{i=0}^{n}\frac{(g(x)-g(a))^{i\alpha}}{\Gamma(i\alpha+1)}\left(D_{a+;g}^{i\alpha}f\right)(a)\right| \leq$$

$$\frac{\theta}{\Gamma\left(\left(n+1\right)\alpha\right)\left(p\left(\left(n+1\right)\alpha-1\right)+1\right)^{\frac{1}{p}}}\left(g\left(x\right)-g\left(a\right)\right)^{\left(n+1\right)\alpha-\frac{1}{q}}, \tag{125}$$

and

$$\left|f\left(x\right)-\sum_{i=0}^{n}\frac{\left(g\left(b\right)-g\left(x\right)\right)^{i\alpha}}{\Gamma\left(i\alpha+1\right)}\left(D_{b-;g}^{i\alpha}f\right)\left(b\right)\right|\leq$$

$$\frac{\theta}{\Gamma\left(\left(n+1\right)\alpha\right)\left(p\left(\left(n+1\right)\alpha-1\right)+1\right)^{\frac{1}{p}}}\left(g\left(b\right)-g\left(x\right)\right)^{\left(n+1\right)\alpha-\frac{1}{q}}, \tag{126}$$

$\forall\, x\in\left[a,b\right]$.

The rest of the proof is as in Theorem 7. □

Applications follow:

Proposition 1. *We assume that* $\left(f\circ\ln x\right)\in AC^{n}\left(\left[e^{a},e^{b}\right]\right)$, *where* $\mathbb{N}\ni n=\lceil\alpha\rceil$, $\alpha>0$. *We also assume that* $\left(f\circ\ln x\right)^{(n)}\circ e^{x}\in L_{\infty}\left(\left[a,b\right]\right)$, $f\in C\left(\left[a,b\right]\right)$. *Set*

$$T_{1}:=\max\left\{\left\|D_{a+;e^{x}}^{\alpha}f\right\|_{L_{\infty}\left(\left[a,b\right]\right)},\left\|D_{b-;e^{x}}^{\alpha}f\right\|_{L_{\infty}\left(\left[a,b\right]\right)}\right\}. \tag{127}$$

Then

(i)

$$\left|\int_{a}^{b}f\left(x\right)e^{x}dx-\sum_{k=0}^{n-1}\frac{1}{\left(k+1\right)!}\left[\left(f\circ\ln x\right)^{(k)}\left(e^{a}\right)\left(e^{t}-e^{a}\right)^{k+1}\right.\right.$$

$$\left.\left.\left(-1\right)^{k}\left(f\circ\ln x\right)^{(k)}\left(e^{b}\right)\left(e^{b}-e^{t}\right)^{k+1}\right]\right|\leq$$

$$\frac{T_{1}}{\Gamma\left(\alpha+2\right)}\left[\left(e^{t}-e^{a}\right)^{\alpha+1}+\left(e^{b}-e^{t}\right)^{\alpha+1}\right], \tag{128}$$

$\forall\, t\in\left[a,b\right]$,

(ii) at $t=\ln\left(\frac{e^{a}+e^{b}}{2}\right)$, *the right hand side of (128) is minimized, and we find:*

$$\left|\int_{a}^{b}f\left(x\right)e^{x}dx-\sum_{k=0}^{n-1}\frac{1}{\left(k+1\right)!}\frac{\left(e^{b}-e^{a}\right)^{k+1}}{2^{k+1}}\right.$$

$$\left.\left[\left(f\circ\ln x\right)^{(k)}\left(e^{a}\right)+\left(-1\right)^{k}\left(f\circ\ln x\right)^{(k)}\left(e^{b}\right)\right]\right|\leq$$

$$\frac{T_{1}}{\Gamma\left(\alpha+2\right)}\frac{\left(e^{b}-e^{a}\right)^{\alpha+1}}{2^{\alpha}}, \tag{129}$$

(iii) if $\left(f\circ\ln x\right)^{(k)}\left(e^{a}\right)=\left(f\circ\ln x\right)^{(k)}\left(e^{b}\right)=0$, *for* $k=0,1,...,n-1$, *we obtain*

$$\left|\int_{a}^{b}f\left(x\right)e^{x}dx\right|\leq T_{1}\frac{\left(e^{b}-e^{a}\right)^{\alpha+1}}{\Gamma\left(\alpha+2\right)2^{\alpha}}, \tag{130}$$

which is a sharp inequality,

(iv) more generally, for $j = 0, 1, 2, ..., N \in \mathbb{N}$, it holds

$$\left| \int_a^b f(x) e^x dx - \sum_{k=0}^{n-1} \frac{1}{(k+1)!} \left(\frac{e^b - e^a}{N} \right)^{k+1} \right.$$

$$\left. \left[j^{k+1} (f \circ \ln x)^{(k)} (e^a) + (-1)^k (N-j)^{k+1} (f \circ \ln x)^{(k)} \left(e^b \right) \right] \right| \leq$$

$$\frac{T_1}{\Gamma(\alpha+2)} \left(\frac{e^b - e^a}{N} \right)^{\alpha+1} \left[j^{\alpha+1} + (N-j)^{\alpha+1} \right], \tag{131}$$

(v) if $(f \circ \ln x)^{(k)} (e^a) = (f \circ \ln x)^{(k)} \left(e^b \right) = 0$, for $k = 1, ..., n-1$, from (131) we obtain

$$\left| \int_a^b f(x) e^x dx - \left(\frac{e^b - e^a}{N} \right) [j f(a) + (N-j) f(b)] \right| \leq$$

$$\frac{T_1}{\Gamma(\alpha+2)} \left(\frac{e^b - e^a}{N} \right)^{\alpha+1} \left[j^{\alpha+1} + (N-j)^{\alpha+1} \right], \tag{132}$$

$j = 0, 1, 2, ..., N$,

(vi) when $N = 2$, $j = 1$, (132) turns to

$$\left| \int_a^b f(x) e^x dx - \left(\frac{e^b - e^a}{2} \right) (f(a) + f(b)) \right| \leq$$

$$\frac{T_1}{\Gamma(\alpha+2)} \frac{\left(e^b - e^a \right)^{\alpha+1}}{2^\alpha}, \tag{133}$$

(vii) when $0 < \alpha \leq 1$, inequality (133) is again valid without any boundary conditions.

Proof. By Theorem 6, for $g(x) = e^x$. □

We continue with

Proposition 2. *Here $f \in C([a,b])$, where $[a,b] \subset (0, +\infty)$. Let $0 < \alpha \leq 1$, and $G_k := D_{a+;\ln x}^{k\alpha} f$, for $k = 0, 1, ..., n+1$; $n \in \mathbb{N}$. We assume that $G_k \circ e^x \in AC([\ln a, \ln b])$ and $(G_k \circ e^x)' \circ \ln x \in L_\infty([a,b])$. Also let $\overline{G_k} := D_{b-;\ln x}^{k\alpha} f$, for $k = 0, 1, ..., n+1$, they fulfill $\overline{G_k} \circ e^x \in AC([\ln a, \ln b])$ and $\left(\overline{G_k} \circ e^x \right)' \circ \ln x \in L_\infty([a,b])$. Set*

$$T_2 := \max \left\{ \left\| D_{a+;\ln x}^{(n+1)\alpha} f \right\|_{\infty,[a,b]}, \left\| D_{b-;\ln x}^{(n+1)\alpha} f \right\|_{\infty,[a,b]} \right\}. \tag{134}$$

Then

(i)

$$\left| \int_a^b \frac{f(x)}{x} dx - \left\{ \sum_{i=0}^{n} \frac{1}{\Gamma(i\alpha+2)} \left[\left(D_{a+;\ln x}^{i\alpha} f \right)(a) \left(\ln \frac{t}{a} \right)^{i\alpha+1} \right. \right. \right.$$

$$\left. \left. \left. + \left(D_{b-;\ln x}^{i\alpha} f \right)(b) \left(\ln \frac{b}{t} \right)^{i\alpha+1} \right] \right\} \right| \leq$$

$$\frac{T_2}{\Gamma((n+1)\alpha+2)} \left[\left(\ln \frac{t}{a} \right)^{(n+1)\alpha+1} + \left(\ln \frac{b}{t} \right)^{(n+1)\alpha+1} \right], \tag{135}$$

$\forall\, t \in [a,b]$,

(ii) at $t = e^{\left(\frac{\ln ab}{2}\right)}$*, the right hand side of (135) is minimized, and we have:*

$$\left| \int_a^b \frac{f(x)}{x} dx - \left\{ \sum_{i=0}^{n} \frac{1}{\Gamma(i\alpha+2)} \frac{\left(\ln \frac{b}{a}\right)^{i\alpha+1}}{2^{i\alpha+1}} \right. \right.$$

$$\left. \left. \left[\left(D_{a+;\ln x}^{i\alpha} f \right)(a) + \left(D_{b-;\ln x}^{i\alpha} f \right)(b) \right] \right\} \right| \leq$$

$$\frac{T_2}{\Gamma((n+1)\alpha+2)} \frac{\left(\ln \frac{b}{a}\right)^{(n+1)\alpha+1}}{2^{(n+1)\alpha}}, \tag{136}$$

(iii) assuming $\left(D_{a+;\ln x}^{i\alpha} f \right)(a) = \left(D_{b-;\ln x}^{i\alpha} f \right)(b) = 0$*,* $i = 0, 1, ..., n$*, we obtain*

$$\left| \int_a^b \frac{f(x)}{x} dx \right| \leq \frac{T_2}{\Gamma((n+1)\alpha+2)} \frac{\left(\ln \frac{b}{a}\right)^{(n+1)\alpha+1}}{2^{(n+1)\alpha}}, \tag{137}$$

which is a sharp inequality,

(iv) more generally, for $j = 0, 1, 2, ..., N \in \mathbb{N}$*, it holds*

$$\left| \int_a^b \frac{f(x)}{x} dx - \left\{ \sum_{i=0}^{n} \frac{1}{\Gamma(i\alpha+2)} \left(\frac{\ln \frac{b}{a}}{N} \right)^{i\alpha+1} \right. \right.$$

$$\left. \left. \left[\left(D_{a+;\ln x}^{i\alpha} f \right)(a) j^{i\alpha+1} + \left(D_{b-;\ln x}^{i\alpha} f \right)(b) (N-j)^{i\alpha+1} \right] \right\} \right| \leq$$

$$\frac{T_2}{\Gamma((n+1)\alpha+2)} \left(\frac{\ln \frac{b}{a}}{N} \right)^{(n+1)\alpha+1} \left[j^{(n+1)\alpha+1} + (N-j)^{(n+1)\alpha+1} \right], \tag{138}$$

(v) if $\left(D_{a+;\ln x}^{i\alpha} f \right)(a) = \left(D_{b-;\ln x}^{i\alpha} f \right)(b) = 0$*,* $i = 1, ..., n$*, from (138) we find:*

$$\left| \int_a^b \frac{f(x)}{x} dx - \left(\frac{\ln \frac{b}{a}}{N} \right) (j f(a) + (N-j) f(b)) \right| \leq$$

$$\frac{T_2}{\Gamma((n+1)\alpha+2)} \left(\frac{\ln \frac{b}{a}}{N} \right)^{(n+1)\alpha+1} \left[j^{(n+1)\alpha+1} + (N-j)^{(n+1)\alpha+1} \right], \tag{139}$$

for $j = 0, 1, 2, ..., N$*,*

(vi) if $N = 2$ *and* $j = 1$*, (139) becomes*

$$\left| \int_a^b \frac{f(x)}{x} dx - \left(\frac{\ln \frac{b}{a}}{2} \right) (f(a) + f(b)) \right| \leq$$

$$\frac{T_2}{\Gamma((n+1)\alpha+2)} \frac{\left(\ln \frac{b}{a}\right)^{(n+1)\alpha+1}}{2^{(n+1)\alpha}}. \tag{140}$$

Proof. By Theorem 7, for $g(x) = \ln x$. □

We could give many other interesting applications that are based in our other theorems, due to lack of space we skip this task.

Funding: This research received no external funding.

Conflicts of Interest: The authors declare no conflict of interest.

References

1. Iyengar, K.S.K. Note on an inequality. *Math. Stud.* **1938**, *6*, 75–76.
2. Anastassiou, G. Advanced Fractional Taylor's formulae. *J. Comput. Anal. Appl.* **2016**, *21*, 1185–1204.
3. Anastassiou, G.; Argyros, I. *Intelligent Numerical Methods: Applications to Fractional Calculus*; Springer: Heidelberg, Germany; New York, NY, USA, 2016.
4. Royden, H.L. *Real Analysis*, 2nd ed.; MacMillan Publishing Co., Inc.: New York, NY, USA, 1968.
5. Royden, H.L.; Fitzpatrick, P.M. *Real Analysis*, 4th ed.; Pearson: New York, NY, USA, 2010.
6. Dragomir, S.S. Inequalities for the Riemann-Stieljes integral of $(p,q) - H-$Dominated integrators with applications. *Appl. Math. E-Notes* **2015**, *15*, 243–260.

MDPI

Article

Duality for Unified Higher-Order Minimax Fractional Programming with Support Function under Type-I Assumptions

Ramu Dubey [1], Vishnu Narayan Mishra [2,*], and Rifaqat Ali [3]

1 Department of Mathematics, J C Bose University of Science and Technology, YMCA, Faridabad 121006, India; rdubeyjiya@gmail.com
2 Department of Mathematics, Indira Gandhi National Tribal University, Lalpur, Amarkantak, Anuppur, Madhya Pradesh 484887, India
3 Department of Mathematics, College of Science and Arts, Muhayil, King Khalid University, 61413 Abha, Saudi Arabia; rifaqat.ali1@gmail.com or rrafat@kku.edu.sa
* Correspondence: vishnunarayanmishra@gmail.com

Received: 5 September 2019; Accepted: 15 October 2019; Published: 3 November 2019

Abstract: This article is devoted to discussing the nondifferentiable minimax fractional programming problem with type-I functions. We focus our study on a nondifferentiable minimax fractional programming problem and formulate a higher-order dual model. Next, we establish weak, strong, and strict converse duality theorems under generalized higher-order strictly pseudo (V, α, ρ, d)-type-I functions. In the final section, we turn our focus to study a nondifferentiable unified minimax fractional programming problem and the results obtained in this paper naturally unify. Further, we extend some previously known results on nondifferentiable minimax fractional programming in the literature.

Keywords: duality; support function; nondifferentiable; strictly pseudo (V, α, ρ, d)-type-I; unified dual; efficient solutions

---

1. Introduction

Minimax is a decision rule used in decision theory, game theory, statistics, and philosophy for minimizing the possible loss for a worst case (maximum loss) scenario. In general, a minimax problem can be formulated as

$$\min_{x \in X} \max_{i} f_i(x), \quad i = 1, 2, 3, ..., m,$$

where $f_i(x)$ is a function defined on the space X. Many minimax problems often arise in engineering design, computer-aided-design, circuit design, and optimal control. Some of the problems arising in engineering, economics, and mathematics are of the following form:

Minimize a function $\Theta(x)$ subject to $x \in \Omega$, where $\Theta(x)$ is one of the following functions:

(a) $\Theta(x) = \max_{y \in H} f(x, y)$,

(b) $\Theta(x) = \max_{y \in H(x)} f(x, y)$,

(c) $\Theta(x) = \max_{y \in H_1(x)} \min_{z \in H_2(x)} f(x, y, z)$,

(d) $\Theta(x) = \max_{y_1 \in H_{11}(x)} \min_{z_1 \in H_{21}(x)}, ..., \max_{y_k \in H_{1k}(x)} \min_{z_k \in H_{2k}(x)} f(x, y_1, ..., y_k, z_1, ..., z_k)$,

where the sets $H(x)$, $H_i(x)$, H_{ij} depend on x and H, Ω are given sets,

(e) $\Theta(x) = \max_i f_i(x),\ i \in \{1,2,3,...,m\}$.

Such problems often appear in the engineering design theory. In recent years, much attention was paid to the problems described. The minimax theory deals with the following problems:

(1) Necessary and sufficient conditions and their geometric interpretation [1,2];
(2) Steepest-descent directions and their applications to constructing numerical methods. The problems have been widely discussed and studied for the function (a);
(3) Saddle points: The problem of finding saddle points is a special case of minimax problems (see survey [3]);
(4) Optimal control problems with a minimax criterion function.

These facts indicate that minimax theory will continue to be an important tool for solving difficult and interesting problems. In addition, minimax methods provide a paradigm for investigating analogous problems. An exciting future with new unified theories may be expected. Optimization problems, in which both a minimization and a maximization process are performed, are known as minimax problems in the area of mathematical programming. For more details, we refer to Stancu-Minasian [4]. Tanimoto [5] applied these optimality conditions to construct a dual problem and established duality theorems. Many researchers have done work related to the same area [6–14].

Fractional programming is an interesting subject which features in several types of optimization problems, such as inventory problem, game theory, and in many other cases. In addition, it can be used in engineering and economics to minimize a ratio of functions between a given period of time and as a utilized resource in order to measure the efficiency of a system. In these sorts of problems, the objective function is usually given as a ratio of functions in fractional programming from (see [15,16]).

Motivated by various concepts of generalized convexity, Liang et al. [17] introduced the concept of (F,α,ρ,d)-convex functions. Hachimi and Aghezzaf [18], with prior definitions of generalized convexity, extended the concept further to (F,α,ρ,d)-type I functions and gave the sufficient optimality conditions and mixed-type duality results for the multiobjective programming problem.

This paper is divided into four sections. Section 2 contains definitions of higher-order strictly pseudo (V,α,ρ,d)-type-I functions. In section 3, we concentrate our discussion on a nondifferentiable minimax fractional programming problem and formulate the higher-order dual model. We establish duality theorems under higher-order strictly pseudo (V,α,ρ,d)-type-I functions. In the final section, we turn our attention to discuss a nondifferentiable mixed-type minimax fractional programming problem and establish duality relations under the same assumptions.

2. Preliminaries and Definitions

Throughout this paper, we use $S' = \{1,2,...,s\}$, $M = \{1,2,...,m\}$ and $(z,w,v,\mu,p) \in R^n \times R^n \times R^n \times R^m_+ \times R^n$.

Definition 1. *Let Q be a compact convex set in R^n. The support function of Q is denoted by $s(x|Q)$ and defined by*

$$s(x|Q) = max\{x^T y : y \in Q\}.$$

The support function $s(x|Q)$, being convex and everywhere finite, has a Clarke subdifferential [8], in the sense of convex analysis. The subdifferential of $s(x|Q)$ is given by

$$\partial s(x|Q) = \{z \in Q \mid z^T x = s(x|Q)\}.$$

For any set S, the normal case to S at a point $x \in S$, denoted by $N_S(x)$ and denoted by

$$N_S(x) = \left\{ y \in R^n : y^T(z - x), \; \forall \, z \in S \right\}.$$

It is readily verified that for a compact convex set $Q \in R^n$, $y \in N_S(x)$ if and only if $s(x|Q) = x^T y$ or equivalently, x is in the Clarke subdifferential of s at y.

Consider the following nondifferentiable minimax fractional programming problem (FP):

$$\textbf{(FP)} \quad \text{Minimize } \frac{\xi(x,y)}{\zeta(x,y)} = \sup_{y \in Y} \frac{f(x,y) + s(x|C)}{g(x,y) - s(x|D)},$$
$$\text{subject to } S = \{x \in X : h_j(x) + s(x|E_j) \leq 0, \; j \in M\},$$

where Y is a compact subject of R^m, $f, \; g : X \times Y \to R$ and $h_j : X \to R$, $i \in S'$ are continuously differentiable functions on $R^n \times R^m$. $f(x,y) + s(x|C) \geq 0$ and $g(x,y) - s(x|D) > 0, \forall \, x \in S$. C, D, and E_j, $j \in M$ are compact convex sets in R^m, and $s(x|C), s(x|D)$, and $s(x|E_j)$, $j \in M$ designate the support functions of compact sets.

$$N(x) = \{i \in S' : h_j(x) = 0\},$$

$$Y(x) = \left\{ y \in Y : \frac{f(x,y) + s(x|C)}{g(x,y) - s(x|D)} = \sup_{z \in Y} \frac{f(x,z) + s(x|C)}{g(x,z) - s(x|D)} \right\}$$

and

$$K(x) = \Bigg\{ (s,t,\bar{y}) \in N \times R^s_+ \times R^m : 1 \leq s \leq n+1, \; t = (t_1, t_2, ..., t_s) \in R^s_+$$
$$\text{with } \sum_{i=1}^{s} t_i = 1, \bar{y} = (\bar{y}_1, \bar{y}_2, ..., \bar{y}_s) \text{ and } \bar{y}_i \in Y(x), \; i \in S \Bigg\}.$$

Assume that $\alpha : X \times X \to R_+ \setminus \{0\}$, $\eta : X \times X \to R^n$, $\rho \in R$ and $d : X \times X \to R$ (satisfying $d(x,y) = 0 \Leftrightarrow x = y$). Let $\phi : X \times Y \to R$ and $\psi_j : X \to R$ be twice differentiable functions.

Definition 2. *$\forall \, j \in M$, $[\phi, \psi_j]$ is said to be higher-order (V, α, ρ, d)-type -I at $\bar{x}$, if $\exists \; \alpha, \; \rho, \; d$, and η such that $\forall \, x \in S$, $y_i \in Y(x)$, and $p \in R^n$, we have*

$$\phi(x, y_i) - \phi(\bar{x}, y_i) - G(\bar{x}, y_i, p) + p^T \nabla_p G(\bar{x}, y_i, p)$$
$$\geq \left\langle \alpha(x, \bar{x}) \{ \nabla \phi(\bar{x}, y_i) + \nabla_p G(\bar{x}, y_i, p) \}, \eta(x, \bar{x}) \right\rangle + \rho_i d^2(x, \bar{x}), \; i \in S'$$

and

$$-\psi_j(\bar{x}) - K_j(\bar{x}, p) + p^T \nabla_p K_j(\bar{x}, p) \geq \left\langle \alpha(x, \bar{x}) \{ \nabla \psi_j(\bar{x}) + \nabla_p K_j(\bar{x}, p) \}, \eta(x, \bar{x}) \right\rangle + \rho_j d^2(x, \bar{x}), \; j \in M.$$

Remark 1. *In the above definition, if the inequalities appear as strict inequalities, then we say that $[\phi, \psi_j]$, $\forall \, j \in M$ is higher-order strict (V, α, ρ, d)-type-I.*

Remark 2. *If $G(\bar{x}, y_i, p) = \frac{1}{2} p^T \nabla^2 \phi(\bar{x}, y_i) p$ and $\rho_i = 0$, $\forall \, i \in S'$, then Definition 2 becomes α-type-I at $\bar{x}$ given by [19].*

Definition 3. *$\forall\, j \in M$, $[\phi, \psi_j]$ is said to be higher-order pseudoquasi (V, α, ρ, d)-type -I at $\bar{x}$, if $\exists\ \alpha,\ \rho,\ d$, and η such that $\forall\ x \in S,\ y_i \in Y(x)$, and $p \in R^n$, we have*

$$\phi(x, y_i) - \phi(\bar{x}, y_i) - G(\bar{x}, y_i, p) + p^T \nabla_p G(\bar{x}, y_i, p) < 0$$

$$\Rightarrow \Big\langle \alpha(x, \bar{x})\{\nabla\phi(\bar{x}, y_i) + \nabla_p G(\bar{x}, y_i, p)\}, \eta(x, \bar{x}) \Big\rangle + \rho_i d^2(x, \bar{x}) < 0,\ \ i \in S'$$

and

$$-\psi_j(\bar{x}) - K_j(\bar{x}, p) + p^T \nabla_p K_j(\bar{x}, p) \leq 0 \Rightarrow \Big\langle \alpha(x, \bar{x})\{\nabla\psi_j(\bar{x}) + \nabla_p K_j(\bar{x}, p)\}, \eta(x, \bar{x}) \Big\rangle + \rho_j d^2(x, \bar{x}) \leq 0,\ j \in M.$$

Remark 3. *In Definition 3, if* $\Big\langle \alpha(x, \bar{x})\{\nabla\phi(\bar{x}, \bar{y}_i) + p^T \nabla_p G(\bar{x}, \bar{y}_i, p)\}, \eta(x, \bar{x}) \Big\rangle + \rho_i d^2(x, \bar{x}) \geq 0$

$$\Rightarrow \phi(x, y_i) - \phi(\bar{x}, y_i) - G(\bar{x}, y_i, p) + p^T \nabla_p G(\bar{x}, y_i, p) > 0,\ i \in S',$$

then $[\phi, \psi_j]$, $\forall\ j \in M$ is higher-order strictly pseudoquasi (V, α, ρ, d)-type-I.

Remark 4. *If $G(\bar{x}, y_i, p) = \frac{1}{2} p^T \nabla^2 \phi(\bar{x}, y_i) p$ and $\rho_i = 0$, $\forall\ i \in S'$, then Definition 3 reduces to α-type-I at $\bar{x}$, given by [19].*

Theorem 1 (Necessary condition). *Ifx^* is an optimal solution of problem (FP) satisfying $< w, x >> 0$, $< v, x > \ > 0$, and $\nabla(h_j(x^*) + < u_j, x^* >)$, $j \in N(x^*)$ are linearly independent, then $\exists\ (s^*, t^*, \bar{y}^*) \in K(x^*)$, $w \in R^n$, $v \in R^n$ and $\mu^* \in R^m_+$ such that*

$$\sum_{i=1}^{s^*} t_i^* \nabla \left(\frac{f_i(x^*, \bar{y}_i) + < w, x^* >}{g_i(x^*, \bar{y}_i) - < v, x^* >} \right) + \sum_{j=1}^{m} \mu_j^* \nabla (h_j(x^*) + < u_j, x^* >) = 0, \tag{1}$$

$$\sum_{j=1}^{m} \mu_j^* (h_j(x^*) + < u_j, x^* >) = 0, \tag{2}$$

$$t_i^* > 0,\ i \in S'^*,\ \sum_{i=1}^{s^*} t_i^* = 1,\ \mu_j^* \geq 0,\ j \in M, \tag{3}$$

$$< w, x^* >= s(x^*|C),\ \ < v, x^* >= s(x^*|D),\ \ < u_j, x^* >= s(x^*|E_j). \tag{4}$$

3. Higher-Order Nondifferentiable Duality Model

The study of higher-order duality is more significant due to the computational advantage over second- and first-order duality as it provides tighter bounds due to presence of more parameters. In the present article, we formulate a new type of duality model for a nondifferentiable minimax fractional programming problem and derive duality theorems under generalized convexity assumptions. Additionally, we use the concept of support function as a nondifferentiable term. Consider the following dual (HFD) of the problem (FP):

$$\textbf{(HFD)} \quad \max_{(s,t,\bar{y}) \in K(z)} \ \sup_{(z,w,v,u,\mu,p) \in H(s,t,\bar{y})} \ \sum_{i=1}^{s} t_i \left[\frac{f(z, \bar{y}_i) + < w, z >}{g(z, \bar{y}_i) - < v, z >} + G(z, \bar{y}_i, p) - p^T \nabla_p G(z, \bar{y}_i, p) \right]$$
$$+ \sum_{i=1}^{m} \mu_j \Big(h_j(z) + < u_j,\ z > + K_j(z, p) - p^T \nabla_p K_j(z, p) \Big),$$

where $H(s,t,\bar{y})$ represents the set of all (z,w,v,u,μ,p) such that

$$\nabla \sum_{i=1}^{s} t_i \left(\frac{f(z,\bar{y}_i) + < w, z >}{g(z,\bar{y}_i) - < v, z >} \right) + \nabla \sum_{j=1}^{m} \mu_j (h_j(z) + < u_j,\ z >)$$

$$+ \sum_{i=1}^{s} t_i \nabla_p G(z,\bar{y}_i,p) + \sum_{j=1}^{m} \mu_j \nabla_p K_j(z,p) = 0, \tag{5}$$

$$t_i \geq 0,\ \sum_{i=1}^{s} t_i = 1,\ \mu_j \geq 0,\ i \in S',\ j \in M, \tag{6}$$

$$(s,t,\tilde{y}) \in K(z). \tag{7}$$

Let T^0 be the feasible set for (HFD).

Theorem 2 (Weak Duality). *Let $x \in S$ and $(z,w,v,\mu,s,t,\bar{y},p) \in T^0$. Let*

(i) $\left[\frac{f(.,\bar{y}_i) + < w, . >}{g(.,\bar{y}_i) - < v, . >},\ h_j(.) + < u_j, . > \right], i \in S', j \in M$ be higher-order (V,α,ρ,d)- type -I at z,

(ii) $\sum_{i=1}^{s} t_i \rho_i + \sum_{j=1}^{m} \mu_j \rho_j \geq 0.$

Then,

$$\sup_{y \in Y} \left(\frac{f(x,y) + < w, x >}{g(x,y) - < v, x >} \right) \geq \sum_{i=1}^{s} t_i \left[\left(\frac{f(z,\bar{y}_i) + < w, z >}{g(z,\bar{y}_i) - < v, z >} \right) + G(z,\bar{y}_i,p) - p^T \nabla_p G(z,\bar{y}_i,p) \right]$$

$$+ \sum_{i=1}^{m} \mu_j \Big(h_j(z) + < u_j, z > + K_j(z,p) - p^T \nabla_p K_j(z,p) \Big). \tag{8}$$

Proof. We shall derive the result by assuming contrary to the above inequality. Suppose

$$\sup_{y \in Y} \left(\frac{f(x,y) + < w, x >}{g(x,y) - < v, x >} \right) < \sum_{i=1}^{s} t_i \left[\left(\frac{f(z,\bar{y}_i) + < w, z >}{g(z,\bar{y}_i) - < v, z >} \right) + G(z,\bar{y}_i,p) - p^T \nabla_p G(z,\bar{y}_i,p) \right]$$

$$+ \sum_{i=1}^{m} \mu_j \Big(h_j(z) + < u_j, z > + K_j(z,p) - p^T \nabla_p K_j(z,p) \Big).$$

This implies

$$\left(\frac{f(x,\bar{y}_i) + < w, x >}{g(x,\bar{y}_i) - < v, x >} \right) < \sum_{i=1}^{s} t_i \left[\left(\frac{f(z,\bar{y}_i) + < w, z >}{g(z,\bar{y}_i) - < v, z >} \right) + G(z,\bar{y}_i,p) - p^T \nabla_p G(z,\bar{y}_i,p) \right]$$

$$+ \sum_{i=1}^{m} \mu_j \Big(h_j(z) + < u_j, z > + K_j(z,p) - p^T \nabla_p K_j(z,p) \Big), \text{ for all } \bar{y}_i\ \in Y(x),\ i \in S'. \tag{9}$$

Further, using $t_i \geq 0, i \in S'$ and $\sum_{i=1}^{s} t_i = 1$, we get

$$\sum_{i=1}^{s} t_i \left(\frac{f(x,\bar{y}_i) + < w, x >}{g(x,\bar{y}_i) - < v, x >} \right) < \sum_{i=1}^{s} t_i \left(\frac{f(z,\bar{y}_i) + < w, z >}{g(z,\bar{y}_i) - < v, z >} + G(z,\bar{y}_i,p) - p^T \nabla_p G(z,\bar{y}_i,p) \right)$$

$$+ \sum_{i=1}^{m} \mu_j \Big(h_j(z) + < u_j, z > + K_j(z,p) - p^T \nabla_p K_j(z,p) \Big). \tag{10}$$

By inequality (7), we obtain

$$\sum_{i=1}^{s} t_i \left(\frac{f(x,\bar{y}_i)+ < w,x >}{g(x,\bar{y}_i)- < v,x >} \right) < \sum_{i=1}^{s} t_i \left(\frac{f(z,\bar{y}_i)+ < w,z >}{g(z,\bar{y}_i)- < v,z >} + G(z,\bar{y}_i,p) - p^T \nabla_p G(z,\bar{y}_i,p) \right)$$
$$+ \sum_{i=1}^{m} \mu_j \Big(h_j(z)+ < u_j,z > +K_j(z,p) - p^T \nabla_p K_j(z,p) \Big). \tag{11}$$

By hypothesis (i), we get

$$\left(\frac{f(x,\bar{y}_i)+ < w,x >}{g(x,\bar{y}_i)- < v,x >} \right) - \left(\frac{f(z,\bar{y}_i)+ < w,z >}{g(z,\bar{y}_i)- < v,z >} \right) - G(z,\bar{y}_i,p) + p^T \nabla_p G(z,\bar{y}_i,p)$$
$$\geq \left\langle \alpha(x,z) \left\{ \nabla \left(\frac{f(z,\bar{y}_i)+ < w,z >}{g(z,\bar{y}_i)- < v,z >} \right) + \nabla_p G(z,\bar{y}_i,p) \right\}, \eta(x,z) \right\rangle + \rho_i d^2(x,z),\ i \in S' \tag{12}$$

and

$$-h_j(z)+ < u_j,z > -K_j(z,p) + p^T \nabla_p K_j(z,p)$$
$$\geq \left\langle \alpha(x,z) \Big\{ \nabla (h_j(z)+ < u_j,z >) + \nabla_p K_j(z,p) \Big\}, \eta(x,z) \right\rangle + \rho_j d^2(x,z),\ j \in M. \tag{13}$$

Multiplying the first inequality by $t_i \geq 0,\ i \in S'$ and the second by $\mu_j \geq 0,\ j \in M$ with $\sum_{i=1}^{s} t_i = 1$, we get

$$\sum_{i=1}^{s} t_i \left[\left(\frac{f(x,\bar{y}_i)+ < w,x >}{g(x,\bar{y}_i)- < v,x >} \right) - \left(\frac{f(z,\bar{y}_i)+ < w,z >}{g(z,\bar{y}_i)- < v,z >} \right) - G(z,\bar{y}_i,p) + p^T \nabla_p G(z,\bar{y}_i,p) \right]$$
$$\geq \left\langle \alpha(x,z) \left\{ \nabla \sum_{i=1}^{s} t_i \left(\frac{f(z,\bar{y}_i)+ < w,z >}{g(z,\bar{y}_i)- < v,z >} \right) + \nabla_p G(z,\bar{y}_i,p) \right\}, \eta(x,z) \right\rangle + \sum_{i=1}^{s} t_i \rho_i d^2(x,z) \tag{14}$$

and

$$-\sum_{j=1}^{m} \mu_j \Big(h_j(z)+ < u_j,z > -K_j(z,p) + p^T \nabla_p K_j(z,p) \Big)$$
$$\geq \left\langle \alpha(x,z) \left\{ \nabla \sum_{j=1}^{m} \mu_j (h_j(z)+ < u_j,z >) + \nabla_p K_j(z,p) \right\}, \eta(x,z) \right\rangle + \sum_{j=1}^{m} \mu_j \rho_j d^2(x,z). \tag{15}$$

The above inequalities yield

$$\sum_{i=1}^{s} t_i \left[\left(\frac{f(x,\bar{y}_i)+ < w,x >}{g(x,\bar{y}_i)- < v,x >} \right) - \left(\frac{f(z,\bar{y}_i)+ < w,z >}{g(z,\bar{y}_i)- < v,z >} \right) \right] - \sum_{j=1}^{m} \mu_j (h_j(z)+ < u_j,z >)$$
$$- \left\{ \sum_{i=1}^{s} t_i \Big(G(z,\bar{y}_i,p) - p^T \nabla_p G(z,\bar{y}_i,p) \Big) - \sum_{j=1}^{m} \mu_j (K_j(z,p) - p^T \nabla_p K_j(z,p)) \right\}$$

$$\geq \left\langle \alpha(x,z) \left\{ \sum_{i=1}^{s} t_i \nabla \left(\frac{f(z,\bar{y}_i)+ < w,z >}{g(z,\bar{y}_i)- < v,z >} \right) + \sum_{j=1}^{m} \mu_j (\nabla h_j(z)+ < u_j,z >) + \sum_{i=1}^{s} t_i \nabla_p G(z,\bar{y}_i,p) \right.\right.$$
$$\left.\left. + \sum_{j=1}^{m} \mu_j \nabla_p K_j(z,p) \right\}, \eta(x,z) \right\rangle + \left(\sum_{i=1}^{s} t_i \rho_i + \sum_{j=1}^{m} \mu_j \rho_j \right) d^2(x,z).$$

The above inequality together with (11), $\alpha(x,z) > 0$, and hypothesis (ii) yield

$$\Big\langle \sum_{i=1}^{s} t_i \nabla\Big(\frac{f(z,\bar{y}_i)+ < w,z >}{g(z,\bar{y}_i)- < v,z >}\Big) + \sum_{j=1}^{m} \mu_j \nabla(h_j(z)+ < u_j,z >)$$

$$+ \sum_{i=1}^{s} t_i \nabla_p G(z,\bar{y}_i,p) + \sum_{j=1}^{m} \mu_j \nabla_p K_j(z,p), \eta(x,z)\Big\rangle < 0, \quad (16)$$

which contradicts (5). This completes the proof. □

Theorem 3 (Strong duality). *Suppose the set* $\Big\{\nabla(h_j(x^*)+ < u_j,x^* >)\Big\}_{j\in N(x^*)}$ *is linearly independent. Let an optimal solution of (FP) be* x^**, further, suppose*

$$G(x^*,\bar{y}_i^*,0) = \nabla_{p^*} G(x^*,\bar{y}_i^*,0) = 0,\ i \in S'^*, \quad (17)$$

$$K_j(x^*,0) = \nabla_{p^*} K_j(x^*,0) = 0,\ j \in M. \quad (18)$$

Then, there exist $(s^*,t^*,\bar{y}^*) \in K(x^*)$ *and* $(x^*,w^*,v^*,u^*,v^*,s^*,t^*,\bar{y}^*,p^*) \in H(s^*,t^*,\bar{y}^*)$ *such that* $(x^*,w^*,v^*,\mu^*,s^*,t^*,\bar{y}^*,p^* = 0) \in T^0$ *and the objectives have the equal values. Moreover, if all the conditions of Weak duality theorem hold for any* $(z,w,v,\mu,s,t,\bar{y},p) \in T^0$*, then* $(x^*,w^*,v^*,u^*,\mu^*,s^*,t^*,\bar{y}^*,p^* = 0)$ *is an optimal solution of (HFD).*

Proof. By Theorem 1, $\exists\ (s^*,t^*,\bar{y}^*) \in K(x^*)$ such that

$$\sum_{i=1}^{s^*} t_i^* \nabla\Big(\frac{f(x^*,\bar{y}_i)+ < w,x^* >}{g(x^*,\bar{y}_i)- < v,x^* >}\Big) + \sum_{j=1}^{m} \mu_j^* \nabla(h_j(x^*)+ < u_j,x^* >) = 0, \quad (19)$$

$$\sum_{j=1}^{m} \mu_j^*(h_j(x^*)+ < u_j,x^* >) = 0, \quad (20)$$

$$t_i^* \geq 0,\ i \in S',\ \sum_{i=1}^{s} t_i^* = 1,\ \mu_j^* \geq 0,\ j \in M, \quad (21)$$

$$< w,x^* >= s(x^*|C),\ < v,x^* >= s(x^*|D),\ < u_j,x^* >= s(x^*|E_j),\ j \in M, \quad (22)$$

which, from (17) and (18), imply $(x^*,w^*,v^*,\mu^*,s^*,t^*,\bar{y}^*,p^* = 0) \in T^0$ and the problems (FP) and (HFD) have the same objective value. The point $(x^*,w^*,v^*,\mu^*,s^*,t^*,\bar{y}^*,p^* = 0)$ is an optimal solution for (HFD) follows from Theorem 2. This completes the proof. □

Theorem 4 (Strict converse duality). *Suppose that* x^* *and* $(z^*,w^*,v^*,v^*,s^*,t^*,\bar{y}^*,p^*)$ *are the optimal solutions of (FP) and (HFD), respectively. Let*

(i) $\Big[\frac{f(.,\bar{y}_i^*)+ < w^*,.>}{g(.,\bar{y}_i^*)- < v^*,.>}, h_j(.)+ < u_j^* >\Big]$, $i \in S'$, $j \in M$ *be higher-order strictly* (V,α,ρ,d)*- type -I and the set* $\{\nabla h_j(x^*)+ < u_j^*,.>, j \in N(x^*)\}$ *be linearly independent,*

(ii) $\sum_{i=1}^{s^*} t_i^* \rho_i^* + \sum_{j=1}^{m} \mu_j^* \rho_j^* \geq 0.$

Then, $z^* = x^*$.

Proof. Suppose contrary to the result that $z^* \neq x^*$. From Theorem 3, we have

$$\sup_{y\in Y}\left(\frac{f(x^*,y^*)+<w^*,x^*>}{g(x^*,y^*)-<v^*,x^*>}\right)\leq\sum_{i=1}^{s^*}t_i^*\left(\frac{f(z^*,\bar{y}_i^*)+<w^*,z^*>}{g(z^*,\bar{y}_i^*)-<v^*,z^*>}\right)+\sum_{i=1}^{m}\mu_j^*(h_j(z^*)+<u_j^*,z^*>$$

$$-\sum_{i=1}^{s^*}t_i^*\left(G(z^*,\bar{y}_i^*,p^*)-p^{*T}\nabla_{p^*}G(z^*,\bar{y}_i^*,p^*)\right)+\sum_{i=1}^{m}\mu_j^*(K_j(z^*,p^*)-p^{*T}\nabla_{p^*}K_j(z^*,p^*)). \tag{23}$$

Thus, we obtain

$$\left(\frac{f(x^*,y_i^*)+<w^*,x^*>}{g(x^*,y_i^*)-<v^*,x^*>}\right)\leq\sum_{i=1}^{s^*}t_i^*\left(\frac{f(z^*,\bar{y}_i^*)+<w^*,z^*>}{g(z^*,\bar{y}_i^*)-<v^*,z^*>}\right)+\sum_{i=1}^{m}\mu_j^*(h_j(z^*)+<u_j^*,z^*>)$$
$$-\sum_{i=1}^{s^*}t_i^*\left(G(z^*,\bar{y}_i^*,p^*)-p^{*T}\nabla_{p^*}G(z^*,\bar{y}_i^*,p^*)\right)+\sum_{i=1}^{m}\mu_j^*(K_j(z^*,\bar{y}_i^*,p^*)$$
$$-p^{*T}\nabla_{p^*}K_j(z^*,\bar{y}_i^*,p^*)),\ \text{for all } \bar{y}_i^*\in Y(x^*),\ i\in S'^*. \tag{24}$$

Following on the lines of Theorem 2, we get

$$\sum_{i=1}^{s^*}t_i^*\left(\frac{f(x^*,y_i^*)+<w^*,x^*>}{g(x^*,y_i^*)-<v^*,x^*>}\right)\leq\sum_{i=1}^{s^*}t_i^*\left(\frac{f(z^*,\bar{y}_i^*)+<w^*,z^*>}{g(z^*,\bar{y}_i^*)-<v^*,z^*>}\right)+\sum_{i=1}^{m}\mu_j^*(h_j(z^*)+<u_j^*,z^*>)$$

$$-\sum_{i=1}^{s^*}t_i^*\left(G(z^*,\bar{y}_i^*,p^*)-p^{*T}\nabla_{p^*}G(z^*,\bar{y}_i^*,p^*)\right)+\sum_{i=1}^{m}\mu_j^*(K_j(z^*,p^*)-p^{*T}\nabla_{p^*}K_j(z^*,p^*)). \tag{25}$$

From hypothesis (i), we have

$$\left(\frac{f(x^*,\bar{y}_i^*)+<w^*,x^*>}{g(x^*,\bar{y}_i)^*-<v^*,x^*>}\right)-\left(\frac{f(z^*,\bar{y}_i^*)+<w^*,z^*>}{g(z^*,\bar{y}_i^*)-<v^*,z^*>}\right)-G(z^*,\bar{y}_i^*,p^*)+p^{*T}\nabla_{p^*}G(z^*,\bar{y}_i^*,p^*)$$

$$>\left\langle\alpha(x^*,z^*)\left\{\nabla\left(\frac{f(z^*,\bar{y}_i^*)+<w^*,z^*>}{g(z^*,\bar{y}_i^*)-<v^*,z^*>}\right)+\nabla_{p^*}G(z^*,\bar{y}_i^*,p^*)\right\},\eta(x^*,z^*)\right\rangle+\rho_i^*d^2(x^*,z^*),\ i\in S'^*$$

and

$$-(h_j(z^*)+<u_j^*,z^*>)-K_j(z^*,p^*)+p^{*T}\nabla_{p^*}K_j(z^*,p^*)$$

$$>\left\langle\alpha(x^*,z^*)\left\{\nabla(h_j(z^*)+<u_j^*,z^*>)+\nabla_{p^*}K_j(z^*,p^*)\right\},\eta(x^*,z^*)\right\rangle+\rho_j^*d^2(x^*,z^*),\ j\in M.$$

Multiplying the first inequality by $t_i^*\geq 0,\ i\in S'$ and the second by $\mu_j^*\geq 0,\ j=1\in M$ with $\sum_{i=1}^{s^*}t_i^*=1$, we get

$$\sum_{i=1}^{s^*}t_i^*\left[\frac{f(x^*,\bar{y}_i^*)+<w^*,x^*>}{g(x^*,\bar{y}_i^*)-<v^*,x^*>}-\frac{f(z^*,\bar{y}_i^*)+<w^*,z^*>}{g(z^*,\bar{y}_i^*)-<v^*,z^*>}\right]-\sum_{i=1}^{s^*}t_i^*\left(G(z^*,\bar{y}_i^*,p^*)\right.$$
$$\left.+p^{*T}\nabla_{p^*}G(z^*,\bar{y}_i^*,p^*)\right)>\left\langle\alpha(x^*,z^*)\left\{\sum_{i=1}^{s^*}t_i^*\nabla\left(\frac{f(z^*,\bar{y}_i^*)+<w^*,x^*>}{g(z^*,\bar{y}_i^*)-<v^*,z^*>}\right)\right.\right.$$

$$\left.\left.+\sum_{i=1}^{s^*}t_i^*\nabla_{p^*}G(z^*,\bar{y}_i^*,p^*)\right\},\eta(x^*,z^*)\right\rangle+\sum_{i=1}^{s^*}t_i^*\rho_i d^2(x^*,z^*) \tag{26}$$

and

$$-\sum_{j=1}^{m}\mu_j^*(h_j(z^*)+<u_j^*,z^*> -K_j(x^*,p^*)+p^{*T}\nabla_{p^*}K_j(z^*,p^*)$$

$$> \left\langle \alpha(x^*,z^*)\left\{\sum_{j=1}^{m}\mu_j^*\nabla(h_j(z^*)+<u_j^*,z^*>)+\sum_{j=1}^{m}\mu_j^*\nabla_{p^*}K_j(x^*,p^*)\right\},\eta(x^*,z^*)\right\rangle+\sum_{j=1}^{m}\mu_j^*\rho_j d^2(x^*,z^*). \quad (27)$$

The above inequalities yield

$$\sum_{i=1}^{s^*}t_i^*\left[\left(\frac{f(x^*,\bar{y}_i^*)+<w^*,x^*>}{g(x^*,\bar{y}_i^*)-<v^*,x^*>}\right)-\left(\frac{f(z^*,\bar{y}_i^*)+<w^*,z^*>}{g(z^*,\bar{y}_i^*)-<v^*,z^*>}\right)\right]-\sum_{j=1}^{m}\mu_j^*(h_j(z^*)+<u_j^*,z^*>)$$
$$-\sum_{j=m}^{m}\mu_j^*(K_j(x^*,p^*)-p^{*T}\nabla_{p^*}K_j(x^*,p^*))-\sum_{i=1}^{s^*}t_i^*\Big(G(z^*,\bar{y}_i^*,p^*)-p^{*T}\nabla_{p^*}G(z^*,\bar{y}_i^*,p^*)\Big)-$$
$$\sum_{j=1}^{m}\mu_j^*\Big(h_j(z^*)+<u_j^*,z^*> -K_j(z^*,p^*)+p^{*T}\nabla_{p^*}K_j(z^*,p^*)\Big)$$

$$> \left\langle \alpha(x^*,z^*)\left[\sum_{i=1}^{s^*}t_i^*\nabla\left(\frac{f(z^*,\bar{y}_i^*)+<w^*,z^*>}{g(z^*,\bar{y}_i^*)-<v^*,z^*>}\right)+\sum_{j=1}^{m}\mu_j^*(\nabla h_j(z^*)+<u_j^*,z^*>)\right.\right.$$

$$\left.\left.+\left\{\sum_{i=1}^{s^*}t_i^*\nabla_{p^*}G(z^*,\bar{y}_i^*,p^*)+\sum_{j=1}^{m}\mu_j^*\nabla_{p^*}K_j(z^*,p^*)\right\}\right],\eta(x^*,z^*)\right\rangle+\left(\sum_{i=1}^{s}t_i^*\rho_i^*+\sum_{j=1}^{m}\mu_j^*\rho_j^*\right)d^2(x^*,z^*).$$

It follows from (11), $\alpha(x^*,z^*)>0$, and hypothesis (ii) that

$$\sum_{i=1}^{s^*}t_i^*\left(\frac{f(x^*,\bar{y}_i^*)+<w^*,x^*>}{g(x^*,\bar{y}_i^*)-<v^*,x^*>}\right) > \sum_{i=1}^{s^*}t_i^*\left(\frac{f(z^*,\bar{y}_i^*)+<w^*,z^*>}{g(z^*,\bar{y}_i^*)-<v^*,z^*>}\right)+\sum_{j=1}^{m}\mu_j^*(h_j(z^*)+<u_j^*,z^*>)$$
$$-\sum_{i=1}^{s^*}t_i^*\Big(G(z^*,\bar{y}_i^*,p^*)+p^{*T}\nabla_{p^*}G(z^*,\bar{y}_i^*,p^*)\Big)-\sum_{j=1}^{m}\mu_j^*\Big(K_j(z^*,p^*)+p^{*T}\nabla_{p^*}K_j(z^*,p^*)\Big),$$

which contradicts (25). Hence, $z^*=x^*$. □

4. Mixed-Type Higher-Order Duality Model

Consider the following higher-order unified dual (HMFD) to (FP):

$$\textbf{(HMFD)} \quad \max_{(s,t,\bar{y})\in K(z)} \sup_{(z,w,v,\mu,p)\in H(s,t,\bar{y})} \sum_{i=1}^{s}t_i\left(\frac{f(z,\bar{y}_i)+<w,z>}{g(z,\bar{y}_i)-<v,z>}\right)+\sum_{j\in J_0}\mu_j(h_j(z)+<u_j,z>)$$
$$+\sum_{i=1}^{s}t_i\Big(G(z,\bar{y}_i,p)-p^T\nabla_pG(z,\bar{y}_i,p)\Big)+\sum_{j\in J_0}\mu_j\Big(K_j(z,p)-p^T\nabla_pK_j(z,p)\Big),$$

where $H(s,t,\bar{y})$ represents the set of all $(z,w,v,,\mu,p)$ such that

$$\nabla\sum_{i=1}^{s}t_i\left(\frac{f(z,\bar{y}_i)+<w,z>}{g(z,\bar{y}_i)-<v,z>}\right)+\nabla\sum_{j=1}^{m}\mu_j(h_j(z)+<u_j,z>)$$

$$+\sum_{i=1}^{s}t_i\nabla_pG(z,\bar{y}_i,p)+\sum_{j=1}^{m}\mu_j\nabla_pK_j(z,p)=0, \quad (28)$$

$$\sum_{j\in J_\beta}\mu_j(h_j(z)+<u_j,z>)+\sum_{j\in J_\beta}\mu_j(K_j(z,p)-p^T\nabla_pK_j(z,p))\geq 0,\ \beta=1,2,...,r, \quad (29)$$

$$t_i \geq 0,\ \sum_{i=1}^{s} t_i = 1,\ \mu_j \geq 0,\ i \in S',\ j \in M, \tag{30}$$

where $J_\beta \subseteq M,\ \beta = 0, 1, 2, ..., r$ with $\bigcup_{\beta=0}^{r} J_\beta = M$ and $J_\beta \bigcap J_\gamma = \phi$, if $\beta \neq \gamma$. Let W^0 be the feasible set for (HMFD).

Theorem 5 (Weak duality). *Let $x \in S$ and $(z, w, v, \mu, s, t, \bar{y}, p) \in W^0$. Let*

(i) $\left[\sum_{i=1}^{s} t_i \left(\frac{f(.,\bar{y}_i) + < w, . >}{g(.,\bar{y}_i) - < v, . >}\right) + \sum_{j \in J_0} \mu_j (h_j(.) + < u_j, . >),\ \sum_{j \in J_\beta} \mu_j (h_j(.) + < u_j, . >)\right],\ \beta = 1, 2, ..., r$ *be higher-order pseudoquasi (V, α, ρ, d)-type -I ,*

(ii) $\sum_{i=1}^{s} t_i \rho_i + \sum_{j=1}^{m} \mu_j \rho_j \geq 0.$

Then,

$$\sup_{y \in Y} \left(\frac{f(x,y) + < w, x >}{g(x,y) - < v, x >}\right) \geq \sum_{i=1}^{s} t_i \left(\frac{f(z,\bar{y}_i) + < w, z > w}{g(z,\bar{y}_i) - < v, x >}\right) + \sum_{j \in J_0} \mu_j (h_j(z) + < u_j, z >)$$

$$+ \sum_{i=1}^{s} t_i \Big(G(z,\bar{y}_i,p) - p^T \nabla_p G(z,\bar{y}_i,p) + \sum_{j \in J_0} \mu_j (K_j(z,p) - p^T \nabla_p K_j(z,p)). \tag{31}$$

Proof. Proof follows on the lines of Theorem 2. □

Theorem 6 (Strong duality). *Suppose the set $\left\{\nabla(h_j(x^*) + < u_j, x^* >)\right\}_{j \in N(x^*)}$ is linearly independent. Let an optimal solution of (FP) be x^*, further, suppose*

$$G(x^*, \bar{y}_i^*, 0) = \nabla_{p^*} G(x^*, \bar{y}_i^*, 0) = 0,\ i \in S'^*, \tag{32}$$

$$K_j(x^*, 0) = \nabla_{p^*} K_j(x^*, 0) = 0,\ j \in M. \tag{33}$$

Then, $\exists\ (s^*, t^*, \bar{y}^*) \in K(x^*)$ and $(x^*, w^*, v^*, u^*, v^*, s^*, t^*, \bar{y}^*, p^*) \in H(s^*, t^*, \bar{y}^*)$ such that $(x^*, w^*, v^*, \mu^*, s^*, t^*, \bar{y}^*, p^* = 0) \in W^0$ and the two objectives have the equal values. In addition, if all the conditions of Weak duality theorem hold for any $(z, w, v, \mu, s, t, u^*, \bar{y}, p) \in W^0$, then $(x^*, w^*, v^*, \mu^*, u^*, s^*, t^*, \bar{y}^*, p^* = 0)$ is an optimal solution of (HMFD).

Proof. The proof can be obtained following the lines of Theorem 3. □

Theorem 7 (Strict converse duality). *Let x^* and $(z^*, w^*, v^*, v^*, s^*, u^*, t^*, \bar{y}^*, p^*)$ be the optimal solutions of (FP) and (HMFD), respectively. Let*

(i) $\left[\frac{f(.,\bar{y}_i^*) + < w^*, >}{g(.,y_i^*) - < v^*, >} + \sum_{j \in J_0} \mu_j^* [h_j + < u_j^*, >], \sum_{j \in J_\beta} \mu_j^* [h_j + < u_j^*, >]\right],\ \beta = 1, 2, ..., r$ *be higher-order strictly pseudo (V, α, ρ, d)- type -I and $\nabla(h_j(x^*) + < u_j^*, x^* >),\ j \in N(x^*)$ be linearly independent,*

(ii) $\sum_{i=1}^{s^*} t_i^* \rho_i + \sum_{j=1}^{m} \mu_j^* \rho_j \geq 0.$

Then, $z^* = x^*$.

Proof. The proof can be derived following the steps of Theorem 4. □

5. Conclusions

In this paper, we discussed higher-order duality theorems for two types of dual models of nondifferentiable minimax fractional programming problems under strictly pseudo (V, α, ρ, d)-type-I functions. The question arises as to whether the second/higher-order duality theorems developed in this paper hold for the complex minimax fractional programming problem. This will orient the future task of the authors.

Author Contributions: Formal Analysis: V.N.M., Editing: R.A. and Investigation: R.D. All authors contributed equally to this research. The research was carried out by all authors. The manuscript was prepared together and they all read and approved the final version.

Funding: The authors extend their appreciation to the "Deanship of Scientific Research" at King Khalid University for funding this work through research groups program under grant number R.G.P.1/152/40.

Acknowledgments: The authors are thankful to the anonymous referees and editor for their valuable suggestions, which have substantially improved the presentation of the paper.

Conflicts of Interest: The authors declare no conflict of interest.

References

1. Beresnev, V.V. Necessary conditions for extremum in a convex maximin problem on connected sets. *Kibernetika* **1972**, *2*, 87–91.
2. Demyanov, V.F. *Minimax, Directional Differentiability*; Leningrad Univ. Press: Leningrad, Russia, 1974.
3. Demyanov, V.F.; Pevnyi, A.B. Numerical methods for finding saddle points. *USSR Comput. Math. Math. Phys.* **1972**, *12*, 11–52. [CrossRef]
4. Stancu-Minasian, I.M. *Fractional Programming, Theory, Methods and Applications*; Kluwer Academic Publishers: Dordrecht, The Netherlands, 1997.
5. Tanimoto, S. Duality for a class of nondifferentiable mathematical programming problems. *J. Math. Anal. Appl.* **1981**, *7*, 283–294. [CrossRef]
6. Liang, Z.A.; Shi, Z.W. Optimality conditions and duality for a minimax fractional programming with generalized convexity. *J. Math. Anal. Appl.* **2003**, *277*, 474–488. [CrossRef]
7. Lai, H.C.; Lee, J.C. On duality theorems for a nondifferentiable minimax fractional programming. *J. Comput. Appl. Math.* **2002**, *146*, 115–126. [CrossRef]
8. Yuan, D.H.; Liu, X.L.; Chinchuluun, A.; Pardalos, P.M. Nondifferentiable minimax fractional programming problems. *J. Optim. Theory Appl.* **2006**, *129*, 185–199. [CrossRef]
9. Mishra, S.K.; Lai, K.K.; Singh, V. Optimality and duality for minimax fractional programming with support function under (C, α, ρ, d)-convexity. *J. Comput. Appl. Math.* **2015**, *274*, 1–10. [CrossRef]
10. Jayswal, A. Optimality and duality for nondifferentiable minimax fractional programming with generalized convexity. *Appl. Math.* **2011**. [CrossRef]
11. Dubey, R.; Mishra, L.N.; Mishra, V.N. Duality relations for a class of a multiobjective fractional programming problem involving support functions. *Am. J. Oper. Res.* **2018**, *08*, 294–311.
12. Dubey, R.; Mishra, V.N. Symmetric duality results for a nondifferentiable multiobjective programming problem with support function under strongly assumptions. *RAIRO-Oper. Res.* **2019**, *53*, 539–558. [CrossRef]
13. Dubey, R.; Mishra, L.N.; Ali, R. Special class of second-order non-differentiable symmetric duality problems with (G, α_f)-pseudobonvexity assumptions. *Mathematics* **2019**, *7*, 763. [CrossRef]
14. Dubey, R.; Mishra, L.N. Nondifferentiable multiobjective higher-order duality relations for unified type dual models under type-I functions. *Adv. Stud. Contemp. Math.* **2019**, *29*, 373–382.
15. Stancu-Minasian, I.M. A sixth bibiliography of fractional programming. *Optimization* **2006**, *55*, 405–428. [CrossRef]
16. Stancu-Minasian, I.M. A seven bibiliography of fractional programming. *Adv. Model. Optim.* **2013**, *15*, 309–386.
17. Liang, Z.A.; Huang, H.X.; Pardalos, P.M. Optimaity conditions and duality for a class of nonlinear fractional programming problems. *J. Optim. Theory Appl.* **2002**, *110*, 611–619. [CrossRef]

18. Hachimi, M.; Aghezzaf, B. Sufficiency and duality in differentiable multiobjective programming involving generalized type I functions. *J. Math. Anal. Appl.* **2004**, *296*, 382–392. [CrossRef]
19. Jayswal, A.; Kummari, K. Second-order duality for nondifferentiable minimax programming problems involving generalized α-type-I functions. *Int. J. Math. Oper. Res.* **2014**, *6*, 393–406. [CrossRef]

Article

Special Class of Second-Order Non-Differentiable Symmetric Duality Problems with (G, α_f)-Pseudobonvexity Assumptions

Ramu Dubey [1], Lakshmi Narayan Mishra [2,*] and Rifaqat Ali [3]

[1] Department of Mathematics, J.C. Bose University of Science and Technology, YMCA, Faridabad 121 006, India
[2] Department of Mathematics, School of Advanced Sciences, Vellore Institute of Technology (VIT) University, Vellore 632 014, India
[3] Department of Mathematics, College of Science, King Khalid University, Abha 9004, Saudi Arabia
* Correspondence: lakshminarayanmishra04@gmail.com

Received: 24 June 2019; Accepted: 15 August 2019; Published: 20 August 2019

Abstract: In this paper, we introduce the various types of generalized invexities, i.e., α_f-invex/α_f-pseudoinvex and (G, α_f)-bonvex/(G, α_f)-pseudobonvex functions. Furthermore, we construct nontrivial numerical examples of (G, α_f)-bonvexity/(G, α_f)-pseudobonvexity, which is neither α_f-bonvex/α_f-pseudobonvex nor α_f-invex/α_f-pseudoinvex with the same η. Further, we formulate a pair of second-order non-differentiable symmetric dual models and prove the duality relations under α_f-invex/α_f-pseudoinvex and (G, α_f)-bonvex/(G, α_f)-pseudobonvex assumptions. Finally, we construct a nontrivial numerical example justifying the weak duality result presented in the paper.

Keywords: symmetric duality; second-order; non-differentiable; (G, α_f)-invexity/(G, α_f)-pseudoinvexity; (G, α_f)-bonvexity/(G, α_f)-pseudobonvexity

---

1. Introduction

Decision making is an integral and indispensable part of life. Every day, one has to make decisions of some type or the other. The decision process is relatively easier when there is a single criterion or objective in mind. The duality hypothesis in nonlinear writing programs is identified with the complementary standards of the analytics of varieties. Persuaded by the idea of second-order duality in nonlinear problems, presented by Mangasarian [1], numerous analysts have likewise worked here. The benefit of second-order duality is considered over first-order as it gives all the more closer limits. Hanson [2] in his examination referred to one model that shows the utilization of second-order duality from a fairly alternate point of view.

Motivated by different ideas of generalized convexity, Ojha [3] formulated the generalized problem and determined duality theorems. Expanding the idea of [3] by Jayswal [4], a new kind of problem has been defined and duality results demonstrated under generalized convexity presumptions over cone requirements. Later on, Jayswal et al. [5] defined higher order duality for multiobjective problems and set up duality relations utilizing higher order $(F, \alpha, \rho d)$-V-Type I suspicions. As of late, Suneja et al. [6] utilized the idea of (F, α, σ)-type I capacities to build up K-K-T-type sufficient optimality conditions for the non-smooth multiobjective fractional programming problem. Many researchers have done work related to the same area [7–9].

The definition of the G-convex function introduced by Avriel et al. [10], which is a further generalization of a convex function where G has the properties that it is a real-valued strictly-increasing, and continuous function. Further, under the assumption of G-invexity, Antczak [11] introduced the concept of the G-invex function and derived some optimality conditions for the constrained problem. In [12], Antczak extended the above notion and proved necessary and sufficient optimality conditions for Pareto-optimal solutions of a multiobjective programming problem. Moreover, defining G-invexity for a locally-Lipschitz function by Kang et al. [13], the optimality conditions for a multiobjective programming are obtained. Recently, Gao [14] introduced a new type of generalized invexity and derived sufficiency conditions under $B-(p,r)-V$-Type-I assumptions.

In this article, we develop the meanings of (G,α_f)-bonvexity/(G,α_f)-pseudo-bonvexity and give nontrivial numerical examples for such kinds of existing functions. We formulate a second-order non-differentiable symmetric dual model and demonstrate duality results under (G,α_f)-bonvexity/(G,α_f)-pseudobonvexity assumptions. Furthermore, we build different nontrivial examples, which legitimize the definitions, as well as the weak duality hypothesis introduced in the paper.

2. Preliminaries and Definitions

Let R^n denote n-dimensional Euclidean space and R^n_+ be its non-negative orthant. Let C_1 and C_2 be closed convex cones in R^n and R^m, respectively, with nonempty interiors. For a real-valued twice differentiable function $g(x,y)$ defined on an open set in $R^n \times R^m$, denote by $\nabla_x g(\bar{x},\bar{y})$ the gradient vector of g with respect to x at $(\bar{x},\bar{y})$ and $\nabla_{xx} g(\bar{x},\bar{y})$ the Hessian matrix with respect to x at $(\bar{x},\bar{y})$. Similarly, $\nabla_{yx} g(\bar{x},\bar{y})$, $\nabla_{xy} g(\bar{x},\bar{y})$, and $\nabla_{yy} g(\bar{x},\bar{y})$ are also defined.

Let $X \subseteq R^n$ be an open set. Let $f : X \to R$ be a differentiable function and $G : I_f(X) \longrightarrow R$, where $I_f(X)$ is the range of f such that G is strictly increasing on the range of f, $\alpha_f : X \times X \to R_+ \setminus \{0\}$ and $\eta : X \times X \to R^n$.

Definition 1. *Let E be a compact convex set in R^n. The support function of E is defined by:*

$$s(y|E) = max\{y^T z : z \in E\}.$$

A support function, being convex and everywhere finite, has a subdifferential, that is there exists a $z \in R^n$ such that:

$$s(z|E) \geq s(y|E) + u^T(z-y), \forall y \in E.$$

The subdifferential of $s(y|E)$ is given by:

$$\partial s(y|E) = \{u \in E : u^T y = s(y|E)\}.$$

For a convex set $F \subset R^n$, the normal cone to F at a point $y \in F$ is defined by:

$$N_F(y) = \{z \in R^n : z^T(u-y) \leq 0, \forall u \in F\}.$$

When E is a compact convex set, $z \in N_E(y)$ if and only if $s(z|E) = y^T z$ or, equivalently, $y \in \partial s(z|E)$.

Definition 2. *The positive polar cone S^* of a cone $S \subseteq R^s$ is defined by:*

$$S^* = \{z \in R^s : y^T z \geq 0\}.$$

Now, we give the definitions of α_f-invex/α_f-pseudoinvex and (G,α_f)-bonvex/(G,α_f)-pseudobonvex functions with respect to η.

Definition 3. *If there exist functions $\alpha_f : Y \times Z \to R_+ \setminus \{0\}$ and $\eta : Y \times Y \to R^n$ s.t. $\forall y \in Y$,*

$$\frac{1}{\alpha_f(y,v)}[f(y) - f(v)] \geq \eta^T(y,v)\nabla_y f(v),$$

then f is called α_f-invex at $v \in Y$ with respect to η.

Definition 4. *If there exists functions $\alpha_f : Y \times Y \to R_+ \setminus \{0\}$ and $\eta : Y \times Y \to R^n$ such that $\forall y \in Y$,*

$$\eta^T(y,v)\nabla_y f(v) \geq 0 \Rightarrow \frac{1}{\alpha_f(y,v)}[f(y) - f(v)] \geq 0,$$

then f is called α_f-pseudoinvex at $v \in Y$ with respect to η.

Definition 5. *$f : Y \longrightarrow R$ is (G, α_f)-bonvex at $v \in Y$, if there exist G, $\alpha_f : Y \times Y \to R_+ \setminus \{0\}$ and $\eta : Y \times Y \longrightarrow R^n$ if $\forall (y,p) \in Y \times R^n$,*

$$\frac{1}{\alpha_f(y,v)}[G(f(y)) - G(f(v)) + \frac{1}{2}p^T\{G''(f(v))\nabla_v f(v)(\nabla_v f(v))^T + G'(f(v))\nabla_{vv} f(v)\}p]:$$

$$\geq \eta^T(y,v)[G'(f(v))\nabla_v f(v) + \{G''(f(v))\nabla_v f(v)(\nabla_v f(v))^T + G'(f(v))\nabla_{vv} f(v)\}p].$$

Definition 6. *$f : Y \longrightarrow R$ is (G, α_f)-pseudobonvex at $v \in Y$, if there exist G, $\alpha_f : Y \times Y \to R_+ \setminus \{0\}$ and a function $\eta : Y \times Y \longrightarrow R^n$ if $\forall (y,p) \in Y \times R^n$,*

$$\eta^T(y,v)[G'(f(v))\nabla_v f(v) + \{G''(f(v))\nabla_v f(v)(\nabla_v f(v))^T + G'(f(v))\nabla_{vv} f(v)\}p] \geq 0:$$

$$\Longrightarrow \frac{1}{\alpha_f(y,v)}[G(f(y)) - G(f(v)) + \frac{1}{2}p^T\{G''(f(v))\nabla_v f(v)(\nabla_v f(v))^T + G'(f(v))\nabla_{vv} f(v)\}p] \geq 0.$$

Remark 1. *If $G(t) = t$, then Definitions 5 and 6 become the α_f-bonvex/α_f-pseudobonvex functions with the same η.*

Now, we present here functions that are (G, α_f)-bonvexity/(G, α_f)-pseudobonvexity, but neither α_f-bonvex/α_f-pseudobonvex nor α_f-invex/α_f-pseudoinvex with the same η.

Example 1. *Let $f : \left[-\frac{\pi}{3}, \frac{\pi}{3}\right] \longrightarrow R$ be defined as*

$$f(y) = y^7, \ \forall\, y \in \left[-\frac{\pi}{3}, \frac{\pi}{3}\right].$$

A function $G : R \longrightarrow R$ is defined as:

$$G(t) = 2t^4.$$

Let $\eta : \left[-\frac{\pi}{3}, \frac{\pi}{3}\right] \times \left[-\frac{\pi}{3}, \frac{\pi}{3}\right] \longrightarrow R$ be given as:

$$\eta(y,v) = y^9 + y^2v^2 + 2yv + 3.$$

Furthermore, $\alpha_f : Y \times Y \to R_+ \setminus \{0\}$ is given by:

$$\alpha_f(y,v) = 2, \ \forall\, y,\ v \in \left[-\frac{\pi}{3}, \frac{\pi}{3}\right].$$

To demonstrate that f is (G, α_f)-bonvex at $v = 0$, we need to demonstrate that

$$\xi = \frac{1}{\alpha_f(y,v)}[G(f(y)) - G(f(v)) + \frac{1}{2}p^T\{G''(f(v))\nabla_v f(v)(\nabla_v f(v))^T + G'(f(v))\nabla_{vv} f(v)\}p]$$
$$- \eta^T(y,v)[G'(f(v))\nabla_v f(v) + \{G''(f(v))(\nabla_v f(v))(\nabla_v f(v))^T + G'(f(v))\nabla_{vv} f(v)\}p] \geq 0.$$

Putting the estimations of f, α_f, η, and G in the above articulation, we get:

$$\xi = [y^{28} - v^{28} + p^2\{588v^{26} + 84v^{26}\}] - (y^9 + y^2v^2 + 2yv + 3)\{1176v^{26} + 168v^{26}\}p$$

for which at $v = 0$, *we get:* $\xi \geq 0, \ \forall y \in \left[-\frac{\pi}{3}, \frac{\pi}{3}\right]$, $\left(\text{clearly, from Figure 1}\right)$.

Therefore, f *is* (G, α_f)*-bonvex at* $v = 0 \in \left[-\frac{\pi}{3}, \frac{\pi}{3}\right]$.

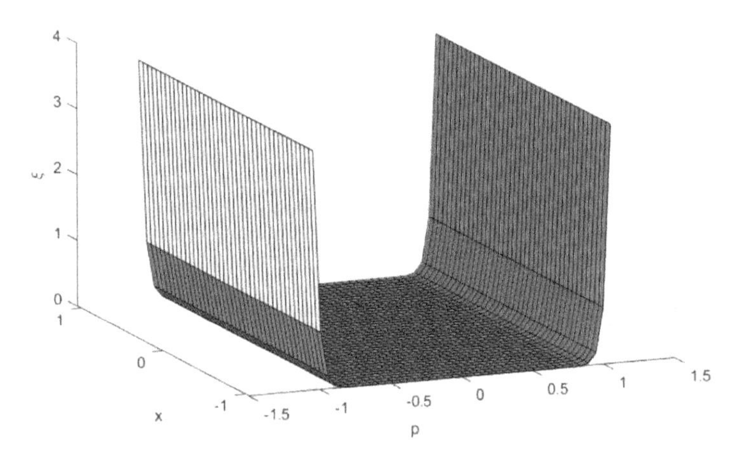

Figure 1. $\xi = y^{28}, \forall y \in [-\frac{\pi}{3}, \frac{\pi}{3}]$, and $\forall\ p$.

Next, let:

$$\delta = \frac{1}{\alpha_f(y,v)}\left[f(y) - f(v) + \frac{1}{2}p^T[\nabla_{vv}f(v)]p\right] - \eta^T(y,v)[\nabla_v f(v) + \nabla_{vv}f(v)p]$$

$$\delta = \frac{1}{2}[y^7 - v^7 + \frac{7}{2}v^5(v+6)p] - 7u^5(y^9 + y^2v^2 + 2yv + 3)(v+6),$$

for which at $v = 0$, *the above equation may not be nonnegative* $\forall\ y \in \left[-\frac{\pi}{3}, \frac{\pi}{3}\right]$ *(see Figure 2).*

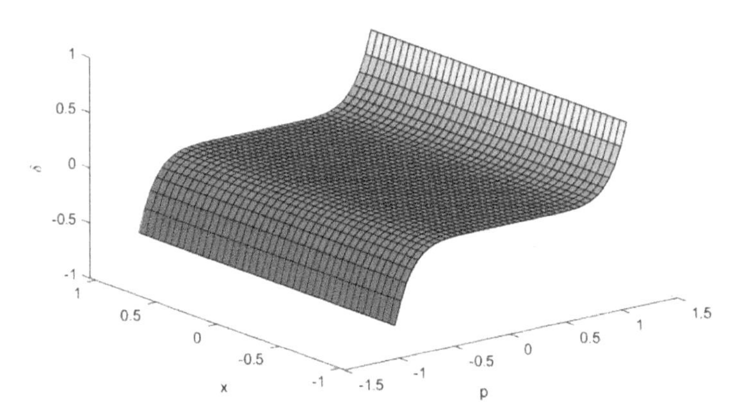

Figure 2. $\delta = \frac{y^7}{2}, \forall y \in [-\frac{\pi}{3}, \frac{\pi}{3}]$, and $\forall\ p$.

Therefore, f *is not* α_f*-bonvex at* $v = 0 \in \left[-\frac{\pi}{3}, \frac{\pi}{3}\right]$ *with the same* η.

Finally,

$$\tau = \frac{1}{\alpha_f(y,v)}\Big[f(y) - f(v)\Big] - \eta^T(y,v)\nabla_v f(v)$$

$$\tau = \frac{1}{2}[y^7 - v^7] - 7v^6(y^9 + y^2v^2 + 2yv + 3).$$

Specifically, at point $y = -\frac{\pi}{3} \in \Big[-\frac{\pi}{3}, \frac{\pi}{3}\Big]$ *and at* $v = 0$*, we find that:*

$$\tau < 0.$$

This shows that f *is not* α_f*-invex with the same* η*.*

Example 2. *Let* $f : [-1,1] \longrightarrow R$ *be defined as:*

$$f(y) = arc(tany).$$

A function $G : R \longrightarrow R$ *is defined as:*

$$G(t) = tant.$$

Let $\eta : [-1,1] \times [-1,1] \longrightarrow R$ *be given as:*

$$\eta(y,v) = -\frac{1}{11}y^{20} + y + 15y^3v^3.$$

Furthermore, $\alpha_f : Y \times Y \to R_+ \setminus \{0\}$ *is given by:*

$$\alpha_f(y,v) = 1,\ \forall\, y,\ v \in [-1,\ 1].$$

Now, we have to claim that f *is* $(G,\ \alpha_f)$*-bonvex at* $v = 0$*. For this, we have to prove that*

$$\begin{aligned}\pi = {} & \frac{1}{\alpha_f(y,v)}[G(f(y)) - G(f(v)) + \frac{1}{2}p^T\{G''(f(v))\nabla_v f(v)(\nabla_v f(v))^T + G'(f(v))\nabla_{vv}f(v)\}p] \\ & - \eta^T(y,v)[G'(f(v))\nabla_v f(v) + \{G''(f(v))\nabla_v f(v)(\nabla_v f(v))^T \\ & + G'(f(v))\nabla_{vv}f(v)\}p] \geq 0.\end{aligned}$$

Substituting the values of $f,\ \alpha_f,\ \eta$*, and* G *in the above expression, we obtain:*

$$\pi = y - v - (-\frac{1}{11}y^{20} + y + 15y^3v^3) \times 1$$

Clearly, from Figure 3, $\pi \geq 0,\ \forall y \in [-1,\ 1]$ *and* $v = 0$*.*
Therefore, f *is* $(G,\ \alpha_f)$*-bonvex at* $v = 0$ *with respect to* η*.*
Suppose,

$$\chi = \frac{1}{\alpha_f(y,v)}[f(y) - f(v) + \frac{1}{2}p^T(\nabla_{vv}f(v)]p) - \eta^T(y,v)[\nabla_v f(v) + \nabla_{vv}f(v)p],$$

$$\chi = arc(tany) - arc(tanv) - \Big(-\frac{1}{11}y^{20} + y + 15y^3v^3\Big)\Big[\frac{1}{1+v^2} - \frac{2vp}{(1+v^2)^2}\Big] - \frac{vp^2}{(1+v^2)^2}$$

which at $v = 0$ *yields:*

$$\chi = arc(tany) + \frac{1}{11}y^{20} - y.$$

$$\chi < 0,\ \forall y \in [-1,1]$$

(from Figure 4).

This implies that f *is not* α_f*-bonvex at* $v = 0$ *with the same* η*.*

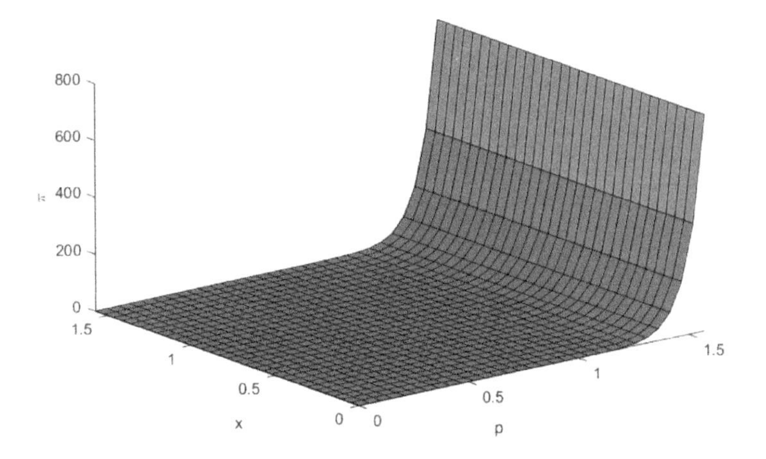

Figure 3. $\pi = \frac{1}{11}y^{20}$, $\forall y \in [-1,1]$, and $\forall$ p.

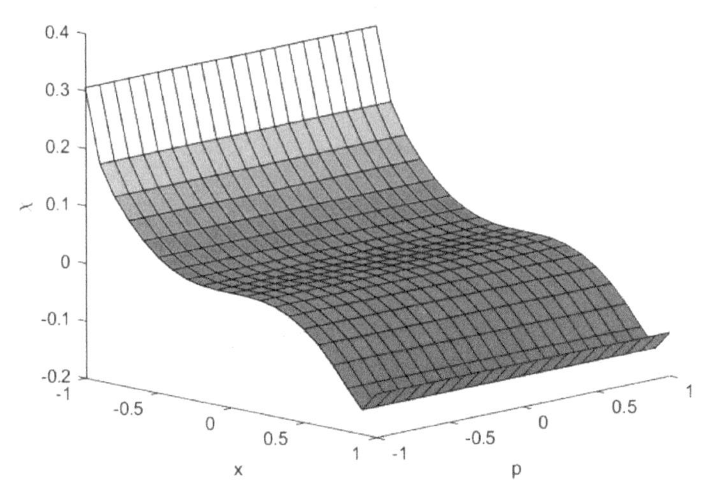

Figure 4. $\varrho = arc(tany) + \frac{1}{11}y^{20} - y$, $\forall y \in [-1,1]$, and $\forall$ p.

Finally,

$$\varrho = \frac{1}{\alpha_f(y,v)}[f(y) - f(v)] - \eta^T(y,v)\nabla_v f(v)$$

$$\varrho = arc(tany) - arc(tanv) - \left(-\frac{1}{11}y^{20} + y + 15y^3v^3\right)\left(\frac{1}{1+v^2}\right)$$

$$\varrho = arc(tany) + \frac{1}{11}y^{20} - y, \text{ at the point } v = 0.$$

At the point $y = 1 \in \big[-1, 1\big]$, *we find that:*

$$\varrho = \frac{\pi}{4} + \frac{1}{11} - 1 < 0.$$

Hence, f *is not* α_f*-invex at* $u = 0$ *with the same* η.

Example 3. *Let* $f : \left[-\frac{\pi}{9}, \frac{\pi}{9}\right] \longrightarrow R$ *be defined as:*

$$f(y) = y^3.$$

A function $G : R \longrightarrow R$ *is defined as:*

$$G(t) = t^4 + t^2 + 9.$$

Let $\eta : \left[-\frac{\pi}{9}, \frac{\pi}{9}\right] \times \left[-\frac{\pi}{9}, \frac{\pi}{9}\right] \longrightarrow R$ *be given as:*

$$\eta(y, v) = y^4 + yv^2 + 2yv^2 + 3.$$

Furthermore, $\alpha_f : Y \times Y \to R_+ \setminus \{0\}$ *is given by:*

$$\alpha_f(y, v) = 9, \ \forall\, y,\ v \in \left[-\frac{\pi}{9}, \frac{\pi}{9}\right].$$

Presently, we need to demonstrate that f *is* (G, α_f)*-pseudobonvex at* $v = 0$ *concerning* η*. For this, we have to show that:*

$$\Delta_1 = \eta^T(y, v)[G'(f(v))\nabla_v f(v) + \{G'(f(v))\nabla_v f(v)(\nabla_v f(v))^T + G'(f(v))\nabla_{vv} f(v)\}p].$$

Putting the estimations of f*,* η*, and* G *in the above articulation, we get:*

$$\Delta_1 = (y^4 + yv^2 + 2yv^2 + 3)[3v^2(4v^9 + 2v^3) + \{9v^4(12v^6 + 2) + 6v(4v^9 + 2v^3)\}p]$$

for which at $v = 0$*, we obtain* $\Delta_1 \geq 0$*,* $\forall\, v \in \left[-\frac{\pi}{9}, \frac{\pi}{9}\right]$*,* $\forall\, p$*.*

Next, $\Delta_2 = \frac{1}{\alpha_f(y, v)}[G(f(y)) - G(f(v)) + \frac{1}{2}p^T\{G''(f(v))\nabla_v f(v)(\nabla_v f(v))^T + G'(f(v))\nabla_{vv} f(v)\}p]$*.*

Substituting the estimations of f*,* α_f*,, and* G *in the above articulation,*

$$\Delta_2 = \frac{1}{9}[(y^{12} + y^6 + 1) - (v^{12} + v^6 + 1) + \frac{p^2}{2}\{9v^4(12v^6 + 2) + 6v(4v^9 + 2v^3)\}]$$

for which at $v = 0$*, we obtain* $\Delta_2 \geq 0$*,* $\forall\, y \left[-\frac{\pi}{9}, \frac{\pi}{9}\right]$*,* $\forall\, p$*. Therefore,* f *is* (G, α_f)*-pseudobonvex at* $v = 0$*.*

Next, consider:

$$\Delta_3 = \eta^T(y, v)[\nabla_v f(v) + \nabla_{vv} f(v)p].$$

Substituting the values of f*,* η*, and* G *in the above expression, we obtain:*

$$\Delta_3 = (y^4 + yv^2 + 2yv^2 + 3)[3v^2 + 6vp],$$

for which at $v = 0$*, we find that* $\Delta_3 \geq 0$*,* $\forall\, y \in \left[-\frac{\pi}{9}, \frac{\pi}{9}\right]$*,* $\forall\, p$*.*

Next,

$$\Delta_4 = \frac{1}{\alpha_f(y, v)}[f(y) - f(v) + \frac{1}{2}p^T\nabla_{vv} f(v)p].$$

Substituting the values of f, α_f, *and G in the above expression, we obtain:*

$$\Delta_4 = \frac{1}{9}[y^3 - v^3 + 3vp^2],$$

for which at $v = 0$, *we get* $\Delta_4 \ngeq 0,\ \forall\, y \in \left[-\frac{\pi}{9}, \frac{\pi}{9}\right]$. *Therefore,* f *is not* $\alpha_f(y,v)$*-pseudobonvex at* $v = 0$.

Next, consider:

$$\Delta_5 = \eta^T(y,v)\nabla_u f(u).$$

Similarly, at $v = 0$, *we find that* $\Delta_5 \geq 0,\ \forall\, y \in \left[-\frac{\pi}{9}, \frac{\pi}{9}\right]$. *Next,*

$$\Delta_6 = \frac{1}{\alpha_f(y,v)}[f(y) - f(v)].$$

In the same way, at $v = 0$, *we find that,*

$$\Delta_6 \ngeq 0,\ \forall\, y \in \left[-\frac{\pi}{9}, \frac{\pi}{9}\right].$$

Hence, f *is not* α_f*-pseudoinvex at* $v = 0 \in \left[-\frac{\pi}{9}, \frac{\pi}{9}\right]$ *with the same* η.

3. Non-Differentiable Second-Order Symmetric Primal-Dual Pair over Arbitrary Cones

In this section, we formulate the following pair of second-order non-differentiable symmetric dual programs over arbitrary cones:

(NSOP) Minimize $W(y,z,r,p) = G(f(y,z)) + s(y|B) - z^T r - \frac{1}{2}p^T[G''(f(y,z)) \nabla_z f(y,z)(\nabla_z f(y,z))^T + G'(f(y,z))\nabla_{zz} f(y,z)]p$

subject to

$$-[G'(f(y,z))\nabla_z f(y,z) - r + \{G''(f(y,z))\nabla_z f(y,z)(\nabla_z f(y,z))^T: + G'(f(y,z))\nabla_{zz} f(y,z)\}p] \in C_2^*, \tag{1}$$

$$z^T[G'(f(y,z))\nabla_z f(y,z) - r + \{G''(f(y,z))\nabla_z f(y,z)(\nabla_z f(y,z))^T + G'(f(y,z))\nabla_{zz} f(y,z)\}p] \geq 0, \tag{2}$$

$$p^T[G'(f(y,z))\nabla_z f(y,z) - r + \{G''(f(y,z))\nabla_z f(y,z)(\nabla_z f(y,z))^T + G'(f(y,z))\nabla_{zz} f(y,z)\}p] \geq 0, \tag{3}$$

$$y \in C_1,\ r \in F. \tag{4}$$

(NSOD) Maximize $T(v,w,t,q) = G(f(v,w)) - s(w|F) + w^T t - \frac{1}{2}q^T[G''(f(v,w)) \nabla_v f(v,w)(\nabla_v f(v,w))^T + G'(f(v,w))\nabla_{vv} f(v,w)]q$

subject to

$$[G'(f(v,w))\nabla_v f(v,w) + t + \{G''(f(v,w))\nabla_v f(v,w)(\nabla_v f(v,w))^T + G'(f(v,w))\nabla_{vv} f(v,w)\}q] \in C_1^*, \tag{5}$$

$$v^T[G'(f(v,w))\nabla_v f(v,w) + t + \{G''(f(v,w))\nabla_v f(v,w)(\nabla_v f(v,w))^T + G'(f(v,w))\nabla_{vv} f(v,w)\}q] \leq 0, \tag{6}$$

$$q^T[G'(f(v,w))\nabla_v f(v,w) + t + \{G''(f(v,w))\nabla_v f(v,w)(\nabla_v f(v,w))^T + G'(f(v,w))\nabla_{vv} f(v,w)\}q] \leq 0, \tag{7}$$

$$w \in C_2,\ t \in B, \tag{8}$$

where C_1^* and C_2^* are positive polar cones of C_1 and C_2, respectively. Let P^0 and Q^0 be feasible solutions of (NSOP) and (NSOD), respectively.

Theorem 1 (Weak duality theorem). *Let $(y,z,r,p) \in P^0$ and $(v,w,t,q) \in Q^0$. Let:*

(i) *$f(.,w)$ and $(.)^T t$ be (G,α_f)-bonvex and α_f-invex at v, respectively, with the same η,*
(ii) *$f(y,.)$ and $(.)^T r$ be (G,α_f)-boncave and α_f-incave at z, respectively, with the same ξ,*
(iii) *$\eta(y,v) + v \in C_1$,*
(iv) *$\xi(w,z) + z \in C_2$.*

Then,

$$W(y,z,r,p) \geq T(v,w,t,q). \tag{9}$$

Proof. From Hypothesis $(iii)$and the dual constraint (5), we obtain

$$(\eta(y,v) + v + q)^T\Big[G'(f(v,w))\nabla_v f(v,w) + t + \{G''(f(v,w))\nabla_v f(v,w) (\nabla_v f(v,w))^T + G'(f(v,w))\nabla_{vv} f(v,w)\}q\Big] \geq 0.$$

The above inequality follows

$$\Longrightarrow \quad \eta^T(y,v)\Big[G'(f(v,w))\nabla_v f(v,w) + t + \{G''(f(v,w))\nabla_v f(v,w)(\nabla_v f(v,w))^T + G'(f(v,w))\nabla_{vv} f(v,w)\}q\Big] \geq -(v+q)\Big[G'(f(v,w))\nabla_v f(v,w) + t: + \{G''(f(v,w))\nabla_v f(v,w)(\nabla_v f(v,w))^T + G'f(v,w)\nabla_{vv} f(v,w)\}q\Big],$$

which upon using (6) and (7) yields

$$\eta^T(y,v)\Big[G'(f(v,w))\nabla_v f(v,w) + t + \{G''(f(v,w))\nabla_v f(v,w)(\nabla_v f(v,w))^T + G'(f(v,w))\nabla_{vv} f(v,w)\}q\Big] \geq 0. \tag{10}$$

Again, from Hypothesis (i), we obtain

$$\frac{1}{\alpha_f(y,v)}[G(f(y,w)) - G(f(v,w)) + \frac{1}{2}q^T\{G''(f(v,w))\nabla_v f(v,w)(\nabla_v f(v,w))^T + G'(f(v,w))\nabla_{vv} f(v,w)\}q] \geq \eta^T(y,v)\Big[G'(f(v,w))\nabla_v f(v,w) + \{G''(f(v,w)): \nabla_v f(v,w)(\nabla_v f(v,w))^T + G'(f(v,w))\nabla_{vv} f(v,w)\}q\Big]$$

and:

$$\frac{1}{\alpha_f(y,v)}[y^Tt - v^Tt] \geq \eta^T(y,v)t.$$

Combining the above inequalities, we get

$$\frac{1}{\alpha_f(y,v)}[G(f(y,w)) + y^Tt - G(f(v,w)) - v^Tt + \frac{1}{2}q^T\{G''(f(v,w))\nabla_v f(v,w)(\nabla_v f(v,w))^T$$
$$+G'(f(v,w))\nabla_{vv}f(v,w)\}q] \geq \eta^T(y,v)\big[G'(f(v,w))\nabla_v f(v,w) + t + \{G''(f(v,w))\nabla_v f(v,w):$$
$$(\nabla_v f(v,w))^T + G'(f(v,w))\nabla_{vv}f(v,w)\}q\big].$$

Using Inequality (10), it follows that

$$\frac{1}{\alpha_f(y,v)}[G(f(y,w)) + y^Tt - G(f(v,w)) - v^Tt + \frac{1}{2}q^T\{G''(f(v,w)):$$
$$\nabla_v f(v,w)(\nabla_v f(v,w))^T + G'(f(v,w))\nabla_{vv}f(v,w)\}q] \geq 0. \tag{11}$$

Similarly, using (ii), (iv), and primal constraints, it follows that

$$\frac{1}{\alpha_f(y,v)}[-G(f(y,w)) + w^Tr + G(f(y,z)) - z^Tr - \frac{1}{2}p^T\{G''(f(y,z))\nabla_z f(y,z):$$
$$(\nabla_z f(y,z))^T + G'(f(y,z))\nabla_{zz}f(y,z)\}p] \geq 0. \tag{12}$$

Adding Inequalities (11) and (12), we get

$$\frac{1}{\alpha_f(y,v)}[G'(f(y,z)) + y^Tt - z^Tr - \frac{1}{2}p^T\{G''(f(y,z))\nabla_z f(y,z)(\nabla_z f(y,z))^T$$
$$+G'(f(y,z))\nabla_{zz}f(y,z)\}p] \geq \frac{1}{\alpha_f(y,v)}[G(f(v,w)) - w^Tr + v^Tt - \frac{1}{2}q^T\{G''(f(v,w)):$$
$$\nabla_v f(v,w)(\nabla_v f(v,w))^T + G'(f(v,w))\nabla_{vv}f(v,w)\}q].$$

Finally, using the inequalities $y^Tt \leq s(y|B)$ and $w^Tr \leq s(w|F)$, we have

$$\frac{1}{\alpha_f(y,v)}[G'(f(y,z)) + s(y|B) - z^Tr - \frac{1}{2}p^T\{G''(f(y,z))\nabla_z f(y,z)(\nabla_z f(y,z))^T$$
$$+G'(f(y,z))\nabla_{zz}f(y,z)\}p] \geq \frac{1}{\alpha_f(y,v)}[G(f(v,w)) - s(w|F) + v^Tt:$$
$$-\frac{1}{2}q^T\{G''(f(v,w))\nabla_v f(v,w)(\nabla_v f(v,w))^T + G'(f(v,w))\nabla_{vv}f(v,w)\}q].$$

Since $\alpha_f \in R_+ \setminus \{0\}$, we obtain

$$[G'(f(y,z)) + s(y|B) - z^Tr - \frac{1}{2}p^T\{G''(f(y,z))\nabla_z f(y,z)(\nabla_z f(y,z))^T$$
$$+G'(f(y,z))\nabla_{zz}f(y,z)\}p] \geq [G(f(v,w)) - s(w|F) + v^Tt - \frac{1}{2}q^T\{G''(f(v,w))\nabla_v f(v,w):$$
$$(\nabla_v f(v,w))^T + G'(f(v,w))\nabla_{vv}f(v,w)\}q].$$

Hence, the result. □

A non-trivial numerical example for legitimization of the weak duality theorem.

Example 4. *Let $f : Y \times Y \longrightarrow R$ $(Y \subseteq R_+)$ be a function given by:*

$$f(y,z) = y^5.$$

Suppose that $G(t) = t^4 + 3$ *and* $B = \{0\} = F$.
Further, let $\eta,\ \xi : Y \times Y \longrightarrow R$ *be given by:*

$$\eta(y,v) = y^2v^2 + y^2v + v + 4 \ \ and \ \ \xi(w,z) = w^2z^2 + wz^2 - z + 9.$$

Furthermore, $\alpha_f : Y \times Y \to R_+ \setminus \{0\}$ *and* $C_1 = R_+,\ C_2 = R_+$.
Putting these values in (NSOP) and (NSOD), we get:

(ENSOP) Minimize $T(y,z,r,p) = y^{20} + 3$
subject to

$$[2y^3 \times 0 + \{2 \times 0 + 2y^3 \times 0\}p] \leq 0,$$

$$z[2y^3 \times 0 + \{2 \times 0 + 2y^3 \times 0\}p] \geq 0,$$

$$p[2y^3 \times 0 + \{2 \times 0 + 2y^3 \times 0\}p] \geq 0,$$

$$p \in R.$$

(ENSOD)Maximize $W(v,w,t,q) = v^{20} - 190q^2 + 3$
subject to

$$v^{18}[v + 19q] \geq 0,$$

$$v^{19}[v + 19q] \leq 0,$$

$$quv^{18}[v + 19q] \leq 0,$$

$$q \in R.$$

Firstly, we will try to prove that all the hypotheses of the weak duality theorem are satisfied:
(i) $f(.,w)$ *is* (G,α_f)*-bonvex at* $v = 0$,

$$\frac{1}{\alpha_f(y,v)}[G(f(y,w)) - G(f(v,w)) + \tfrac{1}{2}q^T[G''(f(v,w))\nabla_v f(v,w)(\nabla_v f(v,w))^T + G'(f(v,w))\nabla_{vv} f(v,w)]q]$$
$$- \eta^T(y,v)[G'(f(v,w))\nabla_v f(v,w) + \{G''(f(v,w))\nabla_v f(v,w)(\nabla_v f(v,w))^T + G' f(v,w)\nabla_{vv} f(v,w)\}q]$$
$$= \frac{1}{\alpha_f(y,v)}[y^{20} - v^{20}] - (y^2v^2 + y^2v + v + 4)[20v^{19} + 380v^{18}q] + 190q^2v^{18}$$
$$= \frac{y^{20}}{\alpha_f(y,v)} \text{ at } v = 0 \in Y$$
$$\geq 0,\ \forall\, q.$$

Obviously, $(.)^T t$ *is* α_f*-invex at* $v = 0 \in Y$.
(ii) $f(y,.)$ *is* (G,α_f)*-boncave at* $z = 0$*, and we obtain*

$$\frac{1}{\alpha_f(y,v)}[G(f(y,v)) - G(f(y,z)) + \tfrac{1}{2}p^T[G''(f(y,z))\nabla_z f(y,z)(\nabla_z f(y,z))^T + G'(f(y,z))\nabla_{zz} f(y,z)]p]$$
$$- \xi^T(v,y)[G'(f(y,z))\nabla_z f(y,z) + \{G''(f(y,z))\nabla_z f(y,z)(\nabla_z f(y,z))^T G'(f(y,z))(\nabla_{zz} f(y,z))\}p],$$
$$= \frac{1}{\alpha_f(y,v)}[(y^{20} + 3) - (y^{20} + 3)] - (w^2z^2 + wz^2 - z + 9)(0),$$
$$= 0 \text{ at } z = 0,\ \forall p.$$

Naturally, $(.)^T r$ *is* α_f*-invex at* $z = 0 \in Y$.
(iii) *Obviously,* $\eta(y,v) \geq 0$ *and* $\xi(w,z) \geq 0$.
Hence, all the assumptions of Theorem 1 hold.

Verification of the weak duality theorem: Let $(y = 2,\ z = 9,\ r = 0,\ p = \frac{1}{2}) \in P^0$ and $(v = 0,\ w = 7,\ t = 0,\ q = \frac{1}{9}) \in Q^0$. To validate the result of the weak duality theorem, we have to show that

$$\Omega = \Big(G(f(y,z) + s(y|B) - z^T r - \tfrac{1}{2}p^T[G'(f(y,z))\nabla_z f(y,z)(\nabla_z f(y,z))^T + G'(f(y,z))$$
$$\nabla_{zz} f(y,z)]p\Big) - \Big(G(f(v,w)) - s(w|F) + w^T t - \tfrac{1}{2}q^T[G'(f(v,w))\nabla_v f(v,w)(\nabla_v f(v,w))^T$$
$$+ G'(f(v,w))\nabla_{vv} f(v,w)]q\Big) \geq 0.$$

Substituting the values in the above expression, we obtain:

$$\Omega = (y^{20} + 3) - (v^{20} - 190q^2 + 3).$$

At the feasible point, the above expression reduces:

$$\Omega \geq 0.$$

Hence, the weak duality theorem is verified.

Remark 2. *Since every bonvex function is pseudobonvex, therefore the above weak duality theorem for the symmetric dual pair (NSOP) and (NSOD) can also be obtained under* (G, α_f)*-pseudobonvex assumptions.*

Theorem 2 (Weak duality theorem). *Let* $(y, z, r, p) \in P^0$ *and* $(v, w, t, q) \in Q^0$. *Let:*

(i) $f(., w)$ *be* (G, α_f)*-pseudobonvex and* $(.)^T t$ *be* α_f*-pseudoinvex at* v *with the same* η,
(ii) $f(y, .)$ *be* (G, α_f)*-pseudoboncave and* $(.)^T r$ *be* α_f*-pseudoinvex at* z *with the same* ξ,
(iii) $\eta(y, v) + v \in C_1$,
(iv) $\xi(w, z) + z \in C_2$.

Then,

$$W(y, z, r, p) \geq T(v, w, t, q).$$

Proof. The proof follows on the lines of Theorem 1. □

Theorem 3 (Strong duality theorem). *Let* $(\bar{y}, \bar{z}, \bar{r}, \bar{p})$ *be an optimum of problem (NSOP). Let:*

(i) $[G''(f(\bar{y}, \bar{z}))\nabla_z f(\bar{y}, \bar{z})(\nabla_z f(\bar{y}, \bar{z}))^T + G'(f(\bar{y}, \bar{z}))\nabla_{zz} f(\bar{y}, \bar{z})]$ *is positive or negative definite,*

(ii) $\Big\{G''(f(\bar{y}, \bar{z}))\nabla_z f(\bar{y}, \bar{z}) - \bar{r} + \{G''(f(\bar{y}, \bar{z}))\nabla_z f(\bar{y}, \bar{z})(\nabla_z f(\bar{y}, \bar{z}))^T + G'(f(\bar{y}, \bar{z}))$
$\nabla_{zz} f(\bar{y}, \bar{z})\}\bar{p}\Big\} \neq 0,$

(iii) $\Big\{\bar{p}^T\{G''(f(\bar{y}, \bar{z}))\nabla_z f(\bar{y}, \bar{z}) - \bar{r} + G''(f(\bar{y}, \bar{z}))\nabla_z f(\bar{y}, \bar{z})(\nabla_z f(\bar{y}, \bar{z}))^T + G'(f(\bar{y}, \bar{z}))$
$\nabla_{zz} f(\bar{y}, \bar{z})\}\Big\} = 0.$

Then, $\bar{p} = 0$, *and there exists* $\bar{t} \in B$ *such that* $(\bar{v}, \bar{w}, \bar{t}, \bar{q})$ *is an optimum for the problem (NSOD).*

Proof. Since $(\bar{y}, \bar{z}, \bar{r}, \bar{p})$ is an efficient solution of (NSOD), therefore by the conditions in [15], such that

$$(y - \bar{y})^T \Big\{\alpha[G'(f(\bar{y}, \bar{z}))\nabla_y f(\bar{y}, \bar{z}) + \bar{t} - \tfrac{1}{2}p^T \nabla_y \{G'(f(\bar{y}, \bar{z}))\nabla_z (f(\bar{y}, \bar{z}))\nabla_z (f(\bar{y}, \bar{z}))^T$$
$$+G''(f(\bar{y}, \bar{z}))\nabla_{zz} f(\bar{y}, \bar{z})p\}] + (\beta - \gamma\bar{z}^T - \delta\bar{p}^T)\nabla_y[G'(f(\bar{y}, \bar{z}))\nabla_y f(\bar{y}, \bar{z}) + \{G'(f(\bar{y}, \bar{z})):$$
$$\nabla_z (f(\bar{y}, \bar{z}))(\nabla_z f(\bar{y}, \bar{z}))^T + G''(f(\bar{y}, \bar{z}))\nabla_{zz} f(\bar{y}, \bar{z})\}]\Big\} \geq 0, \ \forall\, y \in C_1, \tag{13}$$

$$\alpha[G'(f(\bar{y}, \bar{z}))\nabla_z f(\bar{y}, \bar{z}) - \bar{r} - \tfrac{1}{2}p^T \nabla_z \{G'(f(\bar{y}, \bar{z}))\nabla_z (f(\bar{y}, \bar{z}))(\nabla_z f(\bar{y}, \bar{z}))^T$$
$$+G''(f(\bar{y}, \bar{z}))\nabla_{zz} f(\bar{y}, \bar{z})\}p] + (\beta - \gamma\bar{z}^T - \delta\bar{p}^T)[G'(f(\bar{y}, \bar{z}))\nabla_z (f(\bar{y}, \bar{z}))(\nabla_z f(\bar{y}, \bar{z}))^T$$
$$+G''(f(\bar{y}, \bar{z}))\nabla_{zz} f(\bar{y}, \bar{z}) + \nabla_z \{G''(f(\bar{y}, \bar{z}))\nabla_z (f(\bar{y}, \bar{z}))(\nabla_z f(\bar{y}, \bar{z}))^T$$
$$+ G''(f(\bar{y}, \bar{z}))\nabla_{zz} f(\bar{y}, \bar{z})\}] - \gamma[G'(f(\bar{y}, \bar{z}))\nabla_z (f(\bar{y}, \bar{z})) - \bar{r} + \{G''(f(\bar{y}, \bar{z})):$$
$$\nabla_z (f(\bar{y}, \bar{z}))(\nabla_z f(\bar{y}, \bar{z}))^T + G''(f(\bar{y}, \bar{z}))\nabla_{zz} f(\bar{y}, \bar{z})\}\bar{p}] = 0, \tag{14}$$

$(\beta - \alpha\bar{p} - \gamma\bar{z}^T - \delta\bar{p}^T)[G''(f(\bar{y},\bar{z}))\nabla_z(f(\bar{y},\bar{z}))(\nabla_z(f(\bar{y},\bar{z})))^T + G'(f(\bar{y},\bar{z}))$
$\nabla_{zz}f(\bar{y},\bar{z})] - \delta[G'(f(\bar{y},\bar{z}))\nabla_z(f(\bar{y},\bar{z})) - \bar{r} + \{G''(f(\bar{y},\bar{z}))$:

$$\nabla_z f(\bar{y},\bar{z})(\nabla_z f(\bar{y},\bar{z}))^T + G'(f(\bar{y},\bar{z}))\nabla_{zz}f(\bar{y},\bar{z})\}\bar{p}] - \eta = 0, \tag{15}$$

$\beta[G'(f(\bar{y},\bar{z}))\nabla_z(f(\bar{y},\bar{z})) - \bar{r} + \{G'(f(\bar{y},\bar{z}))\nabla_z(f(\bar{y},\bar{z}))(\nabla_z(f(\bar{y},\bar{z})))^T$:

$$+G''(f(\bar{y},\bar{z}))\nabla_{zz}(f(\bar{y},\bar{z}))\}\bar{p}] = 0, \tag{16}$$

$\gamma\bar{z}^T[G(f(\bar{y},\bar{z}))\nabla_z(f(\bar{y},\bar{z})) - \bar{r} + \{G'(f(\bar{y},\bar{z}))(\nabla_z(f(\bar{y},\bar{z})))(\nabla_z(f(\bar{y},\bar{z})))^T$:

$$+G''(f(\bar{y},\bar{z}))\nabla_{zz}(f(\bar{y},\bar{z}))\}\bar{p}] = 0, \tag{17}$$

$\delta\bar{p}^T[G'(f(\bar{y},\bar{z}))\nabla_z(f(\bar{y},\bar{z})) - \bar{r} + \{G'(f(\bar{y},\bar{z}))(\nabla_z(f(\bar{y},\bar{z})))(\nabla_z(f(\bar{y},\bar{z})))^T$:

$$+G''(f(\bar{y},\bar{z}))\nabla_{zz}(f(\bar{y},\bar{z}))\}\bar{p}] = 0, \tag{18}$$

$$(\alpha - \gamma)z + \beta - \delta p \in N_D(t), \tag{19}$$

$$t^T\bar{y} = s(y|B), \tag{20}$$

$$\bar{t} \in \bar{B},\ \bar{r} \in \bar{F}, \tag{21}$$

$$(\alpha, \beta, \gamma, \delta) \neq 0, \tag{22}$$

$$(\alpha, \beta, \gamma, \delta) \geq 0. \tag{23}$$

Premultiplying Equation (15) by $(\beta - \alpha\bar{p} - \gamma\bar{z} - \delta\bar{p})$ and using (16)–(18), we get
$(\beta - \alpha\bar{p} - \gamma\bar{z} - \delta\bar{p})[G'(f(\bar{y},\bar{z}))\nabla_z(f(\bar{y},\bar{z}))(\nabla_z(f(\bar{y},\bar{z})))^T$
$+ G''(f(\bar{y},\bar{z}))\nabla_{zz}(f(\bar{y},\bar{z}))](\beta - \alpha\bar{p} - \gamma\bar{z} - \delta\bar{p}) = 0.$
Using Hypothesis (i), we get:

$$\beta = \alpha\bar{p} + \gamma\bar{z} + \delta\bar{p}. \tag{24}$$

From Equation (15) and Hypothesis (ii), we obtain:

$$\delta = 0. \tag{25}$$

Now, suppose $\alpha = 0$. Then, Equation (14) and Hypothesis (ii) yield $\gamma = 0$, which along with Equations (24) and (25) gives $\beta = 0$. Thus, $(\alpha, \beta, \gamma, \delta) = 0$, a contradiction to Equation (22). Hence, from (23):

$$\alpha > 0. \tag{26}$$

Using Equations (16)–(18), we have
$(\beta - \gamma\bar{z}^T - \delta\bar{p}^T)[G'(f(\bar{y},\bar{z}))\nabla_z(f(\bar{y},\bar{z})) - \bar{r} + \{G'(f(\bar{y},\bar{z}))\nabla_z(f(\bar{y},\bar{z}))$:

$$(\nabla_z(f(\bar{y},\bar{z})))^T + G''(f(\bar{y},\bar{z}))\nabla_{zz}(f(\bar{y},\bar{z}))\}\bar{p}] = 0, \tag{27}$$

and now, Equation (24) gives
$\alpha\bar{p}^T[G'(f(\bar{y},\bar{z}))\nabla_z(f(\bar{y},\bar{z})) - \bar{r} + \{G'(f(\bar{y},\bar{z}))\nabla_z(f(\bar{y},\bar{z})):$

$$(\nabla_z(f(\bar{y},\bar{z})))^T + G''(f(\bar{y},\bar{z}))\nabla_{zz}(f(\bar{y},\bar{z}))\}\bar{p}] = 0, \tag{28}$$

which along with Hypothesis (iii) yields:

$$\bar{p} = 0. \tag{29}$$

Therefore, the equation:

$$\beta = \gamma\bar{z}. \tag{30}$$

Furthermore, it follows from Equations (14), (24), and (29) and Hypotheses $(ii)$and (iv) that:

$$\alpha - \gamma = 0.$$

As $\alpha > 0$, we get:

$$\alpha = \gamma > 0. \tag{31}$$

Therefore, Equation (30) gives:

$$\bar{z} = \frac{\beta}{\gamma} \geq 0. \tag{32}$$

Moreover, Equation (13) together with (24) and using $\bar{p} = 0$ yields
$(y - \bar{y})^T[G'(f(\bar{y},\bar{z}))\nabla_y(f(\bar{y},\bar{z})) - \bar{r} + \{G'(f(\bar{y},\bar{z}))\nabla_z(f(\bar{y},\bar{z}))(\nabla_z(f(\bar{y},\bar{z})))^T:$

$$+G''(f(\bar{y},\bar{z}))\nabla_{zz}(f(\bar{y},\bar{z}))\}\bar{p}] \geq 0,\ \forall\, y \in C_1. \tag{33}$$

Let $y \in C_1$. Then, $y + \bar{y} \in C_1$, as C_1 is a closed convex cone. Upon substituting $y + \bar{y}$ in place of y in (33), we get
$y^T[G'(f(\bar{y},\bar{z}))\nabla_y(f(\bar{y},\bar{z})) - \bar{r} + \{G'(f(\bar{y},\bar{z}))\nabla_z(f(\bar{y},\bar{z}))(\nabla_z(f(\bar{y},\bar{z})))^T:$

$$+G''(f(\bar{y},\bar{z}))\nabla_{zz}(f(\bar{y},\bar{z}))\}\bar{p}] \geq 0, \tag{34}$$

which in turn implies that for all $y \in C_1$, we obtain
$[G'(f(\bar{y},\bar{z}))\nabla_y(f(\bar{y},\bar{z})) - \bar{r} + \{G'(f(\bar{y},\bar{z}))\nabla_z(f(\bar{y},\bar{z}))(\nabla_z(f(\bar{y},\bar{z})))^T:$

$$+G''(f(\bar{y},\bar{z}))\nabla_{zz}(f(\bar{y},\bar{z}))\}\bar{p}] \in C_1. \tag{35}$$

Furthermore, by letting $y = 0$ and $y = 2\bar{y}$, simultaneously in (33), this yields
$\bar{y}^T[G'(f(\bar{y},\bar{z}))\nabla_y(f(\bar{y},\bar{z})) - \bar{r} + \{G'(f(\bar{y},\bar{z}))\nabla_z(f(\bar{y},\bar{z}))(\nabla_z(f(\bar{y},\bar{z})))^T:$

$$+G''(f(\bar{y},\bar{z}))\nabla_{zz}(f(\bar{y},\bar{z}))\}\bar{p}] \geq 0. \tag{36}$$

Using Inequality (31), we get:

$$\bar{z} = \frac{\beta}{\gamma} \in C_2. \tag{37}$$

Thus, $(\bar{y}, \bar{z}, \bar{p} = 0)$ satisfies the dual constraints.

Now, using Equations (30) and (31), we obtain:

$$G'(f(\bar{y},\bar{z}))\nabla_z f(\bar{y},\bar{z}) = \bar{z}^T \bar{t}. \tag{38}$$

Furthermore, $\alpha > 0$, then we obtain $\bar{z} \in N_D(\bar{t})$. Furthermore, D is a compact convex set.

$$\bar{z}^T \bar{t} = s(\bar{z}|D). \tag{39}$$

Thus, after using (20), (29), (38) and (39), we get that the values of the objective functions of (NSOP) and (NSOD) at $(\bar{y},\bar{z},\bar{r},\bar{p}=0)$ and $(\bar{y},\bar{z},\bar{r},\bar{q}=0)$ are the same. By using duality Theorems 1 and 2, it is easily shown that $(\bar{y},\bar{z},\bar{r},\bar{q}=0)$ is an optimal solution of (NSOD). □

Theorem 4 (Strict converse duality theorem). *Let $(\bar{v},\bar{w},\bar{t},\bar{q})$ be an optimum of problem (NSOD). Let:*

(i) $[G''(f(\bar{v},\bar{w}))\nabla_v f(\bar{v},\bar{w})(\nabla_v f(\bar{v},\bar{w}))^T + G'(f(\bar{v},\bar{w}))\nabla_{vv} f(\bar{v},\bar{w})]$ is positive or negative definite,

(ii) $\Big\{G''(f(\bar{v},\bar{w}))\nabla_v f(\bar{v},\bar{w}) + \bar{t} + \{G''(f(\bar{v},\bar{w}))\nabla_v f(\bar{v},\bar{w})(\nabla_v f(\bar{v},\bar{w}))^T + G'(f(\bar{v},\bar{w}))$
$\nabla_{vv} f(\bar{v},\bar{w})\}\bar{q}\Big\} \neq 0,$

(iii) $\Big\{\bar{q}^T\{G''(f(\bar{v},\bar{w}))\nabla_v f(\bar{v},\bar{w}) + \bar{t} + G''(f(\bar{v},\bar{w}))\nabla_v f(\bar{v},\bar{w})(\nabla_v f(\bar{v},\bar{w}))^T$
$+G'(f(\bar{v},\bar{w}))\nabla_{vv} f(\bar{v},\bar{w})\}\Big\} = 0.$

Then, $\bar{q}=0$, and there exists $\bar{r} \in B$ such that $(\bar{y},\bar{z},\bar{r},\bar{p})$ is an optimum for the problem (NSOP).

Proof. The proof follows on the lines of Theorem 3. □

4. Conclusions

In this paper, we considered a new type of non-differentiable second-order symmetric programming problem over arbitrary cones and derived duality theorems under generalized assumptions. The present work can further be extended to non-differentiable higher order fractional programming problems over arbitrary cones. This will orient the future task of the authors.

Author Contributions: All authors contributed equally to this research. The research was carried out by all authors. The manuscript was prepared together and they all read and approved the final version.

Funding: The authors extend their appreciation to the "Deanship of Scientific Research" at King Khalid University for funding this work through research groups program under grant number R.G.P.1/152/40.

Acknowledgments: The authors are thankful to the learned referees whose suggestions improved the present form.

Conflicts of Interest: The authors declare no conflict of interest.

References

1. Mangasarian, O.L. Second and higher-order duality in nonlinear programming. *J. Math. Anal. Appl.* **1975**, *51*, 607–620. [CrossRef]
2. Hanson, M.A. Second-order invexity and duality in mathematical programming. *Opsearch* **1993**, *3*, 313–320.
3. Ojha, D.B. On second-order symmetric duality for a class of multiobjective fractional programming problem. *Tamkang J. Math.* **2009**, *43*, 267–279. [CrossRef]
4. Jayswal, A.; Prasad, A.K. Second order symmetric duality in non-differentiable multiobjective fractional programming with cone convex functions. *Appl. Math. Comput.* **2014**, *45*, 15–33. [CrossRef]
5. Jayswal, A.; Stancu-Minasian, I.M.; Kumar, D. Higher-order duality for multiobjective programming problem involving (F,α,ρ,d)-V-type-I functions. *J. Math. Model. Algorithms* **2014**, *13*, 125–141. [CrossRef]

6. Suneja, S.K.; Srivastava, M.K.; Bhatia, M. Higher order duality in multiobjective fractional programming with support functions. *J. Math. Anal. Appl.* **2008**. [CrossRef]
7. Dubey, R.; Mishra, L.N.; Mishra, V.N. Duality relations for a class of a multiobjective fractional programming problem involving support functions. *Am. J. Oper. Res.* **2018**, *8*, 294–311.
8. Dubey, R.; Mishra, V.N.; Tomar, P. Duality relations for second-order programming problem under (G, α_f)-bonvexity assumptions. *Asian-Eur. J. Math.* **2020**, *13*, 1–17. [CrossRef]
9. Jannelli, A.; Ruggieri, M.; Speciale, M.P. Exact and numerical solutions of time-fractional advection-diffusion equation with a nonlinear source term by means of the Lie symmetries. *Nonlinear Dyn.* **2018**. [CrossRef]
10. Avriel, M.; Diewert, W.E.; Schaible, S.; Zang, I. *Optimality Conditions of G-Type in Locally Lipchitz Multiobjective Programming*; Plenum Press: New York, NY, USA; London, UK, 1987.
11. Antcza, T. New optimality conditions and duality results of *G*-type in differentiable mathematical programming. *Nonlinear Anal.* **2007**, *66*, 1617–1632. [CrossRef]
12. Antczak, T. On *G*-invex multiobjective programming. *Part I Optim. J. Glob. Optim.* **2009**, *43*, 97–109. [CrossRef]
13. Kang, Y.M.; Kim, D.S.; Kim, M.H. Optimality conditions of *G*-type in locally Lipchitz multiobjective programming. *Vietnam J. Math.* **2014**, *40*, 275–285.
14. Gao, X. Sufficiency in multiobjective programming under second-order $B-(p,r)-V$-type Ifunctions. *J. Interdiscip. Math.* **2014**, *17*, 385–402. [CrossRef]
15. Brumelle, S. Optimality conditions of *G*-type in locally Lipchitz multiobjective programming. *Vietnam J. Math.* **1981**, *6*, 159–172.

Article

Viscovatov-Like Algorithm of Thiele–Newton's Blending Expansion for a Bivariate Function

Shengfeng Li [1,*] and Yi Dong [2]

[1] Institute of Applied Mathematics, Bengbu University, Bengbu 233030, China
[2] School of Science, Bengbu University, Bengbu 233030, China
* Correspondence: lsf@bbc.edu.cn; Tel.: +86-552-317-5158

Received: 18 June 2019; Accepted: 30 July 2019; Published: 2 August 2019

Abstract: In this paper, Thiele–Newton's blending expansion of a bivariate function is firstly suggested by means of combining Thiele's continued fraction in one variable with Taylor's polynomial expansion in another variable. Then, the Viscovatov-like algorithm is given for the computations of the coefficients of this rational expansion. Finally, a numerical experiment is presented to illustrate the practicability of the suggested algorithm. Henceforth, the Viscovatov-like algorithm has been considered as the imperative generalization to find out the coefficients of Thiele–Newton's blending expansion of a bivariate function.

Keywords: bivariate function; divided difference; inverse difference; blending difference; continued fraction; Thiele–Newton's expansion; Viscovatov-like algorithm

1. Introduction

The interpolation and expansion of a function are two of the oldest and most interesting branches in both computational mathematics and approximation theory. Most often, they have a natural link with their corresponding algorithms, such as Newton's interpolatory formula and its divided-difference algorithm, Thiele's interpolating continued fraction and its inverse-difference algorithm, Thiele's expansion of a univariate function and its Viscovatov's algorithm, and so on. For the function f being a univariate function, such problems have been extensively investigated, and abundant research results have been achieved. Some surveys and a complete literature for the problems in single variable interpolation and expansion can be found in Cheney [1], Hildebrand [2], Davis [3], Alfio et al. [4], Gautschi [5], Burden et al. [6], and the references therein. However, in comparison to the broad research and application of the univariate interpolation and expansion problems, much less attention has been paid to the problems associated with multivariate interpolation and expansion, and the study of multivariate rational interpolation and expansion is even less. However, fortunately, there exists some literature discussing the multivariate rational interpolation and expansion problems. We mention the works of Baker et al. [7,8], Kuchminskaya [9], Skorobogatko [10], Siemaszko [11], Viscovatov [12], Graves-Morris [13], Cuyt and Verdonk [14–17], Möller [18], Zhu et al. [19], Gu et al. [20,21], Tan et al. [22–28], and the references therein for results concerning the multivariate rational interpolation and expansion.

Skorobogatko applied the idea of the branch to the continued fraction from about the 1960s to the 1980s, which ushered in a new era of the research on the theories and methods of the continued fraction [10]. In 1983, the concept of the Thiele-type interpolation by the continued fraction in one variable was generalized to the multivariate case by Siemaszko [11], and the Thiele-type branched continued fractions were obtained and an algorithm for the computation of the limiting case of branched continued fractions for bivariable functions suggested. Furthermore, in the 1980s, based on the so-called symmetric branched continued fraction, Cuyt et al. [14–16] introduced a symmetric interpolation scheme and studied the expansion of a bivariate function by using this method and technique. By following the prior works, in 1995, Zhu et al. [19,22] discussed the vector-valued rational interpolants by branched continued fractions. In 1997, Gu et al. [20,21] investigated the problem about matrix-valued rational interpolants. In the meantime, Tan et al. engaged in studying bivariate rational interpolants and obtained tremendous scholarly achievements in this field [22–28]. In 2007, Tan summarized the research results concerning the theory of the continued fraction and published the famous book The Theory of Continued Fractions and Their Applications. This book has played an important role in promoting some modern research about the continued fraction. Furthermore, there are a few works and references about the application of the continued fraction in image processing, such as the literature of Hu and Tan [29,30], Li et al. [31].

As we all know, Taylor's expansion of a function is likely to be the best known and most widely-used formula for the function approximation problem. If f is a function of a univariate x and the derivatives of all orders are uniformly bounded in a neighborhood $\mho(\xi)$, then for each x in $\mho(\xi)$, $f(x)$ can be expanded into the following Taylor's formula about ξ:

$$f(x) = C_0 + C_1(x-\xi) + C_2(x-\xi)^2 + \cdots + C_k(x-\xi)^k + \cdots,$$

where $C_k = \frac{1}{k!} f^{(k)}(\xi), k = 0,1,2,\ldots$. On the other hand, the function $f(x)$ can also be expanded about ξ in terms of the continued fraction, which is in the form of the following:

$$f(x) = d_0 + \frac{x-\xi|}{|d_1} + \frac{x-\xi|}{|d_2} + \cdots + \frac{x-\xi|}{|d_n} + \cdots,$$

where $d_k \in \Re, k = 0,1,2,\ldots$. Here, the above formula is called Thiele's expansion for $f(x)$ about ξ. There is a famous algorithm to compute the coefficients $d_0, d_1, d_2, \ldots,$ of Thiele's expansion, which is called Viscovatov's algorithm. We can see the references [16,28].

Motivated by the results concerning the univariate function, in this paper, we consider the rational expansion by Thiele's continued fraction of a bivariate function and give a Viscovatov-like algorithm for the computations of the coefficients. As a preliminary to our discussions, Thiele–Newton's interpolation needs to be introduced first. In the works [25,28], the so-called Thiele–Newton's interpolation was suggested to construct bivariate interpolants by Tan et al. Its main idea is to combine Thiele's interpolating continued fraction in one variable with Newton's interpolating polynomial in another variable to hybridize a new interpolation, which is defined as below:

$$TN_{m,n}(x,y) = t_0(y) + \frac{x-x_0|}{|t_1(y)} + \frac{x-x_1|}{|t_2(y)} + \cdots + \frac{x-x_{m-1}|}{|t_m(y)}, \tag{1}$$

where:

$$\begin{aligned} t_i(y) =& \varphi_{TN}[x_0,\cdots,x_i;y_0] + (y-y_0)\varphi_{TN}[x_0,\cdots,x_i;y_0,y_1] \\ &+ \cdots + (y-y_0)(y-y_1)\cdots(y-y_{n-1})\varphi_{TN}[x_0,\cdots,x_i;y_0,\cdots,y_n] \end{aligned} \tag{2}$$

for $i = 0,1,\ldots,m$, both $X = \{x_i | i \in \mathbb{N}\}$ and $Y = \{y_j | j \in \mathbb{N}\}$ are two sets of points belonging to $\Re$, and $\varphi_{TN}[x_0,\cdots,x_i;\ y_0,\cdots,y_j]$ denotes the blending difference of the function $f(x,y)$ at points $x_0,\ldots,x_i;\ y_0,\ldots,y_j$. Suppose that any blending difference $\varphi_{TN}[x_0,\cdots,x_i;\ y_0,\cdots,y_j]$ exists. Then, one can easily confirm that:

$$TN_{m,n}(x_i,y_j) = f(x_i,y_j), \quad i = 0,1,\ldots,m; \quad j = 0,1,\ldots,n.$$

The limiting case of Thiele's interpolating continued fraction expansion of a univariate function has been discussed in the literature [26]. With the inspiration of the limiting case, Thiele–Newton's expansion of a bivariate function is yielded when all the points in sets $X = \{x_i | i \in \mathbb{N}\}$ and $Y = \{y_j | j \in$

$\mathbb{N}\}$ are coincident with certain points ξ and ζ, respectively, from Equations (1) and (2), or in other words, a bivariate function $f(x,y)$ has Thiele–Newton's expansion of the following form:

$$f(x,y) = l_0(y) + \frac{x-\xi|}{|l_1(y)} + \frac{x-\xi|}{|l_2(y)} + \cdots + \frac{x-\xi|}{|l_m(y)}, \tag{3}$$

where:

$$l_i(y) = a_{i,0} + a_{i,1}(y-\zeta) + a_{i,2}(y-\zeta)^2 + a_{i,3}(y-\zeta)^3 + \cdots \tag{4}$$

for all $i \in \mathbb{N}$. Therefore, there exists a question about how to calculate the unknowns $a_{i,j}, i = 0,1,2,\ldots, j = 0,1,2,\ldots$, in Equation (4).

The aim of this paper is to find an algorithm for the computations of the coefficients of Thiele–Newton's expansion of a bivariate function. The paper is organized as follows. In Section 2, we briefly recall some preliminaries for Thiele's continued fraction and Thiele–Newton's blending interpolation. In Section 3, we suggest Thiele–Newton's blending rational expansion and prove the Viscovatov-like algorithm. In Section 4, numerical examples are given to illustrate the application of the Viscovatov-like algorithm. Throughout the paper, we let $\mathbb{N}$ and $\mathfrak{R}$ stand for the set of natural numbers and the set of real numbers, respectively.

2. Preliminaries

In this section, we briefly review some basic definitions and results for Thiele's continued fraction, Thiele's expansion of a univariate function, and blending interpolation. Some surveys and complete literature about the continued fraction could be found in Cuyt et al. [14–16], Zhu et al. [19], Gu et al. [20,21], and Tan et al. [25,26,28].

Definition 1. *Assume that G is a subset of the complex plane and $X = \{x_i | i \in \mathbb{N}\}$ is a set of points belonging to G. Suppose, in addition, that $f(x)$ is a function defined on G. Let:*

$$f[x_i] = f(x_i), i \in \mathbb{N},$$
$$f[x_i, x_j] = \frac{f[x_i] - f[x_j]}{x_i - x_j},$$
$$f[x_i, x_j, x_k] = \frac{f[x_i, x_k] - f[x_i, x_j]}{x_k - x_j}$$

and:

$$f[x_i, \ldots, x_j, x_k, x_l] = \frac{f[x_i, \ldots, x_j, x_l] - f[x_i, \ldots, x_j, x_k]}{x_l - x_k}.$$

Then, $f[x_i, \ldots, x_j, x_k]$ is called the divided difference of $f(x)$ with respect to points $x_i, \ldots, x_j, x_k$.

Definition 2. *Assume that G is a subset of the complex plane and $X = \{x_i | i \in \mathbb{N}\}$ is a set of points in G. Suppose, in addition, that $f(x)$ is a function defined on G. We let:*

$$\rho[x_i] = f(x_i), i \in \mathbb{N},$$
$$\rho[x_i, x_j] = \frac{x_i - x_j}{\rho[x_i] - \rho[x_j]},$$
$$\rho[x_i, x_j, x_k] = \frac{x_k - x_j}{\rho[x_i, x_k] - \rho[x_i, x_j]}$$

and:

$$\rho[x_i,\ldots,x_j,x_k,x_l] = \frac{x_l - x_k}{\rho[x_i,\ldots,x_j,x_l] - \rho[x_i,\ldots,x_j,x_k]}.$$

Then, $\rho[x_i,\ldots,x_j,x_k]$ *is called the inverse difference of* $f(x)$ *with respect to points* $x_i,\ldots,x_j,x_k$.

Definition 3. *Assume that G is a subset of the complex plane and* $X = \{x_i | i \in \mathbb{N}\} \subseteq G$ *is a set of points. In addition, let* $f(x)$ *be a function defined on G, and let:*

$$R_n(x) = \rho[x_0] + \frac{x - x_0}{\rho[x_0,x_1]} \Big| + \cdots + \frac{x - x_{n-1}}{\rho[x_0,x_1,\ldots,x_n]} \Big|, \quad (5)$$

where $\rho[x_0,x_1,\ldots,x_i], i = 0,1,2,\ldots,n$, *is the inverse difference of* $f(x)$ *with respect to points* $x_0,x_1,\ldots,x_i$. *Then,* $R_n(x)$ *is called Thiele's interpolating continued fraction of order n. It is easy to verify that the rational function satisfies the following conditions:*

$$R_n(x_i) = f(x_i), i = 0,1,2,\ldots,n.$$

When all the points in the set $X = \{x_i | i \in \mathbb{N}\}$ are coincident with a certain point $\xi \in G$, Thiele's expansion of a univariate function $f(x)$ at $x = \xi$ is obtained as follows:

$$f(x) = d_0 + \frac{x-\xi}{d_1}\Big| + \frac{x-\xi}{d_2}\Big| + \cdots + \frac{x-\xi}{d_n}\Big| + \cdots, \quad (6)$$

where $d_k \in \mathfrak{R}, k = 0,1,2,\ldots$. Moreover, if $f(x)$ is a function with derivatives of all orders in a neighborhood $\mho(\xi)$, then Taylor's expansion of the function $f(x)$ at $x = \xi$ is denoted as below:

$$f(x) = \sum_{n=0}^{\infty} C_n^{(0)} (x-\xi)^n,$$

where $C_n^{(0)} = \frac{1}{n!} f^{(n)}(\xi), n = 0,1,2,\ldots$ A famous method, called Viscovatov's algorithm (see [16,28]), is available for the computations of the coefficients $d_0, d_1, d_2, \ldots,$ of Thiele's expansion, which is formulated as follows.

Algorithm 1. *Viscovatov's algorithm to calculate the coefficients* $d_0, d_1, d_2, \ldots$:

$$\begin{aligned} C_i^{(0)} &= f^{(i)}(\xi)/i!, i = 0,1,2,\ldots, \\ d_0 &= C_0^{(0)}, \\ d_1 &= 1/C_1^{(0)}, \\ C_i^{(1)} &= -C_{i+1}^{(0)}/C_1^{(0)}, i \geqslant 1, \\ d_l &= C_1^{(l-2)}/C_1^{(l-1)}, l \geqslant 2, \\ C_i^{(l)} &= C_{i+1}^{(l-2)} - d_l C_{i+1}^{(l-1)}, i \geqslant 1, l \geqslant 2. \end{aligned}$$

Remark 1. *Clearly, by applying Viscovatov's algorithm, we can carry out computations step by step for the coefficients* $d_0, d_1, d_2, \ldots$.

In [25,28], the method known as Thiele–Newton's blending interpolation was suggested to construct bivariate interpolants by Tan et al. Before the method can be introduced, we recall the definition concerning the blending difference.

Definition 4. *Assume that* $\Pi_{m,n} = X_m \times Y_n$, *where* $X_m = \{x_i | i = 0,1,2,\ldots,m\} \subset [a,b] \subset \mathfrak{R}$ *and* $Y_n = \{y_j | j = 0,1,2,\ldots,n\} \subset [c,d] \subset \mathfrak{R}$ *are two sets of points. Suppose that* $f(x,y)$ *is a function of two variables defined on* $D = [a,b] \times [c,d]$. *Let:*

$$\varphi_{TN}[x_i; y_j] = f(x_i, y_j), (x_i, y_j) \in D,$$
$$\varphi_{TN}[x_i; y_p, y_q] = \frac{\varphi_{TN}[x_i; y_q] - \varphi_{TN}[x_i; y_p]}{y_q - y_p},$$
$$\varphi_{TN}[x_i; y_p, \ldots, y_q, y_r, y_s] = \frac{\varphi_{TN}[x_i; y_p, \ldots, y_q, y_s] - \varphi_{TN}[x_i; y_p, \ldots, y_q, y_r]}{y_s - y_r},$$
$$\varphi_{TN}[x_i, x_j; y_p] = \frac{x_j - x_i}{\varphi_{TN}[x_j; y_p] - \varphi_{TN}[x_i; y_p]},$$
$$\varphi_{TN}[x_i, \ldots, x_j, x_k, x_l; y_p] = \frac{x_l - x_k}{\varphi_{TN}[x_i, \ldots, x_j, x_l; y_p] - \varphi_{TN}[x_i, \ldots, x_j, x_k; y_p]}$$

and:

$$\varphi_{TN}[x_i, \ldots, x_l; y_p, \ldots, y_q, y_r, y_s] = \frac{\varphi_{TN}[x_i, \ldots, x_l; y_p, \ldots, y_q, y_s] - \varphi_{TN}[x_i, \ldots, x_l; y_p, \ldots, y_q, y_r]}{y_s - y_r}.$$

Then, $\varphi_{TN}[x_0, \ldots, x_i; y_0, \ldots, y_j]$ *is called Thiele–Newton's blending difference of* $f(x,y)$ *with respect to the set of points* $\Pi_{i,j}$.

Remark 2. *From Definition 4, it is easy to see that the first recurrence relations on Thiele–Newton's blending difference* $\varphi_{TN}[x_0, \ldots, x_i; y_0, \ldots, y_j]$ *are just the inverse difference of* $f(x,y)$ *with respect to the variable* x, *and the second recurrence relations are only the divided difference of* $f(x,y)$ *with respect to the variable* y.

Next, recall Thiele–Newton's interpolation $TN_{m,n}(x,y)$, as shown in Equations (1) and (2). In order to calculate this rational interpolation, we need to utilize the following algorithm whose main operation is matrix transformations (see [23,28]).

Algorithm 2. *Four main steps for the algorithm to calculate Thiele–Newton's interpolation are as follows:*

- **Step 1: Initialization.** For $i = 0,1,\ldots,m;\ j = 0,1,\ldots,n$, let $f_{i,j}^{(0,0)} = f(x_i, y_j)$. Define the following initial information matrix:

$$M_0 = \begin{bmatrix} f_{0,0}^{(0,0)} & f_{1,0}^{(0,0)} & \cdots & f_{m,0}^{(0,0)} \\ f_{0,1}^{(0,0)} & f_{1,1}^{(0,0)} & \cdots & f_{m,1}^{(0,0)} \\ \vdots & \vdots & \ddots & \vdots \\ f_{0,n}^{(0,0)} & f_{1,n}^{(0,0)} & \cdots & f_{m,n}^{(0,0)} \end{bmatrix}.$$

- **Step 2: Thiele's recursion along the X-axis.** For $j = 0,1,\ldots,n;\ p = 1,2,\ldots,m;\ i = p, p+1,\ldots,m$, compute:

$$f_{i,j}^{(p,0)} = \frac{x_i - x_{p-1}}{f_{i,j}^{(p-1,0)} - f_{p-1,j}^{(p-1,0)}}$$

and construct the following information matrix:

$$M_1 = \begin{bmatrix} f_{0,0}^{(0,0)} & f_{1,0}^{(1,0)} & \cdots & f_{m,0}^{(m,0)} \\ f_{0,1}^{(0,0)} & f_{1,1}^{(1,0)} & \cdots & f_{m,1}^{(m,0)} \\ \vdots & \vdots & \ddots & \vdots \\ f_{0,n}^{(0,0)} & f_{1,n}^{(1,0)} & \cdots & f_{m,n}^{(m,0)} \end{bmatrix}.$$

- **Step 3: Newton's recursion along the Y-axis.** For $i = 0, 1, \ldots, m$; $q = 1, 2, \ldots, n$; $j = q, q+1, \ldots, n$, compute:

$$f_{i,j}^{(i,q)} = \frac{f_{i,j}^{(i,q-1)} - f_{i,q-1}^{(i,q-1)}}{y_j - y_{q-1}}$$

and construct the following information matrix:

$$M_2 = \begin{bmatrix} f_{0,0}^{(0,0)} & f_{1,0}^{(1,0)} & \cdots & f_{m,0}^{(m,0)} \\ f_{0,1}^{(0,1)} & f_{1,1}^{(1,1)} & \cdots & f_{m,1}^{(m,1)} \\ \vdots & \vdots & \ddots & \vdots \\ f_{0,n}^{(0,n)} & f_{1,n}^{(1,n)} & \cdots & f_{m,n}^{(m,n)} \end{bmatrix}.$$

- **Step 4: Establish Thiele–Newton's interpolation.** For $i = 0, 1, \ldots, m$, let:

$$t_{i,n}(y) = f_{i,0}^{(i,0)} + (y - y_0) f_{i,1}^{(i,1)} + \cdots + (y - y_0)(y - y_1) \cdots (y - y_{n-1}) f_{i,n}^{(i,n)}.$$

Then, Thiele–Newton's interpolation is established as follows:

$$TN_{m,n}(x, y) = t_{0,n}(y) + \frac{x - x_0|}{|t_{1,n}(y)} + \frac{x - x_1|}{|t_{2,n}(y)} + \cdots + \frac{x - x_{m-1}|}{|t_{m,n}(y)},$$

which satisfies:

$$TN_{m,n}(x_i, y_j) = f(x_i, y_j)$$

for $i = 0, 1, \ldots, m$; $j = 0, 1, \ldots, n$.

Remark 3. *Obviously, for any $i \in \{0, 1, \ldots, m\}$, by using the elements $f_{i,j}^{(i,j)}$, $j = 0, 1, \ldots, n$, in the $(i+1)$th column of the information matrix M_2, Newton's interpolating polynomial $t_{i,n}(y)$ with respect to the variable y can be constructed.*

3. Thiele–Newton's Blending Expansion and the Viscovatov-Like Algorithm

In this section, our main objective is to expound on Thiele–Newton's blending rational expansion of a bivariate function and show the Viscovatov-like algorithm that finds the coefficients of Thiele–Newton's expansion.

3.1. Thiele–Newton's Blending Expansion

Definition 5. *Assume that $\Pi = X \times Y$ with $\Pi \subset D = [a, b] \times [c, d]$, where $X = \{x_i | i = 0, 1, 2, \ldots\} \subset [a, b] \subset \Re$ and $Y = \{y_j | j = 0, 1, 2, \ldots\} \subset [c, d] \subset \Re$ are two sets of points. Suppose, in addition, that the point $(\xi, \zeta) \in D$ and $f(x, y)$ is a bivariate function defined on D. Let all the points in the set $X = \{x_i | i = 0, 1, 2, \ldots\}$ and $Y = \{y_j | j = 0, 1, 2, \ldots\}$ be coincident with the given points ξ and ζ, respectively. Then, Thiele–Newton's* *interpolation $TN_{m,n}(x,y)$ of a bivariate function $f(x,y)$ defined in Section 2 turns into Thiele–Newton's blending expansion of the bivariate function $f(x,y)$ as shown below:*

$$f(x,y) = d_0(y) + \frac{x-\xi}{\lfloor d_1(y)} + \frac{x-\xi}{\lfloor d_2(y)} + \frac{x-\xi}{\lfloor d_3(y)} + \cdots, \tag{7}$$

where:

$$d_i(y) = a_{i,0} + a_{i,1}(y-\zeta) + a_{i,2}(y-\zeta)^2 + a_{i,3}(y-\zeta)^3 + \cdots \tag{8}$$

for any $i \in \mathbb{N}$.

Obviously, a main topic for further discussion is how to calculate the coefficients $d_i(y), i = 0,1,2,\ldots$, in Equation (7), or in other words, how to compute the coefficients $a_{i,j}, i = 0,1,2,\ldots; j = 0,1,2,\ldots$, in Equation (8). In order to handle the problem that we are facing in the bivariate case, we introduce the following algorithm.

3.2. Viscovatov-Like Algorithm

Suppose that $f(x,y)$ is a bivariate function of two variables x and y. If y is held constant, say $y = \zeta$, then $f(x,\zeta)$ is a function of the single variable x. Likewise, $f(\xi,y)$ is also a function of the single variable y when x is regarded as a constant, i.e., $x = \xi$. We use the notation: $D_x^m f(x,y)$ denotes the m-order partial derivative of $f(x,y)$ with respect to x. Similarly, the n-order partial derivative of $f(x,y)$ with respect to y is denoted by $D_y^n f(x,y)$. Furthermore, $D_x^m f(\xi,\zeta)$ and $D_y^n f(\xi,\zeta)$ denote the values of $D_x^m f(x,y)$ and $D_y^n f(x,y)$ about the point $(x,y) = (\xi,\zeta)$, respectively. Let:

$$C_k^{(0)}(y) = \frac{1}{k!} D_x^k f(\xi,y), k = 0,1,2,\ldots.$$

Then, the bivariate function $f(x,y)$ can be expanded formally about the point ξ as follows:

$$f(x,y) = C_0^{(0)}(y) + C_1^{(0)}(y)(x-\xi) + \cdots + C_k^{(0)}(y)(x-\xi)^k + \cdots. \tag{9}$$

From Equations (7)–(9), we give the Viscovatov-like algorithm, which finds out the coefficients of Thiele–Newton's expansion $d_i(y), i = 0,1,2,\ldots$, and $a_{i,j}, i = 0,1,2,\ldots; j = 0,1,2,\ldots$, as described by the following algorithm.

Algorithm 3. *Viscovatov-like algorithm to calculate the coefficients $d_i(y), i = 0,1,2,\ldots$, and $a_{i,j}, i = 0,1,2,\ldots; j = 0,1,2,\ldots$:*

$$\begin{aligned}
C_i^{(0)}(y) &= D_x^i f(\xi,y)/i!, i = 0,1,2,\ldots, \\
d_0(y) &= C_0^{(0)}(y) = f(\xi,y), \\
d_1(y) &= 1/C_1^{(0)}(y), \\
C_i^{(1)}(y) &= -C_{i+1}^{(0)}(y)/C_1^{(0)}(y), i \geqslant 1, \\
d_l(y) &= C_1^{(l-2)}(y)/C_1^{(l-1)}(y), l \geqslant 2, \\
C_i^{(l)}(y) &= C_{i+1}^{(l-2)}(y) - d_l(y)C_{i+1}^{(l-1)}(y), i \geqslant 1, l \geqslant 2, \\
a_{i,j} &= D_y^j d_i(\zeta)/j!, i = 0,1,2,\ldots; j = 0,1,2,\ldots.
\end{aligned}$$

Proof of Algorithm 3. First, we compute the coefficients $d_0(y)$ and $d_1(y)$. Considering the two expansions (7) and (9), we have:

$$C_0^{(0)}(y) + C_1^{(0)}(y)(x-\xi) + C_2^{(0)}(y)(x-\xi)^2 + \cdots = d_0(y) + \frac{x-\xi}{\lfloor d_1(y)} + \frac{x-\xi}{\lfloor d_2(y)} + \frac{x-\xi}{\lfloor d_3(y)} + \cdots. \tag{10}$$

Letting $x = \xi$, from Equation (10), one can clearly get:

$$d_0(y) = C_0^{(0)}(y). \tag{11}$$

Combining Equation (11) with Equation (10), we have:

$$d_1(y) + \frac{x-\xi|}{|d_2(y)} + \frac{x-\xi|}{|d_3(y)} + \cdots = \frac{1}{C_1^{(0)}(y) + C_2^{(0)}(y)(x-\xi) + C_3^{(0)}(y)(x-\xi)^2 + \cdots}. \tag{12}$$

Let $x = \xi$ in Equation (12). Then, we can easily obtain:

$$d_1(y) = \frac{1}{C_1^{(0)}(y)}. \tag{13}$$

Next, by mathematical induction, we shall prove that the following equation:

$$d_l(y) = \frac{C_1^{(l-2)}(y)}{C_1^{(l-1)}(y)} \tag{14}$$

is true for all $l \geqslant 2$.

When $l = 2$, we shall verify that Equation (14) holds. Substituting Equation (13) into Equation (12), we have:

$$\begin{aligned} \frac{x-\xi|}{|d_2(y)} + \frac{x-\xi|}{|d_3(y)} + \cdots &= \frac{1}{C_1^{(0)}(y)\left[1 + \frac{C_2^{(0)}(y)}{C_1^{(0)}(y)}(x-\xi) + \frac{C_3^{(0)}(y)}{C_1^{(0)}(y)}(x-\xi)^2 + \cdots\right]} - \frac{1}{C_1^{(0)}(y)} \\ &= -\frac{\frac{C_2^{(0)}(y)}{C_1^{(0)}(y)}(x-\xi) + \frac{C_3^{(0)}(y)}{C_1^{(0)}(y)}(x-\xi)^2 + \cdots}{C_1^{(0)}(y) + C_2^{(0)}(y)(x-\xi) + C_3^{(0)}(y)(x-\xi)^2 + \cdots}, \end{aligned} \tag{15}$$

which implies that:

$$d_2(y) + \frac{x-\xi|}{|d_3(y)} + \frac{x-\xi|}{|d_4(y)} + \cdots = \frac{C_1^{(0)}(y) + C_2^{(0)}(y)(x-\xi) + C_3^{(0)}(y)(x-\xi)^2 + \cdots}{-\frac{C_2^{(0)}(y)}{C_1^{(0)}(y)} - \frac{C_3^{(0)}(y)}{C_1^{(0)}(y)}(x-\xi) - \frac{C_4^{(0)}(y)}{C_1^{(0)}(y)}(x-\xi)^2 - \cdots}. \tag{16}$$

Let:

$$C_i^{(1)}(y) = -\frac{C_{i+1}^{(0)}(y)}{C_1^{(0)}(y)}, i = 1, 2, 3, \ldots. \tag{17}$$

Then, it follows from the identity (16) that:

$$d_2(y) + \frac{x-\xi|}{|d_3(y)} + \frac{x-\xi|}{|d_4(y)} + \cdots = \frac{C_1^{(0)}(y) + C_2^{(0)}(y)(x-\xi) + C_3^{(0)}(y)(x-\xi)^2 + \cdots}{C_1^{(1)}(y) + C_2^{(1)}(y)(x-\xi) + C_3^{(1)}(y)(x-\xi)^2 + \cdots}. \tag{18}$$

Using $x = \xi$ in Equation (18) yields:

$$d_2(y) = \frac{C_1^{(0)}(y)}{C_1^{(1)}(y)}, \tag{19}$$

which implies that Equation (14) is true for $l = 2$.

When $l \geqslant 3$, assume that Equation (14) holds for any $l = n, n = 3, 4, \ldots$. Then, let us prove that Equation (14) is also true for $l = n + 1$.

By assumption, we have the following equation:

$$d_n(y) = \frac{C_1^{(n-2)}(y)}{C_1^{(n-1)}(y)} \tag{20}$$

holds.

Referring to Equation (18), we assume that the following equation:

$$d_n(y) + \frac{x-\xi}{|\,d_{n+1}(y)} + \frac{x-\xi}{|\,d_{n+2}(y)} + \cdots = \frac{C_1^{(n-2)}(y) + C_2^{(n-2)}(y)(x-\xi) + C_3^{(n-2)}(y)(x-\xi)^2 + \cdots}{C_1^{(n-1)}(y) + C_2^{(n-1)}(y)(x-\xi) + C_3^{(n-1)}(y)(x-\xi)^2 + \cdots} \tag{21}$$

is true, where:

$$C_i^{(k)}(y) = C_{i+1}^{(k-2)}(y) - d_k(y)C_{i+1}^{(k-1)}(y), k = n-2, n-1; n \geq 2; i = 1, 2, 3, \ldots. \tag{22}$$

Combining Equation (20) with Equation (21), one has:

$$\begin{aligned} &\frac{x-\xi}{|\,d_{n+1}(y)} + \frac{x-\xi}{|\,d_{n+2}(y)} + \cdots \\ =&\frac{C_1^{(n-2)}(y) + C_2^{(n-2)}(y)(x-\xi) + C_3^{(n-2)}(y)(x-\xi)^2 + \cdots}{C_1^{(n-1)}(y)\left[1 + \frac{C_2^{(n-1)}(y)}{C_1^{(n-1)}(y)}(x-\xi) + \frac{C_3^{(n-1)}(y)}{C_1^{(n-1)}(y)}(x-\xi)^2 + \cdots\right]} - \frac{C_1^{(n-2)}(y)}{C_1^{(n-1)}(y)} \\ =&\frac{\left(C_2^{(n-2)}(y) - d_n(y)C_2^{(n-1)}(y)\right)(x-\xi) + \left(C_3^{(n-2)}(y) - d_n(y)C_3^{(n-1)}(y)\right)(x-\xi)^2 + \cdots}{C_1^{(n-1)}(y) + C_2^{(n-1)}(y)(x-\xi) + C_3^{(n-1)}(y)(x-\xi)^2 + \cdots}. \end{aligned} \tag{23}$$

Let:

$$C_i^{(n)}(y) = C_{i+1}^{(n-2)}(y) - d_n(y)C_{i+1}^{(n-1)}(y), i = 1, 2, 3, \ldots. \tag{24}$$

Then, Equation (23) is rewritten as follows:

$$d_{n+1}(y) + \frac{x-\xi}{|\,d_{n+2}(y)} + \frac{x-\xi}{|\,d_{n+3}(y)} + \cdots = \frac{C_1^{(n-1)}(y) + C_2^{(n-1)}(y)(x-\xi) + C_3^{(n-1)}(y)(x-\xi)^2 + \cdots}{C_1^{(n)}(y) + C_2^{(n)}(y)(x-\xi) + C_3^{(n)}(y)(x-\xi)^2 + \cdots}, \tag{25}$$

Using the above Equation (25) with $x = \xi$ produces:

$$d_{n+1}(y) = \frac{C_1^{(n-1)}(y)}{C_1^{(n)}(y)}, \tag{26}$$

which means that Equation (14) holds for $l = n + 1$.

As is shown above, Equation (14) is true by mathematical induction for all $l \geqslant 2$. Meanwhile, we show that Equation (24) is also true for any $l = n, n \geqslant 2$.

Moreover, by differentiating Equation (8) j times with respect to the variable y, one has:

$$D_y^j d_i(y) = a_{i,j} j! + a_{i,j+1}\frac{(j+1)!}{1!}(y-\zeta) + a_{i,j+2}\frac{(j+2)!}{2!}(y-\zeta)^2 + \cdots. \tag{27}$$

Notice $y = \zeta$, from Equation (27), and we immediately obtain:

$$a_{i,j} = \frac{D_y^j d_i(\zeta)}{j!} \tag{28}$$

for $i \in \mathbb{N}$ and $j \in \mathbb{N}$.

Therefore, associating Equation (28) with Equations (11), (13), (14), (17), and (24), we have shown the desired conclusion denoted by Algorithm 3. This completes the proof. □

4. Numerical Experiments

In the section, we give the results of numerical experiments to compare the efficiency of Thiele–Newton's blending expansion (7) with series expansion of bivariate functions.

For $|x| < 1$, $|y| < 1$ and $x \neq y$, given the following two test functions:

$$f_1(x,y) = \frac{1}{y-x}\left[\ln(1-x) - \ln(1-y)\right] \tag{29}$$

and:

$$f_2(x,y) = \frac{x^2}{(1-x)(x-y)^2} + \frac{y^2}{(1-y)(x-y)^2} + \frac{2xy\left[\ln(1-x) - \ln(1-y)\right]}{(x-y)^3}, \tag{30}$$

where $\ln(z)$ gives the natural logarithm of z (logarithm to base e). We shall discuss Thiele–Newton's blending expansions of Equations (29) and (30), respectively.

First of all, let us consider Thiele–Newton's blending expansion of the bivariate function $f_1(x,y)$ defined by Equation (29) at the point $(\xi,\zeta) = (0,0)$. Therefore, using the Viscovatov-like algorithm, we can obtain the coefficient using the notation $a_{i,j}^{f_1}$ of Thiele–Newton's expansion of $f_1(x,y)$. Some values of $a_{i,j}^{f_1}, i = 0,1,2,\ldots,m,\ldots; j = 0,1,2,\ldots,n,\ldots$, are shown in Table 1.

Table 1. The coefficients $a_{i,j}^{f_1}$ of Thiele–Newton's expansion of $f_1(x,y)$ given by Equation (29).

$a_{i,j}^{f_1}$	$j=0$	$j=1$	$j=2$	$j=3$	$j=4$	$\cdots$
$i=0$	1	$\frac{1}{2}$	$\frac{1}{3}$	$\frac{1}{4}$	$\frac{1}{5}$	$\cdots$
$i=1$	2	$-\frac{4}{3}$	$-\frac{1}{9}$	$-\frac{8}{135}$	$-\frac{31}{810}$	$\cdots$
$i=2$	$-\frac{3}{4}$	$-\frac{7}{16}$	$-\frac{293}{960}$	$-\frac{299}{1280}$	$-\frac{33869}{179200}$	$\cdots$
$i=3$	16	$-\frac{88}{15}$	$-\frac{191}{225}$	$-\frac{10264}{23625}$	$-\frac{194491}{708750}$	$\cdots$
$\vdots$	$\vdots$	$\vdots$	$\vdots$	$\vdots$	$\vdots$	$\ddots$

Thus, Thiele–Newton's blending expansion of $f_1(x,y)$ at $(\xi,\zeta) = (0,0)$ is denoted in the form:

$$\begin{aligned} f_1(x,y) = R^{f_1}(x,y) =& 1 + \frac{1}{2}y + \frac{1}{3}y^2 + \frac{1}{4}y^3 + \frac{1}{5}y^4 + \cdots \\ &+ \frac{x \rfloor}{\lfloor 2 - \frac{4}{3}y - \frac{1}{9}y^2 - \frac{8}{135}y^3 - \frac{31}{810}y^4 + \cdots} \\ &+ \frac{x \rfloor}{\lfloor -\frac{3}{4} - \frac{7}{16}y - \frac{293}{960}y^2 - \frac{299}{1280}y^3 - \frac{33869}{179200}y^4 + \cdots} \\ &+ \frac{x \rfloor}{\lfloor 16 - \frac{88}{15}y - \frac{191}{225}y^2 - \frac{10264}{23625}y^3 - \frac{194491}{708750}y^4 + \cdots} + \cdots. \end{aligned} \tag{31}$$

For $m = 2, n = 3$, taking into account the truncated Thiele–Newton's blending expansion $R^{f_1}_{m,n}(x,y)$ of $R^{f_1}(x,y)$ expressed by the above Equation (31), one can have:

$$R^{f_1}_{2,3}(x,y) = 1 + \frac{y}{2} + \frac{y^2}{3} + \frac{y^3}{4} + \cfrac{x}{2 - \frac{4}{3}y - \frac{1}{9}y^2 - \frac{8}{135}y^3 - \cfrac{x}{\frac{3}{4} + \frac{7}{16}y + \frac{293}{960}y^2 + \frac{299}{1280}y^3}}. \tag{32}$$

On the other hand, the bivariate function $f_1(x,y)$ defined by Equation (29) can be expanded at the point $(\xi, \zeta) = (0,0)$ by means of the Appell series $F1^{f_1}(a,b,c;d;x,y)$ denoted for $|x| < 1$, $|y| < 1$ and $x \neq y$ by the following bivariate series (see [17]):

$$F1^{f_1}(a,b,c;d;x,y) = \sum_{i,j=0}^{\infty} \frac{(a)_{i+j}(b)_i(c)_j}{(d)_{i+j} i! j!} x^i y^j, \tag{33}$$

where $a = b = c = 1, d = 2$, and the Pochhammer symbol $(\tau)_k$ represents the rising factorial:

$$(\tau)_k = \tau(\tau+1)(\tau+2)\cdots(\tau+k-1) \tag{34}$$

for any $\tau \in \mathfrak{R}^+$ (see [17,32]). In particular, $(1)_0 = 1, (1)_k = k!, (2)_k = (k+1)!$.

For Equation (33), the following polynomial:

$$F1^{f_1}_{m,n}(a,b,c;d;x,y) = \sum_{i=0}^{m} \sum_{j=0}^{n} \frac{(a)_{i+j}(b)_i(c)_j}{(d)_{i+j} i! j!} x^i y^j \tag{35}$$

is defined as the (m,n)-order truncated Appell series, where $m \in \mathbb{N}$ and $n \in \mathbb{N}$.

By Equations (33)–(35), we have:

$$f_1(x,y) = F1^{f_1}(1,1,1;2;x,y) = \sum_{i,j=0}^{\infty} \frac{1}{i+j+1} x^i y^j \tag{36}$$

and for $m = 2, n = 3$, the $(2,3)$-order truncated Appell series is given by:

$$F1^{f_1}_{2,3}(1,1,1;2;x,y) = 1 + \frac{x}{2} + \frac{x^2}{3} + \frac{y}{2} + \frac{xy}{3} + \frac{x^2y}{4} + \frac{y^2}{3} + \frac{xy^2}{4} + \frac{x^2y^2}{5} + \frac{y^3}{4} + \frac{xy^3}{5} + \frac{x^2y^3}{6}. \tag{37}$$

Second, performing similar operations for the bivariate function $f_2(x,y)$ defined by Equation (30), this gives the coefficient of Thiele–Newton's expansion, which is denoted by the notation $a^{f_2}_{i,j}$. Some values of $a^{f_2}_{i,j}, i = 0,1,2,\ldots,m,\ldots; j = 0,1,2,\ldots,n,\ldots$, are listed in Table 2.

Table 2. The coefficients $a^{f_2}_{i,j}$ of Thiele–Newton's expansion of $f_2(x,y)$ given by Equation (30).

$a^{f_2}_{i,j}$	$j=0$	$j=1$	$j=2$	$j=3$	$j=4$	$\cdots$
$i=0$	1	1	1	1	1	$\cdots$
$i=1$	1	$-\frac{4}{3}$	$\frac{5}{18}$	$\frac{4}{135}$	$\frac{17}{1620}$	$\cdots$
$i=2$	-1	$-\frac{7}{6}$	$-\frac{221}{180}$	$-\frac{151}{120}$	$-\frac{10721}{8400}$	$\cdots$
$\vdots$	$\vdots$	$\vdots$	$\vdots$	$\vdots$	$\vdots$	$\ddots$

Therefore, according to the values of $a_{i,j}^{f_2}, i = 0,1,2,\ldots;j = 0,1,2,\ldots$, in Table 2, the Thiele–Newton's blending expansion of $f_2(x,y)$ at $(\xi,\zeta) = (0,0)$ can be written as:

$$\begin{aligned} f_2(x,y) = R^{f_2}(x,y) =& 1 + y + y^2 + y^3 + y^4 + \cdots \\ &+ \frac{x\rfloor}{\lfloor 1 - \frac{4}{3}y + \frac{5}{18}y^2 + \frac{4}{135}y^3 + \frac{17}{1620}y^4 + \cdots} \\ &+ \frac{x\rfloor}{\lfloor -1 - \frac{7}{6}y - \frac{221}{180}y^2 - \frac{151}{120}y^3 - \frac{10721}{8400}y^4 + \cdots} + \cdots . \end{aligned} \tag{38}$$

The corresponding truncated Thiele–Newton's blending expansion $R_{2,3}^{f_2}(x,y)$ of $R^{f_2}(x,y)$ is:

$$R_{2,3}^{f_2}(x,y) = 1 + y + y^2 + y^3 + \frac{x}{1 - \frac{4}{3}y + \frac{5}{18}y^2 + \frac{4}{135}y^3 - \frac{x}{1 + \frac{7}{6}y + \frac{221}{180}y^2 + \frac{151}{120}y^3}}. \tag{39}$$

By a similar technique, consider the Appell series for the bivariate function $f_2(x,y)$ expanded about the point $(\xi,\zeta) = (0,0)$,

$$F1^{f_2}(1,2,2;2;x,y) = \sum_{i,j=0}^{\infty} \frac{(1)_{i+j}(2)_i(2)_j}{(2)_{i+j}i!j!}x^i y^j = \sum_{i,j=0}^{\infty} \frac{(i+1)(j+1)}{i+j+1}x^i y^j. \tag{40}$$

The $(2,3)$-order truncated Appell series for $f_2(x,y)$ is:

$$F1_{2,3}^{f_2}(1,2,2;2;x,y) = 1 + x + x^2 + y + \frac{4}{3}xy + \frac{3}{2}x^2y + y^2 + \frac{3}{2}xy^2 + \frac{9}{5}x^2y^2 + y^3 + \frac{8}{5}xy^3 + 2x^2y^3. \tag{41}$$

Considering the errors, we let:

$$e_{2,3}^{f_k} = f_k(x,y) - R_{2,3}^{f_k}(x,y) \tag{42}$$

and:

$$E_{2,3}^{f_k} = f_k(x,y) - F1_{2,3}^{f_k}(a,b,c;d;x,y) \tag{43}$$

for $k = 1,2$.

Table 3 lists various values of (x,y), together with the values of the bivariate function $f_1(x,y)$, the truncated Thiele–Newton's blending expansion $R_{2,3}^{f_1}(x,y)$, and the truncated Appell series $F1_{2,3}^{f_1}(1,1,1;2;x,y)$. Furthermore, for comparison purposes, the values of errors $e_{2,3}^{f_1}$ and $E_{2,3}^{f_1}$ are given in this table. It can be seen from Table 3 that the error $e_{2,3}^{f_1}$ using the truncated Thiele–Newton's blending expansion $R_{2,3}^{f_1}(x,y)$ is less than when using the truncated Appell series $F1_{2,3}^{f_1}(1,1,1;2;x,y)$, which gives the error $E_{2,3}^{f_1}$. Similarly, displayed in Table 4 are the numerical results for the bivariate function $f_2(x,y)$ defined by Equation (30). Thus, these results illustrate that the approximation by the truncated Thiele–Newton's blending expansion is clearly superior in the two test examples.

Table 3. Comparison of the numerical results by using $R^{f_1}_{2,3}(x,y)$ and $F1^{f_1}_{2,3}(1,1,1;2;x,y)$.

(x,y)	$f_1(x,y)$	$R^{f_1}_{2,3}(x,y)$	$e^{f_1}_{2,3}$	$F1^{f_1}_{2,3}(1,1,1;2;x,y)$	$E^{f_1}_{2,3}$
(0.6,0.5)	2.231435513142	2.175811138576	5.56244×10^{-2}	2.007583333333	2.23852×10^{-1}
(0.5,0.4)	1.823215567940	1.801574172062	2.16414×10^{-2}	1.731400000000	9.18156×10^{-2}
(0.4,0.3)	1.541506798273	1.534197264544	7.30953×10^{-3}	1.506843333333	3.46635×10^{-2}
(0.3,0.2)	1.335313926245	1.333336425463	1.97750×10^{-3}	1.324153333333	1.11606×10^{-2}
(0.2,0.1)	1.177830356564	1.177455592535	3.74764×10^{-4}	1.175210000000	2.62036×10^{-3}
(0.09,0.1)	1.104983618659	1.104936257854	4.73608×10^{-5}	1.104746383333	2.37235×10^{-4}
(0.08,0.09)	1.092907053219	1.092875387558	3.16657×10^{-5}	1.092744392933	1.62660×10^{-4}
(0.07,0.08)	1.081091610422	1.081071421327	2.01891×10^{-5}	1.080985191467	1.06419×10^{-4}
(0.05,0.06)	1.058210933054	1.058204252599	6.68046×10^{-6}	1.058173883333	3.70497×10^{-5}
(0.06,0.05)	1.058210933054	1.058202709844	8.22321×10^{-6}	1.058150458333	6.04747×10^{-5}
(0.04,0.05)	1.047129986730	1.047126709307	3.27742×10^{-6}	1.047111416666	1.85701×10^{-5}
(0.05,0.04)	1.047129986730	1.047125552862	4.43387×10^{-6}	1.047095800000	3.41867×10^{-5}
(0.03,0.02)	1.025650016719	1.025649181797	8.34922×10^{-7}	1.025642954533	7.06219×10^{-6}
(0.02,0.03)	1.025650016719	1.025649615899	4.00820×10^{-7}	1.025647765133	2.25159×10^{-6}
(0.02,0.01)	1.015237146402	1.015236912398	2.34003×10^{-7}	1.015235095400	2.05100×10^{-6}
(0.01,0.02)	1.015237146402	1.015237085235	6.11671×10^{-8}	1.015236857467	2.88935×10^{-7}

Table 4. Comparison of the numerical results by using $R^{f_2}_{2,3}(x,y)$ and $F1^{f_2}_{2,3}(1,2,2;2;x,y)$.

(x,y)	$f_2(x,y)$	$R^{f_2}_{2,3}(x,y)$	$e^{f_2}_{2,3}$	$F1^{f_2}_{2,3}(1,2,2;2;x,y)$	$E^{f_2}_{2,3}$
(0.4,0.3)	2.527646365268	2.541958340395	-1.43120×10^{-2}	2.314840000000	2.12806×10^{-1}
(0.3,0.2)	1.833375742200	1.834880020667	-1.50428×10^{-3}	1.774760000000	5.86157×10^{-2}
(0.2,0.1)	1.399789684856	1.399902542529	-1.12858×10^{-4}	1.387786666667	1.20030×10^{-2}
(0.09,0.1)	1.225048763570	1.225046790051	1.97352×10^{-6}	1.223971000000	1.07776×10^{-3}
(0.08,0.09)	1.197590738753	1.197589594868	1.14389×10^{-6}	1.196860955200	7.29784×10^{-4}
(0.07,0.08)	1.171129067101	1.171128457172	6.09930×10^{-7}	1.170657476267	4.71591×10^{-4}
(0.06,0.07)	1.145615802753	1.145615507616	2.95138×10^{-7}	1.145329149600	2.86653×10^{-4}
(0.05,0.06)	1.121005830888	1.121005702793	1.28095×10^{-7}	1.120845560000	1.60271×10^{-4}
(0.06,0.05)	1.121005830888	1.121006469601	-6.38713×10^{-7}	1.120749100000	2.56731×10^{-4}
(0.04,0.05)	1.097256671169	1.097256621117	5.00525×10^{-8}	1.097177266667	7.94045×10^{-5}
(0.05,0.04)	1.097256671169	1.097256985627	-3.14458×10^{-7}	1.097113306667	1.43365×10^{-4}
(0.03,0.02)	1.052182967898	1.052183005275	-3.73770×10^{-8}	1.052154046400	2.89215×10^{-5}
(0.02,0.03)	1.052182967898	1.052182961331	6.56692×10^{-9}	1.052173533600	9.43430×10^{-6}
(0.02,0.01)	1.030785077555	1.030785083180	-5.62544×10^{-9}	1.030776771467	8.30609×10^{-6}
(0.01,0.02)	1.030785077555	1.030785075750	1.80440×10^{-9}	1.030783868267	1.20929×10^{-6}

5. Conclusions

From Section 3 in the paper, it is clear to see that we generalized Thiele's expansion of a univariate function to the bivariate case. Thus, we obtained a rational approximation method, say Thiele–Newton's blending expansion of a bivariate function. Furthermore, we suggested the Viscovatov-like algorithm, which calculates the coefficients of Thiele–Newton's expansion and gave the proof of this algorithm. Finally, the application of the Viscovatov-like algorithm was given. Numerical experiments and comparisons were presented in Tables 3 and 4, showing that Thiele–Newton's blending expansion performed much better approximation than the polynomial expansion. Moreover, the next step in the research work is the consideration of a vector case by a similar technique.

Author Contributions: The contributions of all of the authors have been similar. All of them have worked together to develop the present manuscript.

Funding: This research was funded by the Project of Leading Talent Introduction and Cultivation in Colleges and Universities of the Education Department of Anhui Province (Grant No. gxfxZD2016270), the Natural Science Key Foundation of the Education Department of Anhui Province (Grant No.KJ2013A183), the Incubation Project of the

National Scientific Research Foundation of Bengbu University (Grant No. 2018GJPY04), and the Project of Quality Curriculums of Education Department of Anhui Province (Grant Nos. 2016gxx087, 2018mooc517).

Acknowledgments: The authors are thankful to the anonymous reviewers for their valuable comments.

Conflicts of Interest: The authors declare no conflict of interest.

References

1. Cheney, E.W. *Introduction to Approximation Theory*; McGraw-Hill: New York, NY, USA, 1966.
2. Hildebrand, F.B. *Introduction to Numerical Analysis*, 2nd ed.; McGraw-Hill: New York, NY, USA, 1974.
3. Davis, P.J. *Interpolation and Approximation*; Dover: New York, NY, USA, 1975.
4. Alfio, Q.; Riccardo, S.; Fausto, S. *Numerical Mathematics*; Springer: New York, NY, USA, 2000.
5. Gautschi, W. *Numerical Analysis*, 2nd ed.; Birkhäuser: Boston, FL, USA, 2011.
6. Burden, A.M.; Faires, J.D.; Burden, R.L. *Numerical Analysis*, 10th ed.; Cengage Learning: Boston, FL, USA, 2014.
7. Baker, G.A. *Essentials of Padé Approximants*; Academic Press: New York, NY, USA, 1975.
8. Baker, G.A.; Graves-Morris, P.R. *Padé Approximants*, 2nd ed.; Cambridge University Press: Cambridge, UK, 1996.
9. Kuchminskaya, K. On approximation of functions by continued and branched continued fractions. *Mat. Met. Fiz. Meh. Polya* **1980**, *12*, 3–10.
10. Skorobogatko, V. *Branched Continued Fractions and Their Applications*; Nauka: Moscow, Russian, 1983.
11. Siemaszko, W. Thiele-type branched continued fractions for two variable functions. *J. Comput. Math.* **1983**, *9*, 137–153. [CrossRef]
12. Viscovatov, B. De la méthode générale pour reduire toutes sortes de quantités en fraction continues. *Mém. Acad. Impériale Sci. St.-Petersbg.* **1805**, *1*, 226–247.
13. Graves-Morris, P.R. Symmetrical formulas for rational interpolants. *J. Comput. Appl. Math.* **1984**, *10*, 107–111. [CrossRef]
14. Cuyt, A.; Verdonk, B. Multivariate rational interpolants. *Computing* **1985**, *34*, 141–161. [CrossRef]
15. Cuyt, A.; Verdonk, B. Multivariate reciprocal differences for branched Thiele contiuned fraction expansions. *J. Comput. Appl. Math.* **1988**, *21*, 145–160. [CrossRef]
16. Cuyt, A.; Verdonk, B. A review of branched contiuned fraction theory for the construction of multivariate rational approximants. *Appl. Numer. Math.* **1988**, *4*, 263–271. [CrossRef]
17. Cuyt, A.; Driver, K.; Tan, J.Q.; Verdonk, B. Exploring multivariate Padé approximants for multiple hypergeometric series. *Adv. Comput. Math.* **1999**, *10*, 29–49. [CrossRef]
18. Möller, H.M. Multivariate rational interpolation: Reconstruction of rational functions. *Int. Ser. Numer. Math.* **1989**, *90*, 249–256.
19. Zhu, G.Q.; Tan, J.Q. The duality of vector valued rational interpolants over rectangular grids. *Chin. J. Num. Math. Appl.* **1995**, *17*, 75–84.
20. Gu, C.Q. Bivariate Thiele-type matrix valued rational interpolants. *J. Comput. Appl. Math.* **1997**, *80*, 71–82.
21. Gu, C.Q.; Zhu, G.Q. Bivariate Lagrange-type vector valued rational interpolants. *J. Comput. Math.* **2002**, *2*, 207–216.
22. Tan, J.Q.; Zhu, G.Q. Bivariate vector valued rational interpolants by branched continued fractions. *Numer. Math. A J. Chin. Univ.* **1995**, *4*, 37–43.
23. Tan, J.Q. Bivariate blending rational interpolants. *Approx. Theory Appl.* **1999**, *15*, 74–83.
24. Tan, J.Q. Bivariate rational interpolants with rectangle-hole structure. *J. Comput. Math.* **1999**, *17*, 1–14.
25. Tan, J.Q.; Fang, Y. Newton–Thiele's rational interpolants. *Numer. Algorithms* **2000**, *24*, 141–157. [CrossRef]
26. Tan, J.Q. The limiting case of Thiele's interpolating continued fraction expansion. *J. Comput. Math.* **2001**, *19*, 433–444.
27. Tan, J.Q.; Jiang, P. A Neville-like method via continued fractions. *J. Comput. Appl. Math.* **2004**, *163*, 219–232. [CrossRef]
28. Tan, J.Q. *The Theory of Continued Fractions and Their Applications*; Science Press: Beijing, China, 2007.
29. Hu, M.; Tan, J.Q.; Xue, F. A new approach to the image resizing using interpolating rational-linear splines by continued fractions. *J. Inf. Comput. Sci.* **2005**, *2*, 681–685.

30. Hu, M.; Tan, J.Q. Adaptive osculatory rational interpolation for image processing. *J. Comput. Appl. Math.* **2006**, *195*, 46–53. [CrossRef]
31. Li, S.F.; Song, L.T.; Xie, J.; Dong, Y. Image inpainting based on bivariate interpolation by continued fractions. In Proceedings of the IEEE International Conference on Computer Science and Automation Engineering, Zhangjiajie, China, 25–27 May 2012; Volume 2, pp. 756–759.
32. Li, S.F.; Dong, Y. k-Hypergeometric series solutions to one type of non-homogeneous k-hypergeometric equations. *Symmetry* **2019**, *11*, 262. [CrossRef]

Article

One-Point Optimal Family of Multiple Root Solvers of Second-Order

Deepak Kumar [1,*], Janak Raj Sharma [1] and Clemente Cesarano [2,*]

[1] Department of Mathematics, Sant Longowal Institute of Engineering and Technology, Longowal, Sangrur 148106, India

[2] Section of Mathematics, International Telematic University UNINETTUNO, Corso Vittorio Emanuele II, 39, 00186 Roma, Italy

* Correspondence: deepak.babbi@gmail.com (D.K.); c.cesarano@uninettunouniversity.net (C.C.)

Received: 6 June 2019; Accepted: 17 July 2019; Published: 21 July 2019

Abstract: This manuscript contains the development of a one-point family of iterative functions. The family has optimal convergence of a second-order according to the Kung-Traub conjecture. This family is used to approximate the multiple zeros of nonlinear equations, and is based on the procedure of weight functions. The convergence behavior is discussed by showing some essential conditions of the weight function. The well-known modified Newton method is a member of the proposed family for particular choices of the weight function. The dynamical nature of different members is presented by using a technique called the "basin of attraction". Several practical problems are given to compare different methods of the presented family.

Keywords: nonlinear equations; multiple roots; one-point methods; optimal convergence

MSC: 65H05; 49M15; 41A25

1. Introduction

Solving nonlinear equations $h(x) = 0$, where function $h(x)$ is defined as $h : \Omega \subseteq R \to R$ in an open interval Ω, is a delightful and demanding task in many applied scientific branches, such as Mathematical Biology, Physics, Chemistry, Economics, and also Engineering, to name a few [1–4]. This is mainly because problems from these areas usually include needing to find the root of a nonlinear equation. The huge value of this subject has led to the development of many numerical methods, with most of them having an iterative nature (see [5–7]). With the advanced technology of computer hardware and the latest software, the topic of solving nonlinear equations by using numerical methods has gained additional significance. Researchers are utilizing iterative methods for approximating the solution, since closed-form solutions cannot be obtained in general. In particular, here we consider iterative methods to compute a multiple root (say, α) with multiplicity $m \geq 1$, i.e., $h^{(k)}(\alpha) = 0$, $k = 0, 1, 2, ..., m-1$ and $h^{(m)}(\alpha) \neq 0$, of the equation $h(x) = 0$.

There are a plethora of methods of an iterative nature with a different order of convergence, constructed to approximate the zeros of Equation $h(x) = 0$ (see [8–18]). The computational efficiency index is a very effective mechanism, defined by Ostrowski in [19] which categorizes the iterative algorithms in the form of their convergence order p_c and the function evaluations d required per iteration. It is formulated as $I = p_c^{1/d}$. The higher the computational efficiency index of an iterative scheme, the better the scheme is.

This idea becomes more rigid with Kung-Traub's conjecture [20], which imposes an upper bound for the convergence order to be limited with fixed functional evaluations. According to this conjecture, an iterative scheme which requires a d number of function evaluations can attain the convergence order $p_c = 2^{d-1}$. The iterative methods which obey Kung-Traub's conjecture are optimal in nature.

The most basic and widely used method is the well-known modified Newton's method:

$$x_{n+1} = x_n - m\frac{h(x_n)}{h'(x_n)} \quad \forall \ n = 0, 1, 2, \ldots. \tag{1}$$

This method can efficiently find the required zero of multiplicity, m with a quadratic order of convergence, provided that the initial approximate x_0 is sufficiently nearer to zero [8]. In Traub's terminology (see [2]), Newton's method (1) is called the one-point method. This classical method attracts many researchers because of its huge applications in several kinds of problems, which are formulated as non-linear equations, differential equations, integral equations, systems of non-linear algebraic equations, and even to random operator equations. However, a common issue and main obstacle in the use of Newton's method is its sensitivity to initial guesses, which must be sufficiently nearer to the exact solution for assured convergence. Developing a criterion for selecting these initial guesses is quite difficult, and therefore, a more effective iterative technique that is globally-convergent is yet to be discovered. Some other important higher order methods that are based on Newton's method (1) have been developed in [11,13,14,21–28].

Recently, Chicharro et al. [28] used the weight function technique to design a class of optimal second-order one-point iterative methods for simple roots, including Newton's method. In this paper, we have applied this technique for the development of a class of optimal second-order one-point methods for multiple roots. The new proposed family contains the modified Newton's method and many other efficient methods. These methods exist when particular weight functions are selected. Therefore, with a wide range of initial approximations, we can select those methods from the family which are able to converge towards exact zero, when Newton's method does not.

The rest of the paper is organized as follows. In Section 2, the technique of the second-order method is developed and its convergence is studied. In Section 3, the basins of attractors are studied to check the stability of the methods. Numerical experiments on different equations are performed in Section 4 to demonstrate the applicability and efficiency of the presented methods. We finish the manuscript with some valuable conclusions in Section 5.

2. The Method

For a known multiplicity $m \geq 1$, we consider the following one–step scheme for multiple roots:

$$x_{n+1} = x_n - G(\nu_n), \tag{2}$$

where the function $G(\nu_n) : \mathbb{C} \to \mathbb{C}$ is differentiable in a neighborhood of "0" with $\nu_n = \frac{h(x_n)}{h'(x_n)}$.

In the next result, we prove a theorem for the order of convergence of the scheme (2).

Theorem 1. *Let $f : \mathbb{C} \to \mathbb{C}$ be a differentiable function in a region in which a multiple zero (say, α) with multiplicity m lies. Suppose that the initial approximate x_0 is sufficiently close to α—then, the iteration scheme defined by (2) has a second-order of convergence, provided that $G(0) = 0$, $G'(0) = m$, and $|G''(0)| < \infty$, and the error is*

$$e_{n+1} = \Big(\frac{2mC_1 - G''(0)}{2m^2}\Big)e_n^2 + O(e_n^3), \tag{3}$$

where $e_n = x_n - \alpha$ and $C_k = \dfrac{m!}{(m+k)!}\dfrac{f^{(m+k)}(\alpha)}{f^{(m)}(\alpha)}$ for $k \in \mathbb{N}$.

Proof. Let the error at the n-th iteration be $e_n = x_n - \alpha$. Using the Taylor's expansion of $f(x_n)$ and $f'(x_n)$ about α, we have that

$$f(x_n) = \frac{f^{(m)}(\alpha)}{m!}e_n^m\Big(1 + C_1e_n + C_2e_n^2 + C_3e_n^3 + O(e_n^4)\Big). \tag{4}$$

and

$$f'(x_n) = \frac{f^{(m)}(\alpha)}{m!} e_n^{m-1} \Big(m + (m+1)C_1 e_n + (m+2)C_2 e_n^2 + (m+3)C_3 e_n^3 + O(e_n^4) \Big). \tag{5}$$

By using (4) and (5), we obtained

$$v_n = \frac{e_n}{m} - \frac{C_1}{m} e_n^2 + \frac{(1+m) - 2mC_1}{m^3} e_n^3 + O(e_n^4).$$

If we write the expansion-of-weight function $G(v_n)$ about the origin by using the Taylor series, then we have that

$$G(v_n) \approx G(0) + vG'(0) + \frac{1}{2} v^2 G''(0). \tag{6}$$

By employing the expression (6) in the scheme (2), we were able to obtain the error equation

$$e_{n+1} = -G(0) + \Big(1 - \frac{G'(0)}{m}\Big) e_n - \Big(\frac{-2C_1 G'(0) + G''(0)}{2m^2}\Big) e_n^2 + O(e_n^3). \tag{7}$$

To obtain the second-order of convergence, the constant term and coefficient of e_n in (7) should simultaneously be equal to zero. This is possible when $G(0)$ and $G'(0)$ have the following values:

$$G(0) = 0, \quad G'(0) = m. \tag{8}$$

By using the above values in (7), the error equation becomes

$$e_{n+1} = \Big(\frac{2mC_1 - G''(0)}{2m^2}\Big) e_n^2 + O(e_n^3). \tag{9}$$

Hence, the second-order convergence is established. □

Some Particular Forms of $G(v_n)$

We were able to obtain numerous methods of the family (2) based on the form of function $G(v)$ that satisfies the conditions of Theorem 1. However, we limited the choices to consider only some simple functions. Accordingly, the following simple forms were chosen:

(1) $G(v_n) = mv_n(1 + a_1 v_n)$ (2) $G(v_n) = \frac{mv_n}{1+a_2 v_n}$ (3) $G(v_n) = \frac{mv_n}{1+a_3 m v_n}$, (4) $G(v_n) = m(e^{v_n} - 1)$
(5) $G(v_n) = m\log[v_n + 1]$ (6) $G(v_n) = m\sin v_n$ (7) $G(v_n) = \frac{v_n}{(\frac{1}{\sqrt{m}} + a_4 v_n)^2}$ (8) $G(v_n) = \frac{v_n^2 + v_n}{\frac{1}{m} + a_5 v_n}$,

where a_1, a_2, a_3, a_4 and a_5 are arbitrary constants.

The corresponding methods to each of the above forms are defined as follows:

Method 1 (M1):

$$x_{n+1} = x_n - mv_n(1 + a_1 v_n).$$

Method 2 (M2):

$$x_{n+1} = x_n - \frac{mv_n}{1 + a_2 v_n}.$$

Method 3 (M3):

$$x_{n+1} = x_n - \frac{mv_n}{1 + a_3 m v_n}.$$

Method 4 (M4):

$$x_{n+1} = x_n - m(e^{v_n} - 1).$$

Method 5 (M5):

$$x_{n+1} = x_n - m\log(v_n + 1).$$

Method 6 (M6):

$$x_{n+1} = x_n - m\sin v_n.$$

Method 7 (M7):

$$x_{n+1} = x_n - \frac{v_n}{(\frac{1}{\sqrt{m}} + a_4 v_n)^2}.$$

Method 8 (M8):

$$x_{n+1} = x_n - \frac{v_n^2 + v_n}{\frac{1}{m} + a_5 v_n}.$$

Remark 1. *The scheme (2) shows a one-point family of second-order methods which needs only two function evaluations—namely, $h(x_n)$ and $h'(x_n)$.*

Remark 2. *Note that the modified Newton's method (1) is the special case of the above methods—M1, M2, M3, and M7—if the corresponding constants a_1, a_2, a_3, and a_4 become zero.*

3. Complex Dynamics of Methods

Our goal here is to check the complex dynamics of new methods with the help of a graphical tool, *the basins of attraction*, of the zeros for a polynomial $P(z)$ in the Argand plane. The nature of the basins of attraction provides important ideas about the stability and convergence of iterative methods. This idea was initially introduced by Vrscay and Gilbert [29]. In recent times, most researchers have been using this concept in their work—see, for example [30,31]. We consider the special cases corresponding to $G(v_n)$ of (2) to analyze the basins of attraction.

The starting approximate z_0 is taken in a region of rectangular shape $R \in \mathbb{C}$ that contains all the zeros of $P(z)$. A method, when it starts from point z_0 in a rectangle, either converges to zero, $P(z)$, or eventually diverges. Therefore, the stopping criterion is 10^{-3} up to a number of 25 iterations.

To show complex geometry, we checked the basins of attraction of the methods M1–M8 on the following four polynomials:

Problem 1. *In this problem, we took the polynomial $P_1(z) = (z^2+4)^2$, which has zeros $\{\pm 2i\}$ with a multiplicity of 2. We used a mesh of 400×400 points in a rectangular frame $D \in \mathbb{C}$ of area $[-2,2] \times [-2,2]$, and gave the color green for "$2i$" and red for "$-2i$". Each initial point from the green region converges towards "$2i$", and from the red region it converges to "$-2i$". Basins obtained for the methods M1–M8 are shown in Figure 1. Analyzing the behavior of the methods, we see that the methods M5 and M6 possess lesser numbers of divergent points, followed by M1, M4, M8, and M2. On the contrary, the method M3 has a higher number of divergent points, followed by M7.*

Problem 2. *Let us consider the polynomial $P_2(z) = (z^3 - z)^3$ having zeros $\{0, \pm 1\}$ with a multiplicity of 3. To see the dynamical structure, we considered a rectangular frame $D = [-2,2] \times [-2,2] \in \mathbb{C}$ with 400×400 mesh points, and gave the colors red, green, and blue to each point in the basins of attraction of -1, 0, and 1, respectively. Basins obtained for the methods M1–M8 are shown in Figure 2. Analyzing the behavior of the methods, we observe that the methods M5 and M6 have wider convergence regions, followed by M1, M4, M8, M2, M3, and M7.*

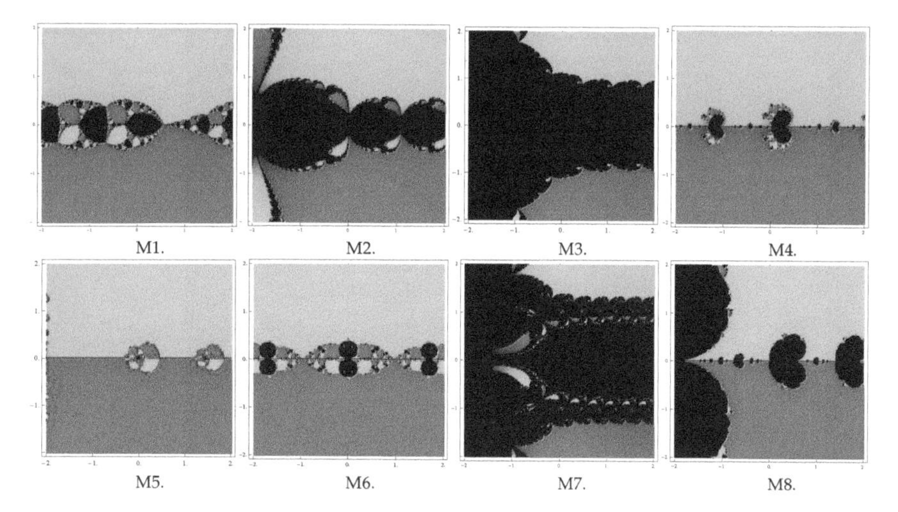

Figure 1. Basins of attraction of M1–M8 for polynomial $P_1(z)$.

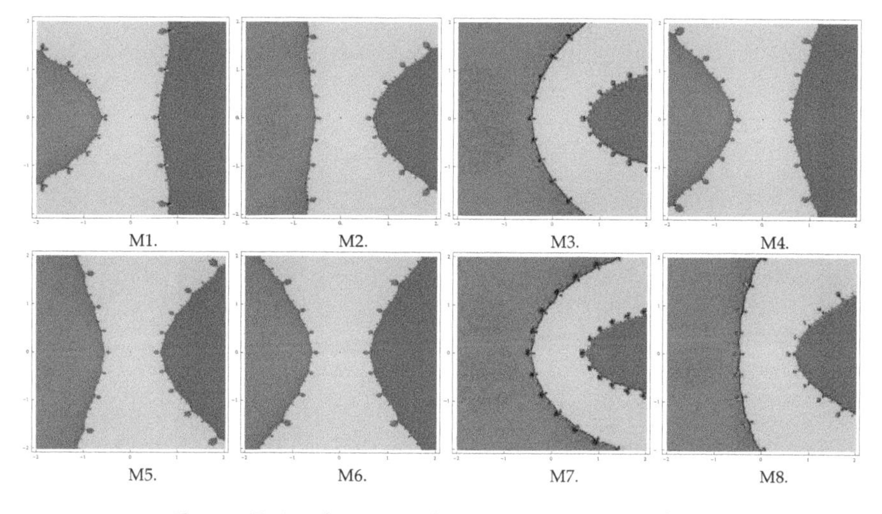

Figure 2. Basins of attraction of M1–M8 for polynomial $P_2(z)$.

Problem 3. *Next, consider the polynomial* $P_3(z) = (z^4 - 6z^2 + 8)^2$ *that has four zeros* $\{\pm 2, \pm 1.414\ldots\}$ *with a multiplicity of 2. To view attraction basins, we considered a rectangular frame* $D = [-2, 2] \times [-2, 2] \in \mathbb{C}$ *with* 400×400 *mesh points and assigned the colors red, blue, green, and yellow to each point in the basin of* $-2, -1.414, \ldots, 1.414\ldots$, *and* 2, *respectively. Basins obtained for the methods M1–M8 are shown in Figure 3. Observing the behavior of the methods, we see that the methods M5, M8, M2, M3, M4, M1, and M6 possess a lesser number of divergent points, and therefore, they show good convergence. On the contrary, the method M7 has a higher number of divergent points.*

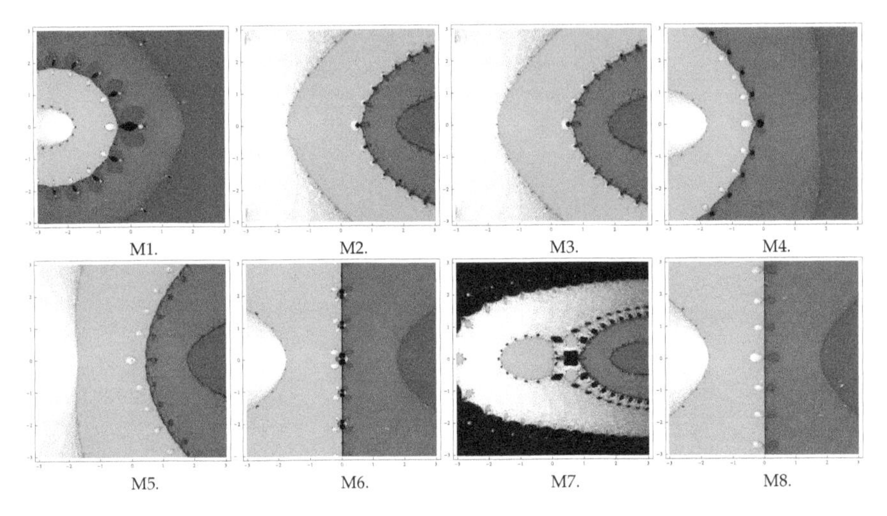

Figure 3. Basins of attraction of M1–M8 for polynomial $P_3(z)$.

Problem 4. *Lastly, we consider the polynomial* $P_4(z) = z^6 - \frac{1}{2}z^5 + \frac{11}{4}(1+i)z^4 - \frac{1}{4}(19+3i)z^3 + \frac{1}{4}(11+5i)z^2 - \frac{1}{4}(11+i)z + \frac{3}{2} - 3i$ *that has six simple zeros* $\{1, -1+2i, -\frac{1}{2} - \frac{i}{2}, i, -\frac{3i}{2}, 1-i\}$. *To view the attraction basins, we considered a rectangle* $D = [-2,2] \times [-2,2] \in \mathbb{C}$ *with* 300×300 *grid points, and assigned the colors red, green, yellow, blue, cyan, and purple to each point in the basin of* 1, $-1+2i$, $-\frac{1}{2} - \frac{1}{2}i$, i, $-\frac{3}{2}i$, *and* $1-i$, *respectively. Basins obtained for the methods M1–M8 are shown in Figure 4. Analyzing the basins of the methods, we observe that the methods M5, M8, M2, M3, M4, and M6 possess a lesser number of divergent points. On the contrary, the methods M1 and M7 have a higher number of divergent points.*

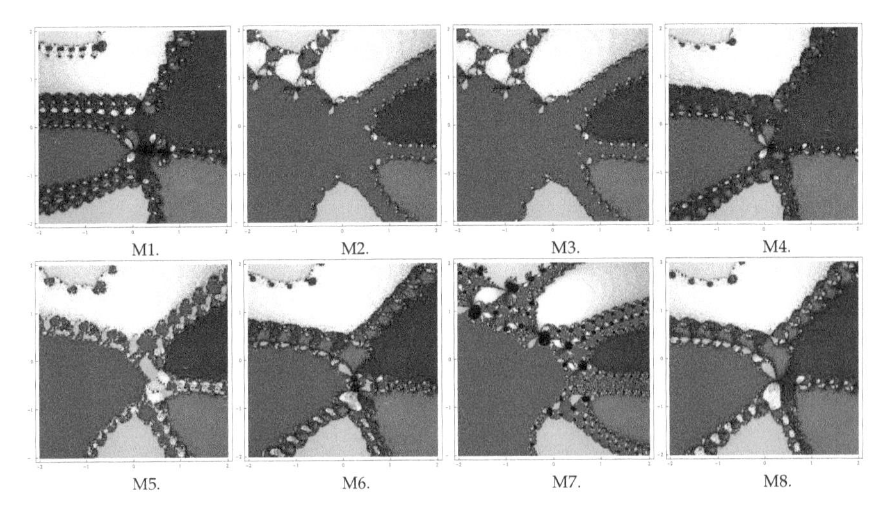

Figure 4. Basins of attraction of M1–M8 for polynomial $P_4(z)$.

From the graphics of the basins, we can give the judgment on the behavior and suitability of any method in the applications. In the event that we pick an initial point z_0 in a zone where various basins of attraction contact one another, it is difficult to anticipate which root will be achieved by the iterative technique that begins in z_0. Subsequently, the choice of z_0 in such a zone is anything but a decent one. Both the dark zones and the zones with various colors are not appropriate for choosing z_0 when we need to obtain a specific root. The most appealing pictures showed up when we had extremely intricate borders between basins of attraction. These borders correspond to the cases where the method is more demanding with respect to the initial point.

4. Numerical Results

In this section, we demonstrate the efficiency, effectiveness, and convergence behavior of the family of new methods by applying them to some practical problems. In this view, we take the special cases M1–M8 of the proposed class and choose $(a_1 = 1/10)$, $(a_2 = 1/4)$, $(a_3 = 1/10)$, $(a_4 = 1/10)$, and $(a_5 = 1/5)$ in the numerical work.

As we know that the constants a_1, a_2, a_3, a_4 and a_5 are arbitrary, there is no particular reason for choosing these values for the constants, and we chose the values randomly. The proposed methods are compared with the existing modified Newton Method (1), also known as MNM.

To verify the theoretical results, we calculate the computational order of convergence (COC) by using the formula (see [32])

$$\text{COC} = \frac{\log|(x_{n+1}-\alpha)/(x_n-\alpha)|}{\log|(x_n-\alpha)/(x_{n-1}-\alpha)|}.$$

The computational work was performed in the programming software, Mathematica, by using multiple-precision arithmetic. Numerical results displayed in Tables 1–4 include: (i) the number of approximations (n) required to converge to the solution such that $|x_{n+1}-x_n| + |f(x_n)| < 10^{-100}$, (ii) values of the last three consecutive errors $|e_n| = |x_{n+1}-x_n|$, (iii) residual error $|f(x_n)|$, and (iv) computational order of convergence (COC).

For testing, we chose four test problems as follows:

Example 1 (Eigenvalue problem). *Eigen value problem is a difficult problem when characteristic polynomial involves a huge square matrix. Finding the zeros of characteristic equation of a square matrix with order more than 4 can even be a challenging task. So, we think about accompanying 9×9 matrix*

$$M = \frac{1}{8}\begin{bmatrix} -12 & 0 & 0 & 19 & -19 & 76 & -19 & 18 & 437 \\ -64 & 24 & 0 & -24 & 24 & 64 & -8 & 32 & 376 \\ -16 & 0 & 24 & 4 & -4 & 16 & -4 & 8 & 92 \\ -40 & 0 & 0 & -10 & 50 & 40 & 2 & 20 & 242 \\ -4 & 0 & 0 & -1 & 41 & 4 & 1 & 0 & 25 \\ -40 & 0 & 0 & 18 & -18 & 104 & -18 & 20 & 462 \\ -84 & 0 & 0 & -29 & 29 & 84 & 21 & 42 & 501 \\ 16 & 0 & 0 & -4 & 4 & -16 & 4 & 16 & -92 \\ 0 & 0 & 0 & 0 & 0 & 0 & 0 & 0 & 24 \end{bmatrix}.$$

The characteristic polynomial of the matrix (M) is given as

$$\begin{aligned} h_1(x) =& x^9 - 29x^8 + 349x^7 - 2261x^6 + 8455x^5 - 17663x^4 + 15927x^3 \\ &+ 6993x^2 - 24732x + 12960. \end{aligned}$$

This function has one multiple zero $\alpha = 3$ with a multiplicity of 4. We chose initial approximations $x_0 = 2.75$ and obtained the numerical results as shown in Table 1.

Table 1. Comparison of performance of methods for Example 1.

Methods	n	$\|e_{n-2}\|$	$\|e_{n-1}\|$	$\|e_n\|$	$f(x_n)$	COC
MNM	7	1.70×10^{-21}	6.84×10^{-43}	1.11×10^{-85}	5.90×10^{-681}	2.000
M1	7	2.79×10^{-21}	1.90×10^{-42}	8.77×10^{-85}	9.90×10^{-674}	2.000
M2	7	2.99×10^{-24}	1.56×10^{-48}	4.27×10^{-97}	8.37×10^{-773}	2.000
M3	6	2.17×10^{-13}	6.50×10^{-27}	5.80×10^{-54}	3.68×10^{-428}	2.000
M4	7	3.39×10^{-18}	4.18×10^{-36}	6.32×10^{-72}	3.53×10^{-570}	2.000
M5	6	5.79×10^{-15}	3.77×10^{-30}	1.60×10^{-60}	5.51×10^{-481}	2.000
M6	7	1.93×10^{-21}	8.86×10^{-43}	1.86×10^{-85}	3.69×10^{-679}	2.000
M7	6	2.28×10^{-13}	7.15×10^{-27}	7.03×10^{-54}	1.71×10^{-427}	2.000
M8	7	6.63×10^{-20}	1.26×10^{-39}	4.60×10^{-79}	1.09×10^{-627}	2.000

Example 2 (Beam Designing Model). *Here, we consider a beam situating problem (see [4]) where a beam of length r unit is inclining toward the edge of a cubical box with the length of the sides being 1 unit each, to such an extent that one end of the bar touches the wall and the opposite end touches the floor, as shown in Figure 5.*

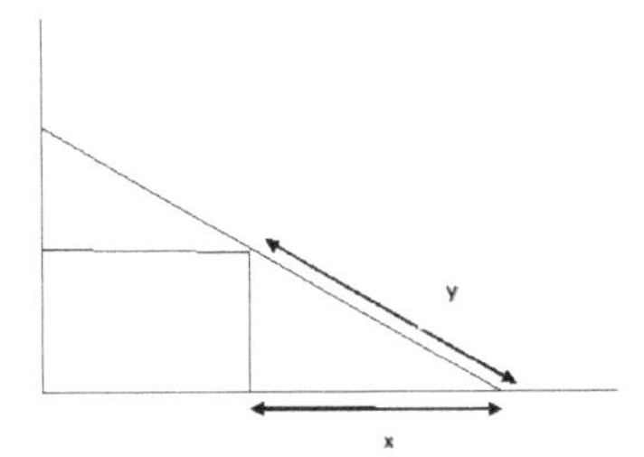

Figure 5. Beam situating problem.

The problem is: What should be the distance be along the bottom of the beam to the floor from the base of the wall? Suppose y is the distance along the edge of the box to the beam from the floor, and let x be the distance from the bottom of the box and of the beam. Then, for a particular value of r, we have

$$x^4 + 4x^3 - 24x^2 + 16x + 16 = 0.$$

The non-negative solution of the equation is a root $x = 2$ with a multiplicity of 2. We consider the initial approximate $x_0 = 3$ to find the root. Numerical results of various methods are shown in Table 2.

Table 2. Comparison of performance of methods for Example 2.

Methods	n	$\|e_{n-2}\|$	$\|e_{n-1}\|$	$\|e_n\|$	$f(x_n)$	COC
MNM	7	1.61×10^{-20}	6.50×10^{-41}	1.06×10^{-81}	1.86×10^{-324}	2.000
M1	7	3.37×10^{-21}	2.55×10^{-42}	1.47×10^{-84}	5.64×10^{-336}	2.000
M2	7	7.19×10^{-18}	1.94×10^{-35}	1.41×10^{-70}	1.34×10^{-279}	2.000
M3	7	2.52×10^{-18}	2.22×10^{-36}	1.73×10^{-72}	2.63×10^{-287}	2.000
M4	6	1.85×10^{-22}	4.10×10^{-47}	2.02×10^{-96}	5.76×10^{-388}	2.000
M5	7	6.46×10^{-16}	2.09×10^{-31}	2.17×10^{-62}	1.34×10^{-246}	2.000
M6	7	1.23×10^{-20}	3.75×10^{-41}	3.52×10^{-82}	2.31×10^{-326}	2.000
M7	7	1.35×10^{-17}	7.17×10^{-35}	2.01×10^{-69}	6.02×10^{-275}	2.000
M8	6	1.34×10^{-17}	9.03×10^{-36}	4.08×10^{-72}	1.66×10^{-287}	2.000

Example 3. *Van der Waals Equation of State, which can be expressed as*

$$\left(P + \frac{a_1 n^2}{V^2}\right)(V - na_2) = nRT,$$

explains the conduct of a real gas by taking in the perfect gas conditions two additional parameters, a_1 and a_2, explicit for every gas. So as to decide the volume V of the gas as far as the rest of the parameters, we are required to explain the nonlinear condition in V.

$$PV^3 - (na_2P + nRT)V^2 + a_1n^2V - a_1a_2n^3 = 0.$$

Given the constants a_1 and a_2 of a specific gas, one can find values for n, P, and T, with the end goal that this condition has three real roots. By utilizing the specific values, we get the accompanying nonlinear function

$$f1(x) = x^3 - 5.22x^2 + 9.0825x - 5.2675,$$

having three real roots. One root among three roots is a multiple zero $\alpha = 1.75$ with a multiplicity of order two, and other one being a simple zero $\xi = 1.72$. However, our desired zero is $\alpha = 1.75$. We considered the initial guess $x_0 = 1.8$ for this problem. Numerical results of various methods are shown in Table 3.

Table 3. Comparison of performance of methods for Example 3.

Methods	n	$\|e_{n-2}\|$	$\|e_{n-1}\|$	$\|e_n\|$	$f(x_n)$	COC
MNM	10	2.22×10^{-22}	8.24×10^{-43}	1.13×10^{-83}	1.36×10^{-331}	2.000
M1	10	1.49×10^{-22}	3.70×10^{-43}	2.27×10^{-84}	2.22×10^{-334}	2.000
M2	10	1.52×10^{-21}	3.88×10^{-41}	2.52×10^{-80}	3.43×10^{-318}	2.000
M3	10	1.05×10^{-21}	1.83×10^{-41}	5.64×10^{-81}	8.54×10^{-321}	2.000
M4	10	3.11×10^{-24}	1.59×10^{-46}	4.15×10^{-91}	2.39×10^{-361}	2.000
M5	10	8.82×10^{-21}	1.32×10^{-39}	2.93×10^{-77}	6.32×10^{-306}	2.000
M6	10	2.42×10^{-22}	9.73×10^{-43}	1.58×10^{-83}	5.16×10^{-331}	2.000
M7	10	1.95×10^{-21}	6.42×10^{-41}	6.92×10^{-80}	1.95×10^{-316}	2.000
M8	9	9.79×10^{-17}	1.57×10^{-31}	4.02×10^{-61}	2.10×10^{-241}	2.000

Example 4. *Lastly, we consider the test function*

$$h_4(x) = (x^2 + 1)\left(2xe^{x^2+1} + x^3 - x\right)\cosh^2\left(\frac{\pi x}{2}\right).$$

The function has a multiple zero $\alpha = i$ of multiplicity 4. We chose the initial approximation $x_0 = 1.25i$ to obtain the zero of the function.

Table 4. Comparison of performance of methods for Example 4.

Methods	n	$\|e_{n-2}\|$	$\|e_{n-1}\|$	$\|e_n\|$	$f(x_n)$	COC
MNM	7	2.87×10^{-15}	2.75×10^{-30}	2.51×10^{-60}	5.82×10^{-478}	2.000
M1	7	2.88×10^{-15}	2.76×10^{-30}	2.53×10^{-60}	6.21×10^{-478}	2.000
M2	7	3.41×10^{-15}	3.95×10^{-30}	5.30×10^{-60}	2.45×10^{-475}	2.000
M3	7	4.43×10^{-15}	6.84×10^{-30}	1.63×10^{-59}	2.14×10^{-471}	2.000
M4	7	5.70×10^{-15}	1.16×10^{-29}	4.75×10^{-59}	1.24×10^{-467}	2.000
M5	7	5.48×10^{-15}	1.07×10^{-29}	4.06×10^{-59}	3.53×10^{-468}	2.000
M6	7	2.99×10^{-15}	2.98×10^{-30}	2.95×10^{-60}	2.10×10^{-477}	2.000
M7	7	4.48×10^{-15}	6.97×10^{-30}	1.69×10^{-59}	2.90×10^{-471}	2.000
M8	7	3.37×10^{-15}	3.82×10^{-30}	4.91×10^{-60}	1.29×10^{-475}	2.000

5. Conclusions

In this paper, we presented a new one-point family of iterative methods with quadratic convergence for computing multiple roots with known multiplicity, based on the weight function technique. Analysis of the convergence showed the second order of convergence under some suppositions regarding the nonlinear function whose zeros are to be obtained. Some efficient and simple cases of the class were presented, and their stability was tested by analyzing complex geometry using a graphical tool—namely, the basin of attraction. The methods were employed to solve some real-world problems, such as the Eigenvalue problem, beam positioning problem, and the Van dar

Waal equation of state, and were also compared with existing methods. Numerical comparison of the results revealed that the presented methods had good convergence behavior, similar to the well-known modified Newton's method.

Author Contributions: The contribution of all the authors have been similar. All of them worked together to develop the present manuscript.

Funding: This research received no external funding.

Acknowledgments: We would like to express our gratitude to the anonymous reviewers for their help with the publication of this paper.

Conflicts of Interest: The authors declare no conflict of interest.

References

1. Argyros, I.K. *Convergence and Applications of Newton-Type Iterations*; Springer: New York, NY, USA, 2008.
2. Traub, J.F. *Iterative Methods for the Solution of Equations*; Chelsea Publishing Company: New York, NY, USA, 1982.
3. Hoffman, J.D. *Numerical Methods for Engineers and Scientists*; McGraw-Hill Book Company: New York, NY, USA, 1992.
4. Zachary, J.L. *Introduction to Scientific Programming: Computational Problem Solving Using Maple and C*; Springer: New York, NY, USA, 2012.
5. Cesarano, C. Generalized special functions in the description of fractional diffusive equations. *Commun. Appl. Ind. Math.* **2019**, *10*, 31–40. [CrossRef]
6. Cesarano, C. Multi-dimensional Chebyshev polynomials: A non-conventional approach. *Commun. Appl. Ind. Math.* **2019**, *10*, 1–19. [CrossRef]
7. Cesarano, C.; Ricci, P.E. Orthogonality Properties of the Pseudo-Chebyshev Functions (Variations on a Chebyshev's Theme). *Mathematics* **2019**, *7*, 180. [CrossRef]
8. Schröder, E. Über unendlich viele Algorithmen zur Auflösung der Gleichungen. *Math. Ann.* **1870**, *2*, 317–365. [CrossRef]
9. Dong, C. A family of multipoint iterative functions for finding multiple roots of equations. *Int. J. Comput. Math.* **1987**, *21*, 363–367. [CrossRef]
10. Geum, Y.H.; Kim, Y.I.; Neta, B. A class of two-point sixth-order multiple-zero finders of modified double-Newton type and their dynamics. *Appl. Math. Comput.* **2015**, *270*, 387–400. [CrossRef]
11. Hansen, E.; Patrick, M. A family of root finding methods. *Numer. Math.* **1977**, *27*, 257–269. [CrossRef]
12. Li, S.; Liao, X.; Cheng, L. A new fourth-order iterative method for finding multiple roots of nonlinear equations. *Appl. Math. Comput.* **2009**, *215*, 1288–1292.
13. Neta, B. New third order nonlinear solvers for multiple roots. *Appl. Math. Comput.* **2008**, *202*, 162–170. [CrossRef]
14. Osada, N. An optimal multiple root-finding method of order three. *J. Comput. Appl. Math.* **1994**, *51*, 131–133. [CrossRef]
15. Sharifi, M.; Babajee, D.K.R.; Soleymani, F. Finding the solution of nonlinear equations by a class of optimal methods. *Comput. Math. Appl.* **2012**, *63*, 764–774. [CrossRef]
16. Sharma, J.R.; Sharma, R. Modified Jarratt method for computing multiple roots. *Appl. Math. Comput.* **2010**, *217*, 878–881. [CrossRef]
17. Victory, H.D.; Neta, B. A higher order method for multiple zeros of nonlinear functions. *Int. J. Comput. Math.* **1983**, *12*, 329–335. [CrossRef]
18. Zhou, X.; Chen, X.; Song, Y. Constructing higher-order methods for obtaining the multiple roots of nonlinear equations. *J. Comput. Appl. Math.* **2011**, *235*, 4199–4206. [CrossRef]
19. Ostrowski, A.M. *Solution of Equations and Systems of Equations*; Academic Press: New York, NY, USA, 1966.
20. Kung, H.T.; Traub, J.F. Optimal order of one-point and multipoint iteration. *J. Assoc. Comput. Mach.* **1974**, *21*, 643–651. [CrossRef]
21. Geum, Y.H.; Kim, Y.I.; Neta, B. A sixth–order family of three–point modified Newton–like multiple–root finders and the dynamics behind their extraneous fixed points. *Appl. Math. Comput.* **2016**, *283*, 120–140. [CrossRef]

22. Behl, R.; Cordero, A.; Motsa, S.S.; Torregrosa, J.R. An eighth-order family of optimal multiple root finders and its dynamics. *Numer. Algor.* **2018**, *77*, 1249–1272. [CrossRef]
23. Zafar, F.; Cordero, A.; Rana, Q.; Torregrosa, J.R. Optimal iterative methods for finding multiple roots of nonlinear equations using free parameters. *J. Math. Chem.* **2017**. [CrossRef]
24. Geum, Y.H.; Kim, Y.I.; Neta, B. Constructing a family of optimal eighth-order modified Newton-type multiple-zero finders along with the dynamics behind their purely imaginary extraneous fixed points. *J. Comput. Appl. Math.* **2018**, *333*, 131–156. [CrossRef]
25. Behl, R.; Zafar, F.; Alshomrani, A.S.; Junjua, M.; Yasmin, N. An optimal eighth-order scheme for multiple zeros of univariate function. *Int. J. Comput. Math.* **2019**, *16*, 1843002. [CrossRef]
26. Behl, R.; Alshomrani, A.S.; Motsa, S.S. An optimal scheme for multiple roots of nonlinear equations with eighth-order convergence. *J. Math. Chem.* **2018**. [CrossRef]
27. Zafar, F.; Cordero, A.; Torregrosa, J.R. An efficient family of optimal eighth-order multiple root finder. *Mathematics* **2018**, *6*, 310. [CrossRef]
28. Chicharro, F.I.; Cordero, A.; Garrido, N.; Torregrosa, J.R. Genertaing root-finder iterative methods of second-order: Convergence and stability. *Axioms* **2019**, *8*, 55. [CrossRef]
29. Vrscay, E.R.; Gilbert, W.J. Extraneous fixed points, basin boundaries and chaotic dynamics for Schröder and König rational iteration functions. *Numer. Math.* **1988**, *52*, 1–16. [CrossRef]
30. Scott, M.; Neta, B.; Chun, C. Basin attractors for various methods. *Appl. Math. Comput.* **2011**, *218*, 2584–2599. [CrossRef]
31. Varona, J.L. Graphic and numerical comparison between iterative methods. *Math. Intell.* **2002**, *24*, 37–46. [CrossRef]
32. Weerakoon, S.; Fernando, T.G.I. A variant of Newton's method with accelerated third-order convergence. *Appl. Math. Lett.* **2000**, *13*, 87–93. [CrossRef]

Article

Some New Oscillation Criteria for Second Order Neutral Differential Equations with Delayed Arguments

Omar Bazighifan [1,†] and Clemente Cesarano [2,*,†]

1 Department of Mathematics, Faculty of Science, Hadhramout University, Hadhramout 50512, Yemen
2 Section of Mathematics, International Telematic University Uninettuno, CorsoVittorio Emanuele II, 39, 00186 Roma, Italy
* Correspondence: c.cesarano@uninettunouniversity.net
† These authors contributed equally to this work.

Received: 10 June 2019; Accepted: 10 July 2019; Published: 11 July 2019

Abstract: In this paper, we study the oscillation of second-order neutral differential equations with delayed arguments. Some new oscillatory criteria are obtained by a Riccati transformation. To illustrate the importance of the results, one example is also given.

Keywords: oscillatory solutions; nonoscillatory solutions; second-order; neutral differential equations

1. Introduction

The main focus of this study was the oscillation criteria of the solution of second-order delay differential equations of the form

$$\left[a(\ell)\left(z'(\ell)\right)^{\beta}\right]' + p(\ell) f(z(\tau(\ell))) = 0, \quad \ell \geq \ell_0, \tag{1}$$

where $z(\ell) = x(\ell) + q(\ell)x(\sigma(\ell))$ and β is a quotient of odd positive integers. Throughout the paper, we always assume that:

(H_1) $a \in C^1([\ell_0, \infty), \mathbb{R}^+), a'(\ell) \geq 0,\ a(\ell) > 0,\ p, q \in C([\ell_0, \infty), [0, \infty)), 0 \leq p(t) < 1, , \sigma, \tau \in C([\ell_0, \infty), \mathbb{R}), \tau(\ell) \leq \ell, \sigma(\ell) \leq \ell, \lim_{\ell \to \infty} \tau(\ell) = \infty$ and $\lim_{\ell \to \infty} \sigma(\ell) = \infty$,

(H_2) $f \in C(\mathbb{R}, \mathbb{R}), f(u)/u^{\beta} \geq k > 0$, for $u \neq 0$.

By a solution of (1), we mean a function $z \in C([\ell_0, \infty), \mathbb{R}),\ \ell_z \geq \ell_\circ$, which has the property $a(\ell)[z'(\ell)]^{\beta} \in C^1([\ell_0, \infty), \mathbb{R})$, and satisfies (1) on $[\ell_z, \infty)$. We consider only those solutions z of (1) which satisfy $\sup\{|z(\ell)| : \ell \geq \ell_z\} > 0$, for all $\ell > \ell_z$. We assume that (1) possesses such a solution. A solution of (1) is called oscillatory if it has arbitrarily large zeros on $[\ell_z, \infty)$, otherwise it is called non-oscillatory. (1) is said to be oscillatory if all its solutions are oscillatory. Likewise, the equation itself is called oscillatory if all of its solutions are oscillatory.

Differential equations are of great importance in the branches of mathematics and other sciences. In 1918, researchers were interested in studying differential equations. Since then, there has been much research on the subject of the oscillation of differential and functional differential equations—see [1–10].

The differential equation in which the highest-order derivative of the unknown function appears both with and without delay is called a neutral delay differential equation. In past years, researchers have been interested in the oscillation of neutral differential equations—see [11–14].

Many authors have discussed the oscillations of second-order differential equations, and have also proposed several ways to achieve oscillation for these equations. For treatments on this subject, we refer the reader to the texts, [15–21]. Here are some of the results that served as motivation for this work.

Cesarano and Bazighifan [22] discussed the equation

$$\left[a(\ell)\, w'(\ell)\right]' + q(\ell)\, f(w(\tau(\ell))) = 0 \tag{2}$$

and used the classical Riccati transformation technique.

Moaaz and Bazighifan [23] considered the oscillatory properties of second-order delay differential equations

$$\left[a(\ell)\left(w'(\ell)\right)^{\beta}\right]' + p(\ell)\, f(w(\tau(\ell))) = 0,$$

under the condition

$$\int_{\ell_0}^{\infty} \frac{1}{a^{\frac{1}{\beta}}(\ell)} d\ell < \infty$$

and he proved it was oscillatory if

$$kq(\ell)\frac{\tau^2(\ell)}{\ell^2} > M.$$

Grace et al. [24] studied the differential equations

$$\left[a(\ell)\left(z'(\ell)\right)^{\beta}\right]' + p(\ell)\, z^{\beta}(\tau(\ell)) = 0, \quad \ell \geq \ell_0,$$

under the conditions

$$\int_{\ell_0}^{\infty} \frac{1}{a^{\frac{1}{\beta}}(\ell)} d\ell = \infty.$$

Trench [25] used the comparison technique for the following

$$\left[a(\ell)\, w'(\ell)\right]' + q(\ell)\, w(\tau(\ell)) = 0,$$

which they compared with the first-order differential equation, and on the condition

$$\int_{\ell_0}^{\infty} \frac{1}{a(\ell)} dz = \infty.$$

In this paper we used the Riccati transformation technique, which differs from those reported in [26] to establish some conditions for the oscillation of (1) under the condition

$$\int_{\ell_0}^{\infty} \frac{1}{a^{\frac{1}{\beta}}(s)} ds < \infty. \tag{3}$$

An example is presented to illustrate our main results.

We begin with the following lemma.

Lemma 1 (See [1], Lemma 2.1). *Let $\beta \geq 1$ be a ratio of two numbers, $G,\ H,\ U,\ V \in \mathbb{R}$. Then,*

$$G^{\frac{\beta+1}{\beta}} - (G-H)^{\frac{\beta+1}{\beta}} \leq \frac{H^{\frac{1}{\beta}}}{\beta}\left[(1+\beta)G - H\right], \quad GH \geq 0,$$

and

$$Uy - Vy^{\frac{\beta+1}{\beta}} \leq \frac{\beta^{\beta}}{(\beta+1)^{\beta+1}}\frac{U^{\beta+1}}{V^{\beta}}, \quad V > 0.$$

2. Main Results

In this section, we state the oscillation criteria for (1). To facilitate this, we refer to the following:

$$B(\ell) := \int_{\ell}^{\infty} \frac{1}{a^{\frac{1}{\beta}}(s)} ds.$$

$$A(\ell) = kq(\ell)(1 - p(\tau(\ell)))^{\beta}.$$

$$D(\tau(\ell)) = B(\ell + \frac{1}{\beta} \int_{\ell_1}^{\ell} B(s) B^{\beta}(\tau(s)) A(s)\, ds.$$

$$\check{D}(\ell) = \exp\left(-\beta \int_{\tau(\ell)}^{\ell} \frac{a(s)^{\frac{-1}{\beta}}}{D(s)} ds\right).$$

$$\Phi(\ell) = \delta(\ell)\left[A(\ell) - \frac{1-\beta}{a^{\frac{1}{\beta}}(\ell)\, \eta^{\beta+1}(\ell)}\right].$$

$$\theta(\ell) = \frac{\delta'_{+}(\ell)}{\delta(\ell)} + \frac{(\beta+1)}{a^{\frac{1}{\beta}}(\ell)\, \eta(\ell)}.$$

$$\rho'_{+}(\ell) := \max\{0, \rho'(\ell)\} \text{ and } \delta'_{+}(\ell) := \max\{0, \delta'(\ell)\}$$

Theorem 1. *Assume that (3) holds. If there exist positive functions $\rho, \delta \in C^1([\ell_0, \infty), (0, \infty))$ such that*

$$\int_{\ell_0}^{\infty} \left[\rho(s) A(s) \check{D}(s) - \frac{a(s)(\rho'_{+}(s))^{\beta+1}}{(\beta+1)^{\beta+1} \rho^{\beta}(s)}\right] ds = \infty \tag{4}$$

and

$$\int_{\ell_0}^{\infty} \left(\Phi(s) - \frac{\delta(s)\, a(s)(\theta(s))^{\beta+1}}{(\beta+1)^{\beta+1}}\right) ds = \infty, \tag{5}$$

then every solution of (1) is oscillatory.

Proof. Let x be a non-oscillatory solution of Equation (1), defined in the interval $[\ell_0, \infty)$. Without loss of generality, we may assume that $x(\ell) > 0$. It follows from (1) that there are two possible cases, for $\ell \geq \ell_1$, where $\ell_1 \geq \ell_0$ is sufficiently large:

$$\begin{aligned} &(C_1) \quad z'(\ell) > 0, \left(a(\ell)(z'(\ell))^{\alpha}\right) < 0, \\ &(C_2) \quad z'(\ell) < 0, \left(a(\ell)(z'(\ell))^{\alpha}\right) < 0. \end{aligned}$$

Assume that Case (C_1) holds. Since $\tau(\ell) \leq t$ and $z'(\ell) > 0$, we get

$$\begin{aligned} x(\ell) &= z(\ell) - p(\ell) x(\tau(\ell)) \\ &\geq (1 - p(\ell)) z(\ell), \end{aligned} \tag{6}$$

which, together with (1), implies that

$$\begin{aligned} \left[a(\ell)(z'(\ell))^{\beta}\right]' &\leq -kq(\ell) f(x(\tau(\ell))) \\ &\leq -kq(\ell) x^{\beta}(\tau(\ell)) \\ &\leq -kq(\ell)(1 - p(\tau(\ell)))^{\beta} z^{\beta}(\tau(\ell)) \\ &\leq -A(\ell) z^{\beta}(\tau(\ell)). \end{aligned} \tag{7}$$

On the other hand, we see

$$\begin{aligned} z(\ell) &= z(\ell_1) + \int_{\ell_1}^{\ell} \frac{1}{a(s)^{\frac{1}{\beta}}} a(s)^{\frac{1}{\beta}} z'(s)\, ds \\ &\geq B(\ell) a(\ell)^{\frac{1}{\beta}} z'(\ell). \end{aligned} \tag{8}$$

Thus, we easily prove that

$$\left(z(\ell) - B(\ell) a(\ell)^{\frac{1}{\beta}} z'(\ell) \right)' = -B(\ell) \left(a(\ell)^{\frac{1}{\beta}} z'(\ell) \right)'.$$

Applying the chain rule, it is easy to see that

$$B(\ell) \left(a(\ell) (z'(\ell))^{\beta} \right)' = \beta B(\ell) \left(a(\ell)^{\frac{1}{\beta}} z'(\ell) \right)^{\beta-1} \left(a(\ell)^{\frac{1}{\beta}} z'(\ell) \right)'.$$

By virtue of (7), the latter equality yields

$$-B(\ell) \left(a(\ell)^{\frac{1}{\beta}} z'(\ell) \right)' = \frac{1}{\beta} B(\ell) \left(a(\ell)^{\frac{1}{\beta}} z'(\ell) \right)^{1-\beta} A(\ell) z^{\beta}(\tau(\ell)).$$

Thus, we obtain

$$\left(z(\ell) - B(\ell) a(\ell)^{\frac{1}{\beta}} z'(\ell) \right)' \geq \frac{1}{\beta} B(\ell) \left(a(\ell)^{\frac{1}{\beta}} z'(\ell) \right)^{1-\beta} A(\ell) z^{\beta}(\tau(\ell)).$$

Integrating from ℓ_1 to ℓ, we get

$$z(\ell) \geq B(\ell) a(\ell)^{\frac{1}{\beta}} z'(\ell) + \frac{1}{\beta} \int_{\ell_1}^{\ell} B(s) \left(a^{\frac{1}{\beta}}(s) z'(s) \right)^{1-\beta} A(s) z^{\beta}(\tau(s))\, ds.$$

From (8), we get

$$\begin{aligned} z(\ell) \geq\ & B(\ell) a(\ell)^{\frac{1}{\beta}} z'(\ell) \\ & + \frac{1}{\beta} \int_{\ell_1}^{\ell} B(s) \left(a^{\frac{1}{\beta}}(s) z'(s) \right)^{1-\beta} A(s) B^{\beta}(\tau(s)) a(\tau(s)) \left(z'(\tau(s)) \right)^{\beta} ds, \end{aligned}$$

and this

$$\begin{aligned} z(\ell) \geq\ & B(\ell) a(\ell)^{\frac{1}{\beta}} z'(\ell) \\ & + \frac{1}{\beta} \int_{\ell_1}^{\ell} B(s) \left(a^{\frac{1}{\beta}}(s) z'(s) \right)^{1-\beta} A(s) B^{\beta}(s) a(s) \left(z'(s) \right)^{\beta} ds, \\ \geq\ & a(\ell)^{\frac{1}{\beta}} z'(\ell) \left(B(\ell) + \frac{1}{\beta} \int_{\ell_1}^{\ell} B(s) B^{\beta}(\tau(s)) A(s)\, ds \right). \end{aligned}$$

Thus, we conclude that

$$z(\tau(\ell)) \geq a(\tau(\ell))^{\frac{1}{\beta}} z'(\tau(\ell)) D(\tau(\ell)). \tag{9}$$

Define the function $\omega(\ell)$ by

$$\omega(\ell) := \rho(\ell) \frac{a(\ell) (z')^{\beta}(\ell)}{z^{\beta}(\ell)}, \tag{10}$$

then $\omega(\ell) > 0$ for $\ell \geq \ell_1$ and

$$\begin{aligned} \omega'(\ell) &= \rho'(\ell)\frac{a(\ell)(z')^{\beta}(\ell)}{z^{\beta}(\ell)} + \rho(\ell)\frac{\left(a(z')^{\beta}\right)'(\ell)}{z^{\beta}(\ell)} - \beta\rho(\ell)\frac{z^{\beta-1}(\ell)z'(\ell)a(\ell)(z')^{\beta}(\ell)}{z^{2\beta}(\ell)}, \\ &= \rho'(\ell)\frac{a(\ell)(z')^{\beta}(\ell)}{z^{\beta}(\ell)} + \rho(\ell)\frac{\left(a(z')^{\beta}\right)'(\ell)}{z^{\beta}(\ell)} - \beta\rho(\ell)a(\ell)\left(\frac{z'(\ell)}{z(\ell)}\right)^{\beta+1}. \end{aligned} \tag{11}$$

From (9), we obtain

$$z(\ell) \geq a(\ell)^{\frac{1}{\beta}} z'(\ell) D(\ell) \tag{12}$$

and this

$$\frac{z'(\ell)}{z(\ell)} \leq \frac{1}{a(\ell)^{\frac{1}{\beta}} D(\ell)}.$$

Integrating the latter inequality from $\tau(\ell)$ to ℓ, we get

$$\frac{z'(\tau(\ell))}{z(\ell)} \geq \exp\left(-\int_{\tau(\ell)}^{\ell} \frac{a(s)^{\frac{-1}{\beta}}}{D(s)} ds\right). \tag{13}$$

Combining (7) and (13), it follows that

$$\begin{aligned} \frac{\left[a(\ell)(z'''(\ell))^{\beta}\right]'}{z^{\beta}(\ell)} &\leq -A(\ell)\left(\frac{z(\tau(\ell))}{z(\ell)}\right)^{\beta} \\ &\leq -A(\ell)\exp\left(-\beta\int_{\tau(\ell)}^{\ell} \frac{a(s)^{\frac{-1}{\beta}}}{D(s)} ds\right) \\ &\leq -A(\ell)\check{D}(\ell). \end{aligned} \tag{14}$$

By (10) and (11), we obtain that

$$\omega'(\ell) \leq \frac{\rho'_{+}(\ell)}{\rho(\ell)}\omega(\ell) - \rho(\ell)A(\ell)\check{D}(\ell) - \frac{\beta}{(\rho(\ell)a(\ell))^{\frac{1}{\beta}}}\omega^{\frac{\beta+1}{\beta}}(\ell).$$

Now, we let

$$G := \frac{\rho'_{+}(\ell)}{\rho(\ell)},\ H := \frac{\beta}{(\rho(\ell)a(\ell))^{\frac{1}{\beta}}},\ y := \omega(\ell).$$

Applying the Lemma 1, we find

$$\frac{\rho'_{+}(\ell)}{\rho(\ell)}\omega(\ell) - \frac{\beta}{(\rho(\ell)a(\ell))^{\frac{1}{\beta}}}\omega(\ell)^{\frac{\beta+1}{\beta}} \leq \frac{a(\ell)(\rho'_{+}(\ell))^{\beta+1}}{(\beta+1)^{\beta+1}\rho^{\beta}(\ell)}.$$

Hence, we obtain

$$\omega'(\ell) \leq -\rho(\ell)A(\ell)\check{D}(\ell) + \frac{a(\ell)(\rho'_{+}(\ell))^{\beta+1}}{(\beta+1)^{\beta+1}\rho^{\beta}(\ell)}. \tag{15}$$

Integrating from ℓ_1 to ℓ, we get

$$\int_{\ell_1}^{\ell}\left[\rho(s)A(s)\check{D}(s) - \frac{a(s)(\rho'_{+}(s))^{\beta+1}}{(\beta+1)^{\beta+1}\rho^{\beta}(s)}\right]ds \leq \omega(\ell_1), \tag{16}$$

which contradicts (4).

Assume that Case (C_2) holds. It follows from $\left(a(\ell)(z'(\ell))^{\beta}\right) \leq 0,$ that we obtain

$$z'(s) \leq \left(\frac{a(\ell)}{a(s)}\right)^{1\backslash\beta} z'(\ell).$$

Integrating from ℓ to ℓ_1, we get

$$z(\ell_1) \leq z(\ell) + a^{1\backslash\beta}(\ell) z'(\ell) \int_{\ell}^{\ell_1} a^{-1\backslash\beta}(s)\, ds. \tag{17}$$

Letting $\ell_1 \to \infty$, we obtain

$$z(\ell) \geq -B(\ell) a(\ell)^{\frac{1}{\beta}} z'(\ell),$$

which implies that

$$\left(\frac{z(\ell)}{B(s)}\right)' \geq 0.$$

Define the function $\psi(t)$ by

$$\psi(t) := \delta(\ell)\left[\frac{a(\ell)(z'(\ell))^{\beta}}{z^{\beta}(\ell)} + \frac{1}{\eta^{\beta}(\ell)}\right], \tag{18}$$

then $\psi(t) > 0$ for $t \geq t_1$ and

$$\begin{aligned} \psi'(\ell) &= \delta'(\ell)\frac{a(\ell)(z'(\ell))^{\beta}}{z^{\beta}(\ell)} + \delta(\ell)\frac{\left(a(\ell)(z'(\ell))^{\beta}\right)'}{z^{\beta}(\ell)} \\ &\quad -\beta\delta(\ell)a(\ell)\frac{(z')^{\beta+1}(\ell)}{z^{\beta+1}(\ell)} + \frac{\alpha\delta(\ell)}{a^{\frac{1}{\beta}}(\ell)\eta^{\beta+1}(\ell)}. \end{aligned}$$

Using (18), we obtain

$$\begin{aligned} \psi'(\ell) &= \frac{\delta'_{+}(t)}{\delta(t)}\psi(\ell) + \delta(\ell)\frac{\left(a(\ell)(z'(\ell))^{\beta}\right)'}{z^{\beta}(\ell)} \\ &\quad -\beta\delta(\ell)a(\ell)\left[\frac{\psi(\ell)}{\delta(\ell)a(\ell)} - \frac{1}{a(\ell)\eta^{\beta}(\ell)}\right]^{\frac{\beta+1}{\beta}} + \frac{\beta\delta(\ell)}{a^{\frac{1}{\beta}}(\ell)\eta^{\beta+1}(\ell)}. \end{aligned} \tag{19}$$

Using Lemma 1 with $G = \frac{\psi(\ell)}{\delta(\ell)a(\ell)},\ H = \frac{1}{a(\ell)\eta^{\beta}(\ell)}$, we get

$$\begin{aligned} \left[\frac{\psi(\ell)}{\delta(\ell)a(\ell)} - \frac{1}{a(\ell)\eta^{\beta}(\ell)}\right]^{\frac{\beta+1}{\beta}} &\geq \left(\frac{\psi(\ell)}{\delta(\ell)a(\ell)}\right)^{\frac{\beta+1}{\beta}} \\ &\quad -\frac{1}{\beta a^{\frac{1}{\beta}}(\ell)\eta(\ell)}\left((\beta+1)\frac{\psi(t)}{\delta(\ell)a(\ell)} - \frac{1}{a(\ell)\eta^{\beta}(\ell)}\right). \end{aligned} \tag{20}$$

From (7), (19), and (20), we obtain

$$\psi'(\ell) \leq \frac{\delta'_+(t)}{\delta(t)}\psi(\ell) - \delta(\ell)A(\ell) - \beta\delta(\ell)a(\ell)\left(\frac{\psi(\ell)}{\delta(\ell)a(\ell)}\right)^{\frac{\beta+1}{\beta}} - \beta\delta(\ell)a(\ell)\left[\frac{-1}{\beta a^{\frac{1}{\beta}}(\ell)\eta(\ell)}\left((\beta+1)\frac{\psi(t)}{\delta(\ell)a(\ell)} - \frac{1}{a(\ell)\eta^{\beta}(\ell)}\right)\right].$$

This implies that

$$\psi'(\ell) \leq \left(\frac{\delta'_+(\ell)}{\delta(\ell)} + \frac{(\beta+1)}{a^{\frac{1}{\beta}}(\ell)\eta(\ell)}\right)\psi(\ell) - \frac{\beta}{(\delta(\ell)a(\ell))^{\frac{1}{\beta}}}\psi^{\frac{\beta+1}{\beta}}(\ell) - \delta(\ell)\left[A(\ell) - \frac{1-\beta}{a^{\frac{1}{\beta}}(\ell)\eta^{\beta+1}(\ell)}\right]. \tag{21}$$

Thus, by (19) yield

$$\psi'(\ell) \leq -\Phi(\ell) + \theta(\ell)\psi(\ell) - \frac{\beta}{(\delta(\ell)a(\ell))^{\frac{1}{\beta}}}\psi^{\frac{\beta+1}{\beta}}(\ell). \tag{22}$$

Applying the Lemma 1 with $U = \theta(\ell), V = \frac{\beta}{(\delta(\ell)a(\ell))^{\frac{1}{\beta}}}$ and $y = \psi(\ell)$, we get

$$\psi'(\ell) \leq -\Phi(\ell) + \frac{\delta(\ell)a(\ell)(\theta(\ell))^{\beta+1}}{(\beta+1)^{\beta+1}}. \tag{23}$$

Integrating from ℓ_1 to ℓ, we get

$$\int_{\ell_1}^{\ell}\left(\Phi(s) - \frac{\delta(s)a(s)(\theta(s))^{\beta+1}}{(\beta+1)^{\beta+1}}\right)ds \leq \psi(\ell_1) - \psi(\ell) \leq \psi(\ell_1),$$

which contradicts (5). The proof is complete. □

Example 1. *As an illustrative example, we consider the following equation:*

$$\left(\ell^2\left(x(\ell) + \frac{1}{3}x\left(\frac{\ell}{2}\right)\right)'\right)' + x\left(\frac{\ell}{3}\right) = 0,\ \ell \geq 1. \tag{24}$$

Let

$$\beta = 1,\ a(\ell) = \ell^2,\ p(\ell) = \frac{1}{3},\ q(\ell) = 1,\ \sigma(\ell) = \frac{\ell}{2},\ \tau(\ell) = \frac{\ell}{3}.$$

If we now set $\delta(\ell) = \rho(\ell) = 1$ and $k = 1$, It is easy to see that all conditions of Theorem 1 are satisfied.

$$B(\ell) := \int_{\ell_0}^{\infty}\frac{1}{a^{1/\beta}(s)}ds = \frac{1}{\ell} < \infty.$$

$$A(\ell) = kq(\ell)(1 - p(\tau(\ell)))^{\beta} = \left(1 - \frac{1}{3}\right) = \frac{2}{3}.$$

$$D(\tau(\ell)) = B(\ell) + \frac{1}{\beta}\int_{\ell_1}^{\ell}B(s)B^{\beta}(\tau(s))A(s)\,ds = \frac{1}{\ell}\int_{\ell_1}^{\ell}\frac{2}{3}\frac{1}{s\tau(s)}$$

$$\check{D}(\ell) = \exp\left(-\beta \int_{\tau(\ell)}^{\ell} \frac{a(s)^{\frac{-1}{\beta}}}{D(s)} ds\right)$$

$$\int_{\ell_0}^{\infty} \left[\rho(s) A(s) \check{D}(s) - \frac{a(s)(\rho'_+(s))^{\beta+1}}{(\beta+1)^{\beta+1} \rho^{\beta}(s)}\right] ds = \int_{\ell_0}^{\infty} \frac{2}{3} ds = \infty$$

and

$$\int_{\ell_0}^{\infty} \left(\Phi(s) - \frac{\delta(s) a(s) (\theta(s))^{\beta+1}}{(\beta+1)^{\beta+1}}\right) ds = \infty.$$

Hence, by Theorem 1, every solution of Equation (24) is oscillatory.

3. Conclusions

This article was interested in the oscillation criteria of the solution of second-order delay differential equations of (1). It has also been illustrated through an example that the results obtained are an improvement on the previous results. Our technique lies in using the generalized Riccati substitution, which differs from those reported in [26]. We offered some new sufficient conditions, which ensure that any solution of Equation (1) oscillates under the condition (3). Equation (1) is a neutral delay differential equation when $\tau(\ell) \leq \ell$, $\sigma(\ell) \leq \ell$. Furthermore, we could study $\tau(\ell) \geq \ell$, and be able to get the oscillation criteria of Equation (1) if $z(\ell) = x(\ell) - q(\ell) x(\sigma(\ell))$ in our future work.

Author Contributions: The authors claim to have contributed equally and significantly in this paper. All authors read and approved the final manuscript.

Funding: The authors received no direct funding for this work.

Acknowledgments: The authors thank the reviewers for for their useful comments, which led to the improvement of the content of the paper.

Conflicts of Interest: There are no competing interests between the authors.

References

1. Agarwal, R.; Zhang, C.; Li, T. Some remarks on oscillation of second order neutral differential equations. *Appl. Math. Comput.* **2016**, *274*, 178–181. [CrossRef]
2. Liang, H.; Li, Q.; Zhang, Z. New oscillatory criteria for higher-order nonlinear neutral delay differential equation. *Non. Anal.* **2008**, *69*, 1719–1731. [CrossRef]
3. Koplatadze, R. Criteria for the oscillation of Solution of differential inequalities and second order equations with retarded argument. *Trudy Instituta Prikladnoj Matematiki Imeni IN Vekua* **1986**, *17*, 104–121.
4. Kiguradze, I.T.; Chanturiya, T.A. *Asymptotic Properties of Solutions of Nonautonomous Ordinary Differential Equations*; Kluwer Academic Publisher: Dordrecht, The Netherlands, 1993.
5. Baculikova, B. Oscillation of second-order nonlinear noncanonical differential equations with deviating argument. *Appl. Math. Lett.* **2018**, *11*, 68–75. [CrossRef]
6. Bazighifan, O.; Elabbasy, E.M.; Moaaz, O. Oscillation of higher-order differential equations with distributed delay. *J. Inequal. Appl.* **2019**, *2019*, 55. [CrossRef]
7. Bazighifan, O. On Oscillatory and Asymptotic Behavior of Fourth Order Nonlinear Neutral Delay Differential Equations. *Int. J. Modern Math. Sci.* **2019**, *17*, 21–30.
8. Assante, D.; Cesarano, C.; Foranaro, C.; Vazquez, L. Higher Order and Fractional Diffusive Equations. *J. Eng. Sci. Technol. Rev.* **2015**, *8*, 202–204. [CrossRef]
9. Cesarano, C.; Foranaro, C.; Vazquez, L. Operational results in bi-orthogonal Hermite functions. *Acta Math. Univ. Comen.* **2016**, *85*, 43–68.
10. Dattoli, G.; Ricci, P.; Cesarano, C. Beyond the monomiality: The monumbrality principle. *J. Comput. Anal. Appl.* **2004**, *6*, 77–83.
11. Gyori, I.; Ladas, G. *Oscillation Theory of Delay Differential Equations with Applications*; Clarendon Press: Oxford, UK, 1991.

12. Fite, W. Concerning the zeros of the solutions of certain differential equations. *Trans. Am. Math. Soc.* **1918**, *19*, 341–352. [CrossRef]
13. Ladde, G.; Lakshmikantham, V.; Zhang, B. *Oscillation Theory of Differential Equations with Deviating Arguments*; Marcel Dekker: New York, NY, USA, 1987.
14. Hale, J.K. Partial neutral functional differential equations. *Rev. Roum. Math. Pures Appl.* **1994**, *33*, 339–344.
15. Litsyn, E.; Stavroulakis, I.P. On the oscillation of solutions of higher order Emden–Fowler state dependent advanced differential equations. *Nonlinear Anal.* **2001**, *47*, 3877–3883. [CrossRef]
16. Cesarano, C.; Pinelas, S.; Al-Showaikh, F.; Bazighifan, O. Asymptotic Properties of Solutions of Fourth-Order Delay Differential Equations. *Symmetry* **2019**, *11*, 628. [CrossRef]
17. Cesarano, C.; Bazighifan, O. Oscillation of fourth-order functional differential equations with distributed delay. *Axioms* **2019**, *8*, 61. [CrossRef]
18. Moaaz, O.; Elabbasy, E.M.; Bazighifan, O. On the asymptotic behavior of fourth-order functional differential equations.*Adv. Differ. Equ.* **2017**, *2017*, 261. [CrossRef]
19. Marin, M.; Ochsner, A. The effect of a dipolar structure on the Holder stability in Green-Naghdi thermoelasticity. *Cont. Mech. Thermodyn* **2017**, *29*, 1365–1374. [CrossRef]
20. Wei, J.J. Oscillation of second order delay differential equation. *Ann. Differ. Equ.* **1988**, *4*, 473–478.
21. Philos, C. On the existence of nonoscillatory solutions tending to zero at ∞ for differential equations with positive delay. *Arch. Math.* **1981**, *36*, 168–178. [CrossRef]
22. Cesarano, C.; Bazighifan, O. Qualitative behavior of solutions of second order differential equations. *Symmetry* **2019**, *11*, 777. [CrossRef]
23. Moaaz, O.; Bazighifan, O. Oscillation criteria for second-order quasi-linear neutral functional differential equation. *Discrete Contin. Dyn. Syst. Ser. S* **2019**, *2019*, 181023.
24. Grace, S.R.; Graef, J.; Tunç, E. Oscillatory behavior of second order damped neutral differential equations with distributed deviating arguments. *Miskolc Math. Notes* **2017**, *18*, 759–769. [CrossRef]
25. Trench, W. Canonical forms and principal systemsfor gneral disconiugat equations. *Trans. Am. Math. Soc.* **1973**, *189*, 319–327. [CrossRef]
26. Chatzarakis, G.E.; Dzurina, J.; Jadlovska, I. New oscillation criteria for second-order half-linear advanced differential equations. *Appl. Math. Comput.* **2019**, *347*, 404–416. [CrossRef]

Article

An Efficient Derivative Free One-Point Method with Memory for Solving Nonlinear Equations

Janak Raj Sharma [1], Sunil Kumar [1] and Clemente Cesarano [2,*]

[1] Department of Mathematics, Sant Longowal Institute of Engineering and Technology, Longowal, Sangrur 148106, India

[2] Section of Mathematics, International Telematic University UNINETTUNO, Corso Vittorio Emanuele II, 39, 00186 Roma, Italy

* Correspondence: c.cesarano@uninettunouniversity.net

Received: 5 June 2019; Accepted: 4 July 2019; Published: 6 July 2019

Abstract: We propose a derivative free one-point method with memory of order 1.84 for solving nonlinear equations. The formula requires only one function evaluation and, therefore, the efficiency index is also 1.84. The methodology is carried out by approximating the derivative in Newton's iteration using a rational linear function. Unlike the existing methods of a similar nature, the scheme of the new method is easy to remember and can also be implemented for systems of nonlinear equations. The applicability of the method is demonstrated on some practical as well as academic problems of a scalar and multi-dimensional nature. In addition, to check the efficacy of the new technique, a comparison of its performance with the existing techniques of the same order is also provided.

Keywords: nonlinear equations; iteration methods; one-point methods; order of convergence

MSC: 65H05; 65H10; 41A58

---

1. Introduction

In this study, we consider the problem of solving the nonlinear equations $F(x) = 0$; wherein $F : \mathbb{D} \subset \mathbb{R}^m \to \mathbb{R}^m$ is a univariate function when $m = 1$ or multivariate function when $m > 1$ on an open domain $\mathbb{D}$, by iterative methods. Univariate function is usually denoted by $f(x)$.

Newton's method [1–3] is one of the basic one-point methods which has quadratic convergence and requires one function and one derivative evaluation per iteration but it may diverge if the derivative is very small or zero. To overcome this problem, researchers have also proposed some derivative free one-point methods, for example, the Secant method [2], the Traub method [2], the Muller method [4,5], the Jarratt and Nudds method [6] and the Sharma method [7]. These methods are classified as one-point methods with memory whereas Newton's method is a one-point method without memory (see Reference [2]). All the above mentioned one-point methods with memory require one function evaluation per iteration and possess order of convergence 1.84 except Secant which has order 1.62.

In this paper, we develop a new efficient one-point method with memory of convergence order 1.84 by using rational linear interpolation. The method consists of deriving the coefficients of a rational function that goes through by three points. Then, the derived coefficients are substituted into the derivative of the considered rational function which, when used in Newton's scheme, gives the new scheme. The formula uses one function evaluation per step and has an efficiency index equal to the efficiency of the aforementioned methods of the same order. However, the main advantages of new method over the existing ones are its simplicity and suitability to solve systems of nonlinear equations.

The contents of the paper are organized as follows: in Section 2, the new method is developed and its convergence is discussed; in Section 3, some numerical examples are considered to verify the theoretical results and to compare the performance of proposed technique with existing techniques; the proposed method is generalized for solving the system of nonlinear equations in Section 4.

2. The Method and Its Convergence

Our aim is to develop a derivative-free iterative method by Newton's scheme

$$x_{n+1} = x_n - \frac{f(x_n)}{f'(x_n)}, \quad n = 0, 1, 2, \ldots, \tag{1}$$

wherein $f'(x_n)$ is approximated by using the rational linear function

$$R(t) = \frac{t - x_n + a}{b(t - x_n) + c}, \tag{2}$$

such that

$$R(x_{n-2}) = f(x_{n-2}), \;\; R(x_{n-1}) = f(x_{n-1}), \;\; R(x_n) = f(x_n), \;\; n = 2, 3, 4, \ldots. \tag{3}$$

Imposing the conditions (3) in (2), we have that

$$\begin{aligned} (b(x_{n-2} - x_n) + c)f(x_{n-2}) &= x_{n-2} - x_n + a, \\ (b(x_{n-1} - x_n) + c)f(x_{n-1}) &= x_{n-1} - x_n + a, \\ cf(x_n) &= a. \end{aligned} \tag{4}$$

Then

$$\begin{aligned} b(x_{n-2} - x_n)f(x_{n-2}) + c(f(x_{n-2}) - f(x_n)) &= x_{n-2} - x_n, \\ b(x_{n-1} - x_n)f(x_{n-1}) + c(f(x_{n-1}) - f(x_n)) &= x_{n-1} - x_n, \end{aligned} \tag{5}$$

equivalently

$$\begin{aligned} bf(x_{n-2}) + cf[x_{n-2}, x_n] &= 1, \\ bf(x_{n-1}) + cf[x_{n-1}, x_n] &= 1, \end{aligned} \tag{6}$$

where $f[s, t] = \frac{f(s) - f(t)}{s - t}$ is the Newton first order divided difference.

Solving for b and c, we obtain that

$$b = \frac{f[x_{n-2}, x_n] - f[x_{n-1}, x_n]}{f[x_{n-2}, x_n]f(x_{n-1}) - f[x_{n-1}, x_n]f(x_{n-2})} \tag{7}$$

and

$$c = \frac{f(x_{n-2}) - f(x_{n-1})}{f[x_{n-1}, x_n]f(x_{n-2}) - f[x_{n-2}, x_n]f(x_{n-1})}. \tag{8}$$

Some simple calculations yield

$$\begin{aligned} R'(x_n) &= \frac{1 - bf(x_n)}{c} \\ &= \frac{f[x_{n-1}, x_n]f[x_{n-2}, x_n]}{f[x_{n-2}, x_{n-1}]}. \end{aligned} \tag{9}$$

Assuming that $f'(x_n)$ is approximately equal to $R'(x_n)$, then, in view of (9) the method (1) can be presented as

$$x_{n+1} = x_n - \frac{f[x_{n-2}, x_{n-1}]}{f[x_{n-1}, x_n] f[x_{n-2}, x_n]} f(x_n). \tag{10}$$

The scheme (10) defines a one-point method with memory and requires one function evaluation per iteration.

In the following theorem, we shall find the order of convergence of (10). We use the concept of R- order of convergence given by Ortega and Rheinboldt [8]. Suppose $\{x_n\}$ is a sequence of approximation generated by an iteration method. If the sequence converges to a zero α of f with R-order $\geq r$, then we write

$$e_{n+1} \sim e_n^r. \tag{11}$$

Theorem 1. *Suppose that $f(x)$, $f'(x)$, $f''(x)$ and $f'''(x)$ are continuous in the neighborhood $\mathbb{D}$ of a zero (say, α) of f. If the initial approximations x_0, x_1 and x_2 are sufficiently close to α, then the R-order of convergence of the method (10) is 1.84.*

Proof. Let $e_n = x_n - \alpha$, $e_{n-1} = x_{n-1} - \alpha$ and $e_{n-2} = x_{n-2} - \alpha$ be the errors in the n-th, $n-1$-th and $n-2$-th iterations, respectively. Using Taylor's expansions of $f(x_n)$, $f(x_{n-1})$ and $f(x_{n-2})$ about α and taking into account that $f(\alpha) = 0$ and $f'(\alpha) \neq 0$, we have that

$$f(x_n) = f'(\alpha)\left[e_n + A_2 e_n^2 + A_3 e_n^3 + \cdots\right], \tag{12}$$

$$f(x_{n-1}) = f'(\alpha)\left[e_{n-1} + A_2 e_{n-1}^2 + A_3 e_{n-1}^3 + \cdots\right], \tag{13}$$

$$f(x_{n-2}) = f'(\alpha)\left[e_{n-2} + A_2 e_{n-2}^2 + A_3 e_{n-2}^3 + \cdots\right], \tag{14}$$

where $A_1 = 1$ and $A_i = (1/i!) f^{(i)}(\alpha)/f'(\alpha)$, $i = 2, 3, 4, \ldots$

Using Equations (12) and (13), we have

$$f[x_{n-1}, x_n] = f'(\alpha)(1 + A_2(e_n + e_{n-1}) + A_3(e_n^2 + e_{n-1}^2 + e_n e_{n-1}) + \cdots). \tag{15}$$

Similarly we can obtain

$$f[x_{n-2}, x_n] = f'(\alpha)(1 + A_2(e_n + e_{n-2}) + A_3(e_n^2 + e_{n-2}^2 + e_n e_{n-2}) + \cdots), \tag{16}$$

$$f[x_{n-2}, x_{n-1}] = f'(\alpha)(1 + A_2(e_{n-2} + e_{n-1}) + A_3(e_{n-2}^2 + e_{n-1}^2 + e_{n-2} e_{n-1}) + \cdots). \tag{17}$$

Using Equations (12), (15)–(17) in (10), we obtain that

$$\begin{aligned} e_{n+1} &= e_n - \frac{e_n + A_2 e_n^2 + A_3 e_n^3 + A_2(e_{n-2}e_n + e_{n-1}e_n) + A_3(e_n e_{n-1} e_{n-2}) + \cdots}{1 + A_2(e_n + e_{n-2}) + A_2(e_n + e_{n-1}) + A_2^2(e_n^2 + e_n e_{n-2} + e_{n-1}e_n + e_{n-1}e_{n-2}) + \cdots} \\ &= (A_2^2 - A_3) e_n e_{n-1} e_{n-2} + \cdots, \end{aligned}$$

that is

$$e_{n+1} \sim e_n e_{n-1} e_{n-2}. \tag{18}$$

From (11), we have that

$$e_n \sim e_{n+1}^{\frac{1}{r}}, \tag{19}$$

$$e_{n-1} \sim e_n^{\frac{1}{r}} \tag{20}$$

and

$$e_{n-2} \sim e_{n-1}^{\frac{1}{r}} \sim e_n^{\frac{1}{r^2}}. \tag{21}$$

Combining (18), (20) and (21), it follows that

$$e_{n+1} \sim e_n e_n^{\frac{1}{r}} e_n^{\frac{1}{r^2}} = e_n^{1+\frac{1}{r}+\frac{1}{r^2}}. \tag{22}$$

Comparison of the exponents of e_n on the right hand side of (11) and (22) leads to

$$r^3 - r^2 - r - 1 = 0,$$

which has a unique positive real root 1.84. That means the order r of method (10) is 1.84. □

Remark 1. *According to Ostrowski's formula [9] for the efficiency measure of an iterative method of order r; if c is the computational cost measured in terms of the number of evaluations of the function f and its derivatives that are required for each iteration, then the efficiency index of the method is given by $r^{1/c}$. Thus the efficiency index of Newton's method is* 1.414*, the Secant method is* 1.62 *whereas in the case of the Muller, Jarratt-Nudds, Traub, Sharma and new methods* (10) *this index is* 1.84.

3. Numerical Results

We check the performance of the new method (10), now denoted by NM, using the computational software package Mathematica [10] with multiple-precision arithmetic. For comparison purposes, we consider the Muller method (MM), the Traub method (TM), the Jarratt-Nudds method (JNM) and the Sharma method (SM). These methods are given as follows:

Muller method (MM):

$$x_{n+1} = x_n - \frac{2a_2}{a_1 \pm \sqrt{a_1^2 - 4a_0a_2}},$$

where

$$\begin{aligned}
a_0 &= \frac{1}{D}\big[(x_n - x_{n-2})(f(x_n) - f(x_{n-1})) - (x_n - x_{n-1})(f(x_n) - f(x_{n-2}))\big],\\
a_1 &= \frac{1}{D}\big[(x_n - x_{n-2})^2(f(x_n) - f(x_{n-1})) - (x_n - x_{n-1})^2(f(x_n) - f(x_{n-2}))\big],\\
a_2 &= f(x_n),\\
D &= (x_n - x_{n-1})(x_n - x_{n-2})(x_{n-1} - x_{n-2}).
\end{aligned}$$

Traub method (TM):

$$x_{n+1} = x_n - \frac{f(x_n)}{f[x_n, x_{n-1}]} + \frac{f(x_n)f(x_{n-1})}{f(x_n) - f(x_{n-2})}\Big(\frac{1}{f[x_n, x_{n-1}]} - \frac{1}{f[x_{n-1}, x_{n-2}]}\Big).$$

Jarratt-Nudds method (JNM):

$$x_{n+1} = x_n + \frac{(x_n - x_{n-1})(x_n - x_{n-2})f(x_n)(f(x_{n-1}) - f(x_{n-2}))}{(x_n - x_{n-1})(f(x_{n-2}) - f(x_n))f(x_{n-1}) + (x_n - x_{n-2})(f(x_n) - f(x_{n-1}))f(x_{n-2})}.$$

Sharma method (SM):

$$x_{n+1} = x_n - \frac{2f(x_n)(bf(x_n) - d)}{c \pm \sqrt{c^2 - 4af(x_n)(bf(x_n) - d)}},$$

where

$$c = \frac{a(h_1\delta_2 - h_2\delta_1) + b\delta_1\delta_2(h_1\delta_1 - h_2\delta_2)}{\delta_2 - \delta_1},$$
$$d = \frac{a(h_2 - h_1) + b(h_2\delta_2^2 - h_1\delta_1^2)}{\delta_2 - \delta_1},$$
$$h_k = x_n - x_{n-k},$$
$$\delta_k = \frac{f(x_n) - f(x_{n-k})}{x_n - x_{n-k}}, \quad k = 1, 2.$$

We consider five examples for numerical tests as follows:

Example 1. *Let us consider Kepler's equation;* $f_1(x) = x - \alpha_1 \sin(x) - K = 0$*, where* $0 \leq \alpha_1 < 1$ *and* $0 \leq K \leq \pi$*. A numerical study, based on different values of parameters K and* α_1*, has been performed in [11]. We solve the equation taking* $K = 0.1$ *and* $\alpha_1 = 0.25$*. For this set of values the solution* α *is* 0.13320215082857313*.... The numerical results are shown in Table 1.*

Table 1. Comparison of performance of methods for function $f_1(x)$, taking $x_0 = 0.5, x_1 = -0.3$, $x_2 = 0.1$.

Methods	n	$\lvert x_4 - x_3 \rvert$	$\lvert x_5 - x_4 \rvert$	$\lvert x_6 - x_5 \rvert$	COC	CPU-Time
MM	7	2.860(−4)	2.271(−7)	1.184(−13)	1.82	0.0952
TM	7	2.832(−4)	2.247(−7)	1.143(−13)	1.82	0.0944
JNM	7	2.846(−4)	2.259(−7)	1.163(−13)	1.82	0.1246
SM ($a = 1, b = 1$)	7	2.850(−4)	2.262(−7)	1.169(−13)	1.82	0.1107
SM ($a = 1, b = 2$)	7	2.845(−4)	2.258(−7)	1.162(−13)	1.82	0.0973
SM ($a = 1, b = -1$)	7	2.897(−4)	2.302(−7)	1.239(−13)	1.82	0.0984
NM	7	2.670(−4)	2.116(−7)	1.013(−13)	1.82	0.0921

Example 2. *Next, we consider isentropic supersonic flow across a sharp expansion corner (see Reference [12]). The relationship between the Mach number before the corner (i.e.,* M_1*) and after the corner (i.e.,* M_2*) is expressed by*

$$f_2(x) = b^{1/2}\left(\tan^{-1}\left(\frac{M_2^2-1}{b}\right)^{1/2} - \tan^{-1}\left(\frac{M_1^2-1}{b}\right)^{1/2}\right) - \left(\tan^{-1}(M_2^2-1)^{1/2} - \tan^{-1}(M_1^2-1)^{1/2}\right) - \delta,$$

where $b = \frac{\gamma+1}{\gamma-1}$ *and* γ *is the specific heat ratio of the gas. We take values* $M_1 = 1.5$*,* $\gamma = 1.4$ *and* $\delta = 10^0$*. The solution* α *of this problem is* 1.8411294068501996*.... The numerical results are shown in Table 2.*

Table 2. Comparison of performance of methods for function $f_2(x)$, taking $x_0 = 1.1, x_1 = 2.3, x_2 = 1.7$.

Methods	n	$\lvert x_4 - x_3 \rvert$	$\lvert x_5 - x_4 \rvert$	$\lvert x_6 - x_5 \rvert$	COC	CPU-Time
MM	7	8.212(−3)	3.223(−5)	3.369(−9)	1.83	0.3312
TM	7	8.228(−3)	4.906(−5)	6.104(−9)	1.83	0.3434
JNM	7	8.220(−3)	4.048(−5)	4.636(−9)	1.83	0.3163
SM ($a = 1, b = 1$)	7	8.215(−3)	3.537(−5)	3.841(−9)	1.83	0.3754
SM ($a = 1, b = 2$)	7	8.217(−3)	3.752(−5)	4.175(−9)	1.83	0.3666
SM ($a = 1, b = -1$)	7	8.207(−3)	2.724(−5)	2.660(−9)	1.83	0.3627
NM	7	8.228(−3)	4.905(−5)	5.395(−9)	1.83	0.3024

Example 3. *Consider the equation governing the L-C-R circuit in electrical engineering [13]*

$$L\frac{d^2q}{dt^2} + R\frac{dq}{dt} + \frac{q}{C} = 0,$$

whose solution $q(t)$ is

$$q(t) = q_0 e^{-Rt/2L} \cos\left(\sqrt{\frac{1}{LC} - \left(\frac{R}{2L}\right)^2}\, t\right),$$

where at $t = 0$, $q = q_0$.

A particular problem as a case study is given as: *Assuming that the charge is dissipated to 1 percent of its original value ($q/q_0 = 0.01$) in $t = 0.05$ s, with $L = 5$ Henry and $C = 10^{-4}$ Farad. Determine the proper value of R?*

Using the given numerical data, the problem is given as

$$f_3(x) = e^{-0.005x} \cos\left(\sqrt{2000 - 0.01x^2}\,(0.05)\right) - 0.01 = 0,$$

where $x = R$. Solution of this problem is, $\alpha = 328.15142908514817....$ Numerical results are displayed in Table 3.

Table 3. Comparison of performance of methods for function $f_3(x)$, taking $x_0 = 430, x_1 = 200, x_2 = 315$.

Methods	n	$\lvert x_4 - x_3 \rvert$	$\lvert x_5 - x_4 \rvert$	$\lvert x_6 - x_5 \rvert$	COC	CPU-Time
MM	7	4.446(−1)	2.182(−3)	3.303(−8)	1.83	0.2075
TM	7	6.515(−1)	4.078(−3)	1.381(−7)	1.84	0.2185
JNM	7	1.259(−1)	1.767(−4)	2.058(−10)	1.83	0.1721
SM ($a = 1, b = 1$)	7	4.446(−1)	2.182(−3)	3.303(−8)	1.83	0.2126
SM ($a = 1, b = 2$)	7	4.446(−1)	2.182(−3)	3.303(−8)	1.83	0.1979
SM ($a = 1, b = -1$)	7	4.446(−1)	2.182(−3)	3.303(−8)	1.83	0.2034
NM	7	1.818(−1)	3.112(−4)	6.976(−10)	1.83	0.1568

Example 4. *Law of population growth is given as (see References [14,15])*

$$\frac{dN(t)}{dt} = \lambda N(t) + \nu,$$

where $N(t)$ = population at time t, λ = constant birth rate of population and ν = constant immigration rate. The solution of this differential equation is given by

$$N(t) = N_0 e^{\lambda t} + \frac{\nu}{\lambda}(e^{\lambda t} - 1),$$

where N_0 is initial population.

A particular problem for the above model can be formulated as: *Suppose that a certain population consists of 1,000,000 people initially. Further suppose that 435,000 people immigrate into the community in the first year and 1,564,000 people are present at the end of one year. Determine the birth rate (λ) of this population.*

To find the birth rate, we will solve the equation

$$f_4(x) = 1564 - 1000e^x - \frac{435}{x}(e^x - 1) = 0,$$

wherein $x = \lambda$. Solution of this problem is, $\alpha = 0.10099792968574979....$ The numerical results are given in Table 4.

Table 4. Comparison of performance of methods for function $f_4(x)$, taking $x_0 = -0.4, x_1 = 0.5$, $x_2 = 0.05$.

Methods	n	$\lvert x_4 - x_3\rvert$	$\lvert x_5 - x_4\rvert$	$\lvert x_6 - x_5\rvert$	COC	CPU-Time
MM	7	1.464(−3)	4.958(−6)	5.588(−11)	1.83	0.1924
TM	7	3.061(−3)	1.670(−5)	7.659(−10)	1.84	0.1884
JNM	7	7.093(−4)	1.013(−6)	2.558(−12)	1.82	0.1811
SM ($a = 1, b = 1$)	7	3.061(−3)	1.670(−5)	7.659(−10)	1.84	0.2194
SM ($a = 1, b = 2$)	7	3.061(−3)	1.670(−5)	7.659(−10)	1.84	0.2033
SM ($a = 1, b = -1$)	7	3.061(−3)	1.670(−5)	7.659(−10)	1.84	0.1875
NM	7	1.980(−3)	1.078(−6)	8.160(−12)	1.85	0.1727

Example 5. *Next, we consider an example of academic interest, which is defined by*

$$f_5(x) = \begin{cases} x^3 \ln x^2 + x^5 - x^4, & x \neq 0, \\ 0, & x = 0. \end{cases}$$

It has three zeros. Note that $\alpha = 0$ is the multiple zero of multiplicity 3. We consider the zero $\alpha = 1$ in our work. Numerical results are displayed in Table 5.

Table 5. Comparison of performance of methods for function $f_5(x)$, taking $x_0 = 1.2, x_1 = 0.9, x_2 = 1.05$.

Methods	n	$\lvert x_4 - x_3\rvert$	$\lvert x_5 - x_4\rvert$	$\lvert x_6 - x_5\rvert$	COC	CPU-Time
MM	8	3.206(−3)	5.057(−5)	2.720(−8)	1.84	0.0943
TM	9	1.090(−2)	9.025(−4)	5.898(−6)	1.83	0.0821
JNM	8	4.915(−3)	1.525(−4)	1.955(−7)	1.85	0.0798
SM ($a = 1, b = 1$)	8	1.010(−2)	7.066(−4)	3.901(−6)	1.85	0.0942
SM ($a = 1, b = 2$)	8	1.048(−2)	7.960(−4)	4.777(−6)	1.83	0.0933
SM ($a = 1, b = -1$)	9	1.185(−2)	1.188(−3)	9.274(−6)	1.83	0.0931
NM	8	1.930(−3)	4.728(−5)	1.766(−8)	1.85	0.0775

Numerical results shown in Tables 1–5 contain the required iterations n, computed estimated error $|x_{n+1} - x_n|$ in first three iterations (wherein A(-h) denotes $A \times 10^{-h}$), computational order of convergence (COC) and CPU time (CPU-time) are measured during the execution of the program. Computational order of convergence (COC) is computed by using the formula [16]

$$\mathrm{COC} = \frac{\ln(|x_{n+1} - x_n|/|x_n - x_{n-1}|)}{\ln(|x_n - x_{n-1}|/|x_{n-1} - x_{n-2}|)}.$$

The necessary iterations (n) are obtained so as to satisfy the criterion $(|x_{n+1} - x_n| + |f(x_n)|) < 10^{-100}$. The first two initial approximations x_0 and x_1 are chosen arbitrarily, whereas third x_2 is taken as the average of these two. From the numerical results displayed in Tables 1–5, we can conclude that the accuracy of the new method (NM) is either equal to or better than existing methods. Moreover, it requires less CPU-time compared with that of existing methods. This character makes it more efficient than the existing ones.

4. Generalized Method

We end this work with a method for solving a system of nonlinear equations $F(x) = 0$; $F : \mathbb{D} \subset \mathbb{R}^m \to \mathbb{R}^m$ is the given nonlinear function $F = (f_1, f_2, ...f_m)^T$ and $x = (x_1, ..., x_m)^T$. The divided difference $F[x, y]$ of F is a matrix of order $m \times m$ (see Reference [2], p. 229) with elements

$$F[x,y]_{ij} = \frac{f_i(x_1, ..., x_j, y_{j+1}, ..., y_m) - f_i(x_1, ..., x_{j-1}, y_j, ..., y_m)}{x_j - y_j}, \quad 1 \le i, j \le m. \tag{23}$$

Keeping in mind (10), we can write the corresponding method for the system of nonlinear equations as:

$$x^{(n+1)} = x^{(n)} - F[x^{(n-1)}, x^{(n)}]^{-1} F[x^{(n-2)}, x^{(n-1)}] F[x^{(n-2)}, x^{(n)}]^{-1} F(x^{(n)}), \tag{24}$$

where $F[\cdot, \cdot]^{-1}$ is the inverse of the divided difference operator $F[\cdot, \cdot]$.

Remark 2. *The computational efficiency of an iterative method for solving the system $F(x) = 0$ is calculated by the efficiency index $E = r^{1/C}$, (see Reference [17]), where r is the order of convergence and C is the total cost of computation. The cost of computation C is measured in terms of the total number of function evaluations per iteration and the number of operations (that means products and divisions) per iteration. The various evaluations and operations that contribute to the cost of computation are described as follows. For the computation of F in any iterative function we evaluate m scalar functions f_i, $(1 \le i \le m)$ and when computing a divided difference $F[x, y]$, we evaluate $m(m-1)$ scalar functions, wherein $F(x)$ and $F(y)$ are evaluated separately. Furthermore, one has to add m^2 divisions from any divided difference. For the computation of an inverse linear operator, a linear system can be solved that requires $m(m-1)(2m-1)/6$ products and $m(m-1)/2$ divisions in the LU decomposition process, and $m(m-1)$ products and m divisions in the resolution of two triangular linear systems. Thus, taking into account the above considerations of evaluations and operations for the method (24), we have that*

$$C = \frac{2}{3}m^3 + 8m^2 - \frac{8}{3}m \quad \text{and} \quad E = 1.84^{\frac{3}{2m^3+24m^2-8m}}.$$

Next, we apply the generalized method on the following problems:

Example 6. *The following system of m equations (selected from [18]) is considered:*

$$\sum_{j=1, j\neq i}^{m} x_j - e^{-x_i} = 0, \quad 1 \le i \le m.$$

In particular, we solve this problem for $m = 10, 30, 50, 100$ by selecting initial guesses $x^{(0)} = \{2, 2, \overset{m}{\cdots}, 2\}^T$, $x^{(1)} = \{-1, -1, \overset{m}{\cdots}, -1\}^T$ and $x^{(2)} = \{\frac{1}{2}, \frac{1}{2}, \overset{m}{\cdots}, \frac{1}{2}\}^T$ towards the corresponding solution:

$$\alpha = \{0.100488400337\ldots, 0.100488400337\ldots, \overset{10}{\cdots}, 0.100488400337\ldots\}^T,$$

$$\alpha = \{0.033351667835\ldots, 0.033351667835\ldots, \overset{30}{\cdots}, 0.033351667835\ldots\}^T,$$

$$\alpha = \{0.020003975040\ldots, 0.020003975040\ldots, \overset{50}{\cdots}, 0.020003975040\ldots\}^T,$$

$$\alpha = \{0.010000498387\ldots, 0.010000498387\ldots, \overset{100}{\cdots}, 0.010000498387\ldots\}^T.$$

Numerical results are displayed in Table 6.

Table 6. Performance of new method (NM) for Example 6.

m	n	$\|\|x_4 - x_3\|\|$	$\|\|x_5 - x_4\|\|$	$\|\|x_6 - x_5\|\|$	COC	CPU-Time
10	7	1.139(−2)	7.395(−5)	1.310(−9)	1.84	1.935
30	7	6.776(−3)	1.937(−5)	5.181(−11)	1.84	16.832
50	7	5.251(−3)	9.485(−6)	9.630(−12)	1.84	57.704
100	7	3.691(−3)	3.463(−6)	9.131(−13)	1.84	407.912

Example 7. *Consider the system of m equations (selected from Reference [19]):*

$$\tan^{-1}(x_i) + 1 - 2 \sum_{j=1, j\neq i}^{m} x_j^2 = 0, \quad 1 \leq i \leq m.$$

Let us solve this problem for $m = 10, 30, 50, 100$ *with initial values* $x^{(0)} = \{-1, -1, \overset{m}{\cdots}, -1\}^T$, $x^{(1)} = \{0, 0, \overset{m}{\cdots}, 0\}^T$ *and* $x^{(2)} = \{-0.5, -0.5, \overset{m}{\cdots}, -0.5\}^T$ *towards the corresponding solutions:*

$$\alpha = \{-0.209906976944\ldots, -0.209906976944\ldots, \overset{10}{\cdots}, -0.209906976944\ldots\}^T,$$
$$\alpha = \{-0.123008700800\ldots, -0.123008700800\ldots, \overset{30}{\cdots}, -0.123008700800\ldots\}^T,$$
$$\alpha = \{-0.096056797272\ldots, -0.096056797272\ldots, \overset{50}{\cdots}, -0.096056797272\ldots\}^T,$$
$$\alpha = \{-0.0685903131070\ldots, -0.0685903131070\ldots, \overset{100}{\cdots}, -0.0685903131070\ldots\}^T.$$

Numerical results are displayed in Table 7.

Table 7. Performance of new method (NM) for Example 7.

m	n	$\|\|x_4 - x_3\|\|$	$\|\|x_5 - x_4\|\|$	$\|\|x_6 - x_5\|\|$	COC	CPU-Time
10	9	7.661(−2)	1.423(−2)	1.304(−4)	1.84	3.386
30	10	4.195(−1)	5.623(−2)	6.824(−3)	1.84	25.600
50	10	6.603(−1)	5.572(−2)	1.354(−2)	1.84	87.531
100	10	1.076	2.307(−2)	1.106(−2)	1.84	593.691

In Tables 6 and 7 we have shown the results of the new method only, because the other methods are not applicable for nonlinear systems. We conclude that there are numerous one-point iterative methods for solving a scalar equation $f(x) = 0$. Contrary to this fact, such methods are rare for multi-dimensional cases, that is, for approximating the solution of $F(x) = 0$. Since the method uses first divided difference, a drawback of the method is that if at some stage (say j) the denominator $x_j = y_j$ in the Formula (23), then the method may fail to converge. However, this situation is rare since we have applied the method successfully on many other different problems. In the present work, an attempt has been made to develop an iterative scheme which is equally suitable for both categories viz. univariate and multivariate functions.

Author Contributions: The contribution of all the authors has been equal. All of them have worked together to prepare the manuscript.

Funding: This research received no external funding.

Conflicts of Interest: The authors declare no conflict of interest.

References

1. Argyros, I.K. *Convergence and Applications of Newton-Type Iterations*; Springer: New York, NY, USA, 2008.
2. Traub, J.F. *Iterative Methods for the Solution of Equations*; Prentice-Hall: Englewood Cliffs, NJ, USA, 1964.

3. Kumar, D.; Sharma, J.R.; Cesarano, C. An efficient class of Traub-Steffensen-type methods for computing multiple zeros. *Axioms* **2019**, *8*, 65. [CrossRef]
4. Gerald, C.F.; Wheatley, P.O. *Applied Numerical Analysis*; Addison-Wesley: Reading, MA, USA,1994.
5. Muller, D.E. A method of solving algebraic equations using an automatic computer. *Math. Comp.* **1956**, *10*, 208–215. [CrossRef]
6. Jarratt, P.; Nudds, D. The use of rational functions in the iterative solution of equations on a digital computer. *Comput. J.* **1965**, *8*, 62–65. [CrossRef]
7. Sharma, J. R. A family of methods for solving nonlinear equations using quadratic interpolation. *Comput. Math. Appl.* **2004**, *48*, 709–714. [CrossRef]
8. Ortega, J.M.; Rheinboldt, W.C. *Iterative Solution of Nonlinear Equations in Several Variables*; Academic Press: New York, NY, USA, 1970.
9. Ostrowski, A.M. *Solution of Equations and Systems of Equations*; Academic Press: New York, NY, USA; London, UK, 1960; p. 20.
10. Wolfram, S. *The Mathematica Book*, 5th ed.; Wolfram Media: Champaign, IL, USA, 2003.
11. Danby, J.M.A.; Burkardt, T.M. The solution of kepler's equation. *Celest. Mech.* **1983**, *40*, 95–107. [CrossRef]
12. Hoffman, J.D. *Numerical Methods for Engineers and Scientists*; McGraw-Hill Book Company: New York, NY, USA, 1992.
13. Chapra, S.C.; Canale, R.P. *Numerical Methods for Engineers*; McGraw-Hill Book Company: New York, NY, USA, 1988.
14. Burden, R.L.; Faires, J.D. *Numerical Analysis*; Brooks/Cole: Boston, MA, USA, 2005.
15. Assante, D.; Cesarano, C.; Fornaro, C.; Vazquez, L. Higher order and fractional diffusive equations. *J. Eng. Sci. Technol. Rev.* **2015**, *8*, 202–204. [CrossRef]
16. Weerakoon, S.; Fernando, T.G.I. A variant of newton's method with accelerated third-order convergence. *Appl. Math. Lett.* **2000**, *13*, 87–93. [CrossRef]
17. Cordero, A.; Hueso, J.L.; Martínez, E.; Torregrosa, J.R. A modified Newton-Jarratt's composition. *Numer. Algorithms* **2010**, *55*, 87–99. [CrossRef]
18. Grau-Sànchez, M.; Noguera, M.; Amat, S. On the approximation of derivatives using divided difference operators preserving the local convergence order of iterative methods. *J. Comput. Appl. Math.* **2013**, *237*, 363–372. [CrossRef]
19. Xiao, X.Y.; Yin, H.W. Increasing the order of convergence for iterative methods to solve nonlinear systems. *Calcolo* **2016**, *53*, 285–300. [CrossRef]

MDPI
St. Alban-Anlage 66
4052 Basel
Switzerland
Tel. +41 61 683 77 34
Fax +41 61 302 89 18
www.mdpi.com

Mathematics Editorial Office
E-mail: mathematics@mdpi.com
www.mdpi.com/journal/mathematics

Lightning Source UK Ltd
Milton Keynes UK
UKHW051042151220
375215UK00003B/213